Treating the Troubled Family

Also by Nathan W. Ackerman

• *The Psychodynamics of Family Life* (1958)

Treating the Troubled Family

Nathan W. Ackerman

Basic Books, Inc., Publishers | *New York*
London

To THE FAMILY INSTITUTE

Fifth Printing

© 1966 by Nathan W. Ackerman
   Library of Congress Catalog Card Number: 66–27943
   Manufactured in the United States of America
   Designed by *Sophie Adler*

It is not only man's concept of matter which must come from science but also man's concept of himself. . . . At this stage of specialization of our knowledge, to determine what is specifically human in man requires a veritable cracking of the concept of man. . . . If the concept is cracked, the release of spiritual energy will be voluminous enough to make physical nuclear energy behave. It might be powerful enough to light the lamps of peace and keep them burning.

—Ana María O'Neill, quoted in the preface to
Man's Emerging Mind, by N. J. Berrill (1955)

Preface

Elsewhere I have written: "In the present era the extraordinary acceleration of social change crowds all of history into the life space of a single family. We ask: Is man's capacity to adapt to almost any living condition reaching the breaking point? Is the unique flexibility of the human family failing? Can the family take it?"

Troubled families are everywhere today. Family relations are out of kilter. After an upset, the family seems less able to bounce back and regain its balance. It looks for all the world as if it is falling apart. Unlike Humpty Dumpty, however, it may well pull itself together. But at what cost? And will it ever be the same again?

Close observers of family life clash sharply in their judgments. The optimistic view is that the modern family is thriving; it is merely changing its face to fit the times. The pessimistic view is that the family shows unmistakable signs of disorganization and decay. Will the family, as we have known it, survive or die? But posing this question in all-or-none terms is, I believe, misleading. The real issue is a different one: What is the social and emotional cost, the toll in suffering, breakdown, and mental illness the contemporary family is forced to pay as it engages in a desperate struggle to adapt to a world in crisis? The issues are crucial: What is the present condition of the human family? How did it get that way? How would we like it to be? The social disorders of family living magnify the vulnerability of family members to emotional and mental disorder. What can we do about it?

The development of a method of psychotherapy for the whole

family is at least a partial answer. This type of treatment makes use of a primary group, the family; it deals, not with the isolated individual patient, but with the family as an organic whole. It focuses on the interactional effects of disturbances within the group, and applies its technique to the relationship between the psychosocial functions of the family unit and the emotional destiny of its members. The goal of family psychotherapy is not merely to remove symptoms or to "adjust" personality to environment, but, more than that, to create a new way of living.

All that I know about troubled people I have learned from treating them, both as individuals and as families. While recognizing my debt to therapeutic work, I must confess I felt some qualms about publishing at this early stage a book on the psychotherapy of the whole family. There is, I believe, good reason for hesitancy. Somehow it seems easier to write about the theory of the family, to work toward building a conceptual framework for "the psychodynamics of family life." By contrast, it is far more difficult and hazardous to translate the infinite complexities and nuances of the therapeutic process to the written word.

Twenty-five years ago, Lawson Lowrey, an astute and gifted observer of the mental-health scene, startled me with the declaration that, although there was voluminous literature in child psychiatry, there was not yet a single authoritative work on child psychotherapy. This is no longer so, of course; there are now many books on child psychotherapy. But is there, even today, a single authoritative work on any type of psychotherapy? Perhaps not. The challenge of communicating the very core of the therapeutic process by the written word is an extremely sensitive one. Who of us can really do it? Through the years I learned this lesson only too well. Repeatedly, one or another of my colleagues pointed out to me that what I do in psychotherapy and what I write are not the same. I took this observation to heart. Again and again I tried to paint a picture in words of what really happens in the psychotherapeutic struggle and, by my standards, I failed.

Nevertheless, the pressure to pin down on the printed page the principles and practices of family psychotherapy is, today, so strong that it has brought forth a spate of books in the field. All of these, including the present volume, must be judged to be a mere beginning.

In any case, it is the utter frustration of these past efforts that explains the avid hope of our time for a more adequate recording of treatment sessions with the use of sound tape, closed-circuit TV, and motion pictures. The value of a permanent recording of therapeutic experience in motion pictures is self-evident. It is, in my view, the only known method to date that provides a satisfactory permanent record of a Gestalt, a merging of the image of face, voice, emotion, and bodily expression. It depicts action and reaction in faithful sequence and is a highly suitable instrument for the systematic study of what goes on inside and between minds.

A number of the families used as case illustrations in this book have been filmed for purposes of both research and professional training. The film records of two of these families have been edited and have now been distributed to over five hundred training centers, medical colleges, departments of psychiatry, mental health clinics, child guidance clinics, and family service agencies. For the purposes of this book, I have tried to communicate the vital essence of the therapeutic process through verbatim records of actual sessions, coupled with interpretive comment, sequence by sequence. Taking into account the limitations of the written word, we dare to try again; we must!

N.W.A.

New York
August 1966

Acknowledgments

In the preparation of this book, I owe much to many people. First and foremost, I want to express my appreciation to the troubled families who, with great faith and dignity, joined me in the struggle to get well and stay well.

I am deeply indebted to the Jewish Family Service of New York City, to its directors, Frances L. Beatman and Sanford N. Sherman, and to my talented case consultant in the Family Mental Health Clinic, Celia Mitchell, as well as to many other members of the staff who, for nearly ten years, shared with me a devotion to the problems of disturbed families.

To Marjorie Behrens, my research associate, mentor, and ever-willing helper, I owe thanks beyond measure.

To Dr. Lawrence Kolb, Director of the Department of Psychiatry, Columbia University, go my thanks for the privilege of conducting the seminar on family psychotherapy at the Psychiatric Institute. The psychiatrists in training at Columbia deserve much for the rich and evocative nature of their discussions and questions.

To Drs. Israel Zwerling and Andrew Ferber of the Day Hospital of the Albert Einstein Medical College, I am indebted for sharing with me their confrontation of the controversial issues in the field.

I extend my gratitude to Dimmes Bishop, whose wise and efficient editing carried me through the publication of both *The Psychodynamics of Family Life* and *Treating the Troubled Family*.

I express my thanks to the *International Journal of Social Psychiatry* for permission to use some previously published material pertinent to the content of this book. I also wish to mention the journal *Family Process,* which has been for me the richest kind of education in the phenomena of family life, and in the endlessly fascinating challenge of family psychotherapy.

Last, and most important, I offer my deep appreciation to The Family Institute, its Board of Directors, and its professional staff, whose unstinting encouragement enables me to carry on the work of helping troubled families.

N.W.A.

Contents

Treating the Troubled Family

1

Crisis and Therapy

DR. A.: Bill, you heaved a sigh as you sat down tonight.

Therapist instantly fastens on a piece of nonverbal behavior, the father's sigh.

FATHER: Just physical, not mental.

DR. A.: Who are you kidding?

Therapist challenges father's evasive response.

FATHER: I'm kidding no one.

DR. A: Hmmm . . .

Therapist registers disbelief, a further pressure for a more honest response.

FATHER: Really not. . . . Really physical. I'm tired because I put in a full day today.

DR. A.: Well, I'm tired every day, and when I sigh it's never purely physical.

An example of therapist's use of his own emotions to counter an insincere denial.

FATHER: Really?

DR. A.: What's the matter?

FATHER: Nothing. Really!

DR. A.: Well, your own son doesn't believe that.

Therapist now exploits son's gesture, a knowing grin, to penetrate father's denial and evoke a deeper sharing of feelings.

FATHER: Well, I mean, nothing . . . nothing could cause me to sigh especially today or tonight.

DR. A.: Well, maybe it isn't so special, but . . . How about it, John?

Therapist stirs son to unmask father.

SON: I wouldn't know.

Now son wipes grin off his face, and turns evasive, like father.

DR. A.: You wouldn't know? How come all of a sudden you put on a poker face? A moment ago you were grinning very knowingly.

Therapist counters by challenging son, who took pot shot from sidelines, and then backed away.

SON: I really wouldn't know.

DR. A.: You . . . Do you know anything about your pop?

SON: Yeah.

DR. A.: What do you know about him?

SON: Well, I don't know, except that I know some stuff.

DR. A.: Well, let's hear.

This is the beginning of a family therapy session.[1] In the room with the therapist is a family composed of four people: the parents and two children. The son, John, aged sixteen, is the older of the two. The mother is a speech teacher; the father is a businessman. There have been recurrent crises in this family, engendered by parental quarrels over money and a basic sexual maladjustment.

The family was initiated into family therapy following the crisis situation in which the younger child, Peg, eleven years old, threatened to stab her brother and her two parents with a kitchen knife. This explosive attack was precipitated by Peg's discovery that her parents and her brother had conspired to deceive her about the disappearance of her dog. They told her that the dog had died, whereas in fact her mother, wanting to be rid of the animal, surrendered him to the S.P.C.A. This is typical of the family's habit of indulging in small "white lies." In this instance the conspiracy to lie about the dog was initiated by the mother, who then brought the father and brother into it. Her brother, however, gave the

[1] This is the second exploratory interview with this family.

secret away; he "let the dog out of the bag," so to speak. When Peg woke up to this betrayal, she reacted first with depression and then with a furious tantrum.

Until a few months back, Peg was considered an adjusted child. She was compliant, did well in school, and made friends. By contrast, John was regarded as a chronic and serious behavior problem. He had had periodic tantrums since childhood, sharp shifts of mood, periods of excitement followed by periods of depression, feelings of inferiority, and sexual anxiety. He was failing in school.

The interview which follows illustrates the stage-by-stage shift from preoccupation with the children's problems to a confrontation of the basic disorder of the marital partnership.

Verbatim Record	Interpretive Comment
DR. A. (*to John*): Well, let's hear.	
SON: My . . . well, I . . . (*Laughs.*)	
FATHER: He's nailed down.	Earlier son pinned father down; now father pins son down.
DR. A.: He's a man?	Referring to father.
SON: Yeah.	
FATHER: Come on, come on, come on. Dr. A. wants information from you.	Father makes a demanding gesture with his open palm—in effect: *give!*
SON: Eh, all right, I'll tell you, Dr. A.	
DR. A.: Your father uses his hand, you know, not like your mother.	
FATHER: Give, give, give.	
DR. A.: Mother's gesture is this, and Pop's gesture is give.	Therapist dramatically enacts the contrast of father's and mother's gestures (mother's being an accusing forefinger).
SON: Ah, I don't have much to say, to tell the truth. I can't . . . He's just a normal man, I mean, he's my father. He's a good guy.	
MOTHER: May I make a suggestion?	Mother intrudes between therapist and son.

DR. A.: What's your suggestion?

MOTHER: Well, uh, I have been keeping an anecdotal record of the time that has elapsed since we were here. Not every minute of the time, but anything that I think is important enough to relate.

Mother keeps dossier on family.

DR. A.: Um-hum.

MOTHER: Now, I think this is good for many reasons. When you read it, you sort of get a better view of things, and, uh, if you'd like me to read it, I will. If you feel you'd rather ask questions, you can. But that's my suggestion.

DR. A.: Well, I'm glad you called my attention to that notebook in your lap there. You come armed with a notebook . . .

Therapist hints at mother's use of her notebook as a weapon.

MOTHER: . . . and I've been keeping this record since last week because I think it's very important. You forget very quickly what people say and how they say it unless you write it down right away. Now, this is something that I do for children in my class, that I have to for case histories, and I think it's a wonderful idea.

In this second interview, mother comes prepared to justify her position.

DR. A.: Well now, what have you there? A "case history" on your whole family?

Mother keeps a dossier on her family. Gives them a mark as she does with bad children in the classroom.

MOTHER: Yes.

DR. A.: Marvelous! How long is it?

Therapist is amused. Injects a note of ironic humor.

MOTHER: It's not that long. I just started it. (*To father*) There's some here that you didn't see last night.

FATHER: Oh, you cheated!

Father's tone is banteringly competitive.

MOTHER: I didn't cheat. I just didn't tell you there was more to it, that's all. You read the front of the book. . . .

FATHER: That's cheating, isn't it?

Father is aware of and points up mother's insincerity.

MOTHER: Oh, no, it isn't. So if you would like me to read it . . . It's sort of a little résumé of my thinking in the last week.

DR. A.: Fire away!

Therapist's choice of phrase dramatizes mother's weapon.

MOTHER: But I was quite disturbed last week; in the middle of the week, very disturbed.

DR. A.: You're picking your fingernails, Bill.

Therapist calls attention to father's urge to pick on himself.

FATHER: No, I was . . . I had a little hangnail.

MOTHER: That's a nervous ailment of his. He picks at his feet, at a rash there, and he picks at his fingers. That's a nervous ailment of his.

Mother instantly picks this up to accent her critical attack on father's bad habits.

SON: Pretty disgusting.

Son injects a dirty, contemptuous note.

DR. A.: Pretty disgusting, you say?

Therapist turns instantly to son; he feels and responds to the contagion of hostility in this family.

SON (to mother): How about your nervous habits?

Son sides with father. Launches counterattack on mother.

MOTHER: I have quite a few.

SON: Yeah, like sitting . . . never mind. Quite a few.

Mother is sitting with legs crossed, exhibiting her figure. Son initiates a reproach of her, but changes his mind. He is caught in conflict by mother's seductive posture.

MOTHER: I said I have a few.

SON: Yes, and they're pretty bad.

MOTHER: All right.

DR. A.: What's the matter? Are you sore at Mother because she's picking pieces out of Poppa's fingers?

> Therapist confronts son with his urge to pick critically at mother.

SON: So what? So he has that nervous habit. So don't we all?

DR. A.: What kind of piece would you like to pick out of Momma?

> Therapist's choice of words hints at son's defensiveness concerning his erotic interest in mother.

SON: She has some pretty disgusting habits.

> A veiled allusion to the link of dirt and sex.

DR. A.: Well, what are they?

MOTHER: I'll tell you what they are.

> Mother rushes in to shut son's mouth.

FATHER: Now wait a minute. . . .

> The tendency to cut in, cut down, and cut out one another is characteristic of this family.

DR. A.: She's talking.

MOTHER: Well, John, you don't have to be bashful. This is to give information. You don't have to . . .

DR. A.: He's not bashful!

> Therapist challenges mother's intrusion.

MOTHER: . . . You don't have to be embarrassed, if I'm not.

DR. A.: Hold it, hold it, hold it. Now, John . . .

> Again, therapist hushes mother, so son can have his say.

SON: Well, I don't exactly know how to put it, if you want the truth.

> Son, with characteristic ambivalence, backs off.

MOTHER: Well, that's why I was going to put it for you.

> Mother just will not be stopped.

SON: Yeah, well, I . . . Maybe she has some better words for the thing.

> Son capitulates.

DR. A.: No, no, no, no, now give, John. . . . It's that same old insincere ritual. You first, Alfonse. Let's not be scared around these here parts. You started something. Finish it!

Therapist uses father's gesture with open palm—*give!* Here with the tone of his voice therapist emphasizes son's evasiveness and resistance to facing the basic conflict—and this is characteristic of every member of this family, despite all the projective accusations.

SON: Ah, well, I'll tell you, she belches.

Finally, son exposes mother, anxiously and indecisively.

DR. A.: She belches?

SON: Consistently, repeatedly, and disgustingly.

Now his accusation gathers force.

MOTHER: That's right. I swallow air. I went to a doctor many years ago about it. It's a nervous habit and when I'm very upset evidently I swallow . . .

DR. A. (*to son*): When Momma belches, whose face does she belch into?

FATHER: Mine most of the time.

The secret is out.

SON: His!

Son, grinning broadly, points dramatically to father.

MOTHER: Well, let me read what's in here. Maybe this will give you . . .

Mother reverts to her secret weapon, the "case record" on her whole family.

DR. A.: That's the worst habit? No others?

Son and mother both laugh, in tacit recognition of other dirty habits.

DR. A.: Pop's tensing up because he knows all about Momma's habits.

SON: Then ask him.

DR. A.: Only belching in Pop's face.

Responding to the contagion of feeling, therapist heightens the drama.

MOTHER: (*Giggles.*)

DR. A.: Oh, Mom likes that. Look at her giggle.

He makes prompt use of nonverbal attitudes.

MOTHER: You know why I'm giggling?

DR. A.: Why?

MOTHER: I asked Bill as a favor to me that he should keep some kind of a record of our relationship. I feel there's lots to be desired in it. Maybe if we can get it down on paper, you can help us with it. So he did write it down. And there were several things he wrote—they were mostly about things I don't care to discuss in front of the children. However, one of the things was about the belching. And I giggled because I refuse to take it seriously. Well, some of this stuff is pretty rugged. I mean, it's what I think and it's not complimentary in some respects. And he read it. And for the first time since we're married, which is twenty years, he didn't get angry.

Mother whets children's curiosity about her private relationship with father, while making an insincere gesture of protecting them.

FATHER: More, dear.

Notice context and timing of "dear." Father's tone is teasing and competitive.

MOTHER: All right, it's a little more than twenty. He didn't get angry. And I can honestly say that's the first time that he ever acted like the kind of man I hoped he was. He didn't get angry at what was in this notebook.

Mother now talks down to father.

DR. A.: Well, my, my—that's quite a bit of progress. Last week you said he wasn't a man at all.

MOTHER: He . . . most of the time, he, he doesn't react the way I would like him to. I can honestly say this is the first time he acted the way I would like him to and the way I

Mother again talks like "speecher-teacher" (which is daughter's characterization of her).

would expect him to. The first time since we're married. It was a pleasure to see him not get angry at something that was the truth.

DR. A.: Look at his tongue, look at his tongue.

Therapist again makes use of father's nonverbal gesture. He is sticking his tongue out in hidden ridicule of mother.

MOTHER: He doesn't always follow the middle course. Either he's too easy to get along with, or for *nothing* he'll get angry.

DR. A.: I asked you to look at his tongue.

MOTHER: Well, I didn't see his tongue.

DR. A: Why didn't you look?

Stresses mother's ignoring of father's nonverbal attitude.

MOTHER: Well, I was talking to you, so I was looking at you.

DR. A.: Why do you have eyes for me only? What about your husband?

MOTHER: Well, I think when you talk to somebody you should look at them, which is something he doesn't do, which I've criticized.

FATHER: Did you see that finger go?

This is mother's characteristic gesture—an accusing forefinger.

SON: (*Laughs.*)

MOTHER: Excuse me. Which is something I've criticized him for *many* times. I think . . .

Mother ignores her own non-verbal communication and begins another speech.

DR. A.: Well, while you talk about him, he has his tongue in a very special position.

Therapist refuses her evasion.

MOTHER: Well, I don't know why. I don't know why at all.

DAUGHTER: Like this.

MOTHER: Well, he was laughing to himself. I don't know why.

Mother denies she is butt of attack. Again, turns it back to father.

FATHER: No, I really appreciated your compliment.

SON: What a family!

Son covers his eyes with hand and laughs.

FATHER: It's a habit of maybe forty or forty-five years. Whenever I write, I can just sign my name, my tongue'll be out.

DR. A.: You mean you stick your tongue out when you concentrate?

FATHER: Yeah. Whenever I do anything.

MOTHER: To get unduly upset over nothing, and raise the roof, and get really nasty and mean . . .

DR. A.: Uh, how does he do that?

MOTHER: Well, if I read these notes you'll know how he does it. Otherwise I can't really describe it to you, my inner feelings, that's the only way I can tell you. . . .

Again, mother turns to her weapon, her "case history" on the family.

DR. A.: Before you read your notes now, I'd just like to ask Pop one question. Uh, when she belches in your face . . .

Therapist disarms mother of her weapon and focuses on the critical problem, the marital relationship.

FATHER: Well, her belching does something to me that, that I just can't explain. It's like waving a red flag in front of my face . . .

Here father speaks with animated conviction.

DR. A.: Hmmm.

FATHER: . . . and the thing that aggravates me more than anything is that with certain company in the house, she can control it beautifully.

DR. A.: Well, uh, when was the last time she belched in your face?

An example of therapist's role in pinning problem

down to a specific
situation.

MOTHER: I really think there is something psychological. When I lie down I begin to swallow air, I don't know why.

DAUGHTER: Excuse me, but just now . . .

The effort to come to grips with the marital conflict is interrupted by the children.

MOTHER: All right, don't interrupt.

DAUGHTER: He, he said if you talk about that lipstick mark, I'll kill you.

At this juncture, brother whispers into sister's ear: "Don't you dare talk about my date with a girl friend." Yet he puts the idea into her head.

FATHER: Oh, stop.

MOTHER: Never mind, that's silly.

DAUGHTER: Just for that, I'm going to talk.

DR. A.: Now, every time we concentrate on the love life between Ma and Pa, you two kids start cutting up.

Therapist confronts the children directly with their competitive intrusion on the problems of the parents' love life.

SON: That's right. 'Cause I don't like it one bit.

DR. A.: Would you rather talk about your love life?

SON: No. I'd rather talk about nobody's love life.

DAUGHTER: I'd like to say something.

DR. A.: Yes, Peg.

DAUGHTER: Well, he has some marks on his neck and I was teasing him and saying it was lipstick marks from his girl friend. And he said, "If you say that in front of Dr. A., I'll murder you." And I didn't like . . . what he said.

The children compete with parents in exhibiting their erotic interests and problems.

MOTHER: John hasn't got a sense of humor when it comes to things he's touchy about. He doesn't want to discuss his report card, which I said I would discuss tonight. He said, "You better not, or else."

Mother engages in a distraction. She wants defensively to get away from sex.

DR. A.: Well, John, uh . . .

John contemptuously turns his back on the whole family.

MOTHER: Would you mind turning around and acting like a man? Now please turn around and sit up.

DR. A. (*to daughter*): . . . talking about his special date with a girl friend, with the doors locked, and Peg felt so alone. 'Cause after all, John's your boy friend, isn't he?

Therapist interprets the submerged romance between brother and sister.

DAUGHTER: No.

DR. A.: No?

DAUGHTER: He's a brat.

DR. A.: He's a brat? But John's also sore at me because he doesn't like it when we talk with Ma and Pa here about their love life. He wants to pretend like he knows from nothing about their love life.

Therapist provokes awareness of the undercurrent of guilt and anxiety about sex.

SON: Will you please stop touching me? Keep your hands off me!

Mother makes a restraining gesture toward John, who turns instantly hostile. He is furious with mother and sister.

DR. A. (*to daughter*): You didn't like it when he had that girl in the apartment?

Therapist brings jealousy problem into the open.

DAUGHTER: No.

DR. A.: What were you so sore about?

DAUGHTER: 'Cause I had nothing to do, and when I wanted to get something out of the kitchen he told me to go out.

DR. A.: Well, he wanted a little privacy with his girl friend.

Therapist supports son's valid right to a girl friend.

DAUGHTER: Yeah, to smooch.

DR. A.: Smooch. Well, what's wrong with a smooch? Is it a terrible thing for a guy like John to smooch a little bit with a girl friend and get lipstick on his neck?

Therapist challenges daughter's hypocritical gesture that smooching is bad.

DAUGHTER: Yes, it's wrong.

DR. A.: What, it's wrong? It's bad?

DAUGHTER: Yes.

DR. A.: The only thing I know that's bad about it is, he got the lipstick on his neck.

Therapist uses humor to ease tension.

DAUGHTER: Yeah, so it's evidence.

DR. A.: Oh, you want to hang the man on the evidence.

He points sharply to daughter's punitiveness.

DAUGHTER: Well, when we leave— he's going to murder me.

DR. A.: You two kids just pulled us right out of your parents' bed. We were in there, the double bed, Mom was belching into Pop's face, and that's where you interrupted the story.

Therapist neutralizes children's competitive, exhibitionistic intrusion, and focuses once more on the problem of mother's belching in bed.

MOTHER: I wouldn't put it quite so. But I do, uh, begin to swallow air, and I don't know why. Now maybe what I have written here will have some bearing on the subject.

Again, mother executes a characteristic retreat to her "notebook."

DR. A.: Well, you can read that in just a moment. Bill can't stand it when you belch into his face in bed. It torments him no end!

Once again, therapist foils this diversionary move.

FATHER: Well, did you ever try, or think that you wanted to kiss a woman, and just when you're about to do it, have her belch in your face?

With therapist's support, father comes to his own defense.

DR. A.: I'm, I'm terribly sympathetic with you.

Therapist's tone of voice points up the problem dramatically.

FATHER: I mean, this is something, unless you wear a gas mask.

Father gets heated up.

DR. A.: Smells bad?

FATHER: It blows your head to one side, and it's really very unhappy. And I just hope you never have the experience.

DR. A.: You mean, an explosion of gas? Hmmm?

Note the therapist's choice of phrase, suggesting the equation of belching with anal explosion.

FATHER: Yeees. To say the least.

MOTHER: This is silly!

Mother is now sharply defensive.

DR. A.: At the very moment you want to kiss her?

FATHER: Well, you're afraid. And I'm serious and sincere.

MOTHER: Well, I think this is just partly an excuse on his part.

Mother initiates a counter-attack.

FATHER: I didn't say it happened every night, but there are nights when you will blame it on what you've eaten, there'll be nights when you'll blame it on what you drank, there'll be nights when you'll blame it on being upset, and other nights you'll blame it on not sleeping enough the day before,

DR. A.: Mother always has an excuse.

FATHER: But the belching is there.

DR. A.: Peg, she just loves this, oh boy, does she love it.

Daughter is now rolling in her seat with a burst of laughter. She is empathically allied with mother and gets a big bang out of father's discomfort.

FATHER: I'm not saying it to be funny particularly, but uh . . .

DAUGHTER: 'Cause I wanna get him as mad as he got me today.

The competitive theme is reasserted. Again, daughter pushes her relations with brother into the foreground.

DR. A.: Now just a minute, we're in your parents' bed. Can we stay there a few minutes? Or won't you let us? Now suppose you move over, again, next to John, 'cause we've got a problem between Mom and Pa here, we've got to know what to do with this gas.

The halting of this intrusion is an illustration of therapist's active assertion of control. He now seats the two parents together, to confront them with the issue of mother's explosion of gas.

DAUGHTER: I don't want to go near him.

Daughter doesn't easily surrender.

MOTHER: Well, uh, I'll leave out anything that has to do with, with bed, because if it's going to disturb them, then I think it should be left out.

Mother's gesture of protecting children is not sincere; it is a provocation, a teaser.

DR. A.: Well, John, it isn't really that you don't know about this. You just want to make out you don't know.

Therapist challenges son's defensive denial of interest in parents' sexual problem. This is not kept secret at home; if anything, it is brashly exhibited.

SON: I don't want you to talk about it in my presence. Now you can talk about anything you want, which I think is wrong, in anyone else's presence, but I don't want to be present.

This remark again is an insincere protest of innocence.

MOTHER: Well, then, why don't you leave?

Mother is hostile to son, over-anxious to get rid of him.

SON: All right, I'll leave.

FATHER: Why don't you let Dr. A. decide whether he's to leave or not?

Father undercuts mother, supports therapist's authority.

MOTHER: Oh, excuse me, oh, I'm sorry, I thought . . .

DR. A.: That's all right, sit down. . . . If we come to a point, John, where

Therapist clarifies the situation, but presses his question.

. . . it seems really sensible that both children leave, I'll ask both of you to leave, if we want to deal with the very private part of the relations between Ma and Pa. But I want to know, what bothers you so about it? You know that every pa and ma kiss.

SON: I certainly do. But that isn't . . .

DR. A.: Well, do you think since we're all here together it might be useful for you to stay with us and see why you are so distressed?

DR. A.: . . . it might be so, that you don't want to be in on the thing when we talk about the private love life of Ma and Pa because if you are, you're afraid that Ma and Pa, and I too, might invade your private love life.

Therapist confronts son with his personal anxiety about sex.

SON: No. That, that isn't possible, because nobody knows about my private love life, except me, and that's . . .

Again, a denial.

DAUGHTER: Except me!

Daughter injects self aggressively (like mother).

DR. A.: You insist on your privacy.

SON: That's right.

DR. A.: All right. But look, I can't keep you here. The door is wide open, but if you can tolerate it, I would prefer that you stay with us, because I'm interested in helping the whole family.

Here, therapist emphasizes the shared quality of conflict experienced in this family.

SON: Well, as far as I'm concerned, the second it began it was too much for me, but if you want me to stay, I will.

DR. A.: I'd prefer it.

Son is mollified. He really wants to stay.

SON: O.K. Whatever you say.

DAUGHTER: I don't want to go home tonight. He's going to kill me.

Daughter again intrudes her conflict with brother, beneath

which is hidden her romantic attachment to him.

DR. A.: I think you're just jealous of that girl he had, that's all.

Therapist interprets undercurrent emotion, jealousy.

DAUGHTER: I'm not jealous of that ugly girl.

DR. A.: Ooh, she was ugly, was she?

Therapist raises voice meaningfully.

DAUGHTER: Yes.

DR. A.: You mean you're prettier?

SON: Look, I'm going to smack her right in her face if she doesn't shut her mouth, and I'm telling you.

FATHER: John, stop.

SON: Look, do you mind if I leave?

Now son is enraged and walks out.

DR. A.: Uh, Peg, you say his girl friend was ugly. Are you much prettier than she?

DAUGHTER: I think so.

DR. A.: Oh, well, you're pretty jealous then.

DAUGHTER: I am not jealous of her.

DR. A.: Oh, don't kid me now.

Therapist uses plain language to press his point.

DAUGHTER: I'm not!

DR. A.: You're a pretty good romancer yourself, you know. You're a great teaser, you are. You and John both. Well, anyhow, let's get back to Ma and Pa. Well now, what'd you do last night when she belched in your face? You wanted to kiss her and she belched.

Therapist interprets daughter's sexual provocation of her brother. He then returns to parents' sexual problem.

FATHER: No, I didn't want to kiss her. And I merely said that it is very unhappy to kiss a woman and have her belch in your face.

This is easy to understand.

DR. A.: You know, you sound so reasonable right now that I don't believe a word that's coming out of your mouth. You're not that reasonable when you get belched at, are you?

This is a good example of therapist's use of a blunt confrontation.

FATHER: Yes, I do get sore. I turn around and, uh, I have at times left the bed and gone inside, and read the newspaper, and read a magazine, or other things. I've criticized her for it. . . .

Father backs off. Daughter leaves room to join brother outside. Therapist is now alone with the two parents.

DR. A.: Hmmm. All right, folks, here's your chance to talk in plain English now, about your sex life.

Therapist, with plain talk, presses the question.

MOTHER: All right, let me read the part I wrote about that. Bill is under the impression that he should not be the pursuer in bed. I think that when you feel you're loved, that when you feel you—this is my thinking now—when you feel you're loved and wanted, sex is spontaneous, and you don't even think about who is making the advances. Sex should be an outcome of love and understanding during the day. And shouldn't be a separate thing. Bill has never acted as if he was really sorry after doing something wrong. There is no discussion which ends up in a better understanding of a problem. Now, I have some other things, uh, in the back here.

Mother finally gets her way. She reads from the "notebook" a bill of particulars against her husband. Her voice is harsh, hammerlike. She reveals here her characteristic self-righteous, preaching attitude.

FATHER: This is what was held out on me.

Father is sarcastic.

MOTHER: Uh, I did write some things that I think are, if you want to hear the gory details, then, I mean I feel where you're professional people and I can, uh, say those, too, if you want me to.

Note term "gory."

DR. A.: Yes. Fire away.

MOTHER: Well, I can't find that particular part of it, but, uh, about the . . .

DR. A.: Say it right out of your mind.

MOTHER: All right, uh, this has been going on for many years, this has not happened since Peg's tantrums. Our sex life I don't think is a normal one. Though I have never discussed it with anybody, so I don't know what the normal is. But I do know that Bill's needs are very different from mine. I think that if, if he didn't have a wife, I don't think he would require anything, for long periods of time. This is my impression. I am a great deal more sensitive and warmer, and my needs are very different. Now I told him after a long time that I thought this wasn't right, he should see a doctor about it. Well, he knew it wasn't right, I didn't have to tell him. Now this is something he should think of himself. I shouldn't have to tell him to go to see a doctor. And even after I did, he didn't go to a doctor.

DR. A.: You thought there was something very wrong.

MOTHER: There *is* something wrong.

DR. A.: With him as a man?

FATHER: Yes.

MOTHER: Yes, I really do.

DR. A.: He doesn't have enough sexual desire for you?

MOTHER: Yes, and if there was a reason for it, if he doesn't love me enough, that's one thing. Maybe he loved me when we were married and doesn't any more. Those things happen. But whatever it is, it should come out in the open. If we, if we aren't meant for each other, we should find

Mother gropes for her place in the notebook.

Mother goes on and on, like a phonograph record.

She exposes father's impotence. Belittles his masculinity.

out and decide what to do about it. But you don't just ignore a problem, that doesn't help it any. So we finally discussed it with the doctor who . . .

DR. A.: Well, let's come back to you two. Where were we now?

MOTHER: Well, uh, about the sex problem, if you want the gory details, I'll tell them to you. Is this the place and time for it?

Again, mother refers to "the gory details."

DR. A.: Certainly.

MOTHER: All right. Bill has the feeling that he cannot use contraceptives. Now this is something I don't know why. Now I don't mind using contraceptives; however, I feel this is a premeditated form of sex. You've got to think, maybe you will feel like it, maybe you won't. So I don't feel it's something to use all the time, for that reason alone. I think it should . . .

Mother launches a "lecture," a righteous preachment on their sex problem.

DR. A.: You talking about a diaphragm or a rubber?

MOTHER: No, the diaphragm. So I don't feel it should be used all the time, because you can't always tell how you're going to feel ten minutes later. Now he evidently has discarded the thought of contraceptives completely. So it leaves me with the use of a diaphragm. And frankly, it's something that I don't feel like using all the time. . . . So that limits us in another way. Another thing, there's the constant . . .

DR. A.: You want him to use a rubber rather than . . .

MOTHER: Not always, just, I feel that if the burden is shared, that's better than somebody having it all alone. Another thing, there is constant fear

Note choice of word "burden."

on my part of pregnancy. Which is almost an abnormal fear. Because when you take care, you shouldn't become pregnant. However, I feel there's always that chance, and I think that if I were ever pregnant again, I would jump out of the nearest window. I just am petrified of it like the plague. If your experiences with children are happy ones, I don't suppose you feel quite that way, but my experience has not been that kind. So that I feel that I never want . . .

Mother elaborates on her fear of pregnancy; it is "like the plague."

DR. A.: Have you always been scared of being pregnant?

Therapist elicits relevant background.

MOTHER: Well, not at the beginning, when we were first married . . .

DR. A.: You've been married over twenty years?

MOTHER: . . . because then I wanted to have a baby. So that I wasn't afraid then, but after I had John, I knew what babies were like, or the kind I had, anyway.

Note the persecutory feeling toward children.

DR. A.: What happened with John?

MOTHER: Well, he was a horror. But I mean a horror.

John is a "horror," mother's persecutor.

DR. A.: What do you mean by that?

MOTHER: He never slept. He never ate. He cried all the time. It was simply worth your life to go through the days and nights. So much so, that I changed pediatricians. I didn't know what to do to shut him up. He simply didn't shut up, day or night. And didn't eat anything, he was, he was the most miserable baby I've ever seen. Now maybe this was my fault. . . .

DR. A.: You wanted that pregnancy then?

MOTHER: Certainly.

MOTHER: . . . four years, and I had a miscarriage before he was born. The torture came after he was born. For ten years I don't think we slept a night. And I tell you, I just was ready to go to an insane asylum. Because what he did tonight was practically what he did all the time . . . morning, noon, and night. You couldn't spend an hour with that child without wanting to jump out of your skin.

In this special context, note mother's choice of word "torture."

The child drove her "crazy."

DR. A.: So then you had a private persecutor?

Therapist pinpoints mother's feeling of "torture."

MOTHER: Yes.

DR. A.: What'd you do about sex, then?

Back to sex.

MOTHER: You mean? When?

DR. A.: After John was born.

MOTHER: We did the same thing we've been doing, it was a very intermittent thing, and uh, it has never really been right, I don't think.

DR. A.: What's the matter with it?

MOTHER: I think it's all wrong.

Mother makes sweeping indictment.

DR. A.: That doesn't tell me much. You said Bill wasn't any part of a man.

Therapist asks for specifics.

MOTHER: I didn't mean quite that. I think that Bill is able to react properly if conditions are right, if everything is right, I think he's as much of a man as anybody else. But evidently things aren't right.

Mother projects onto father the requirement of perfect conditions for sexual relations.

DR. A.: You mean in order to respond to you sexually, to rise to the occasion, he has to have perfect conditions, is that right?

Note here therapist's choice of phrase: "to rise to the occasion."

MOTHER: Evidently.

FATHER: I would say that is not an unfair statement.

DR. A.: What are the perfect conditions?

FATHER: Peace of mind, for one thing, and I would say not the knowledge that I must make the first move, all the time. We even had a standing joke when we were first married. Somebody told her that the woman must always be the pursued one, and that before the sexual act, it's the husband's job to put her in the mood. And I will not accept this as a fact. I feel that this is wrong. . . .

Father turns contentious. He now launches into a speech to justify his position. Both parents refer repeatedly to the need for "peace of mind," but they are collusive in maintaining a state of war.

DR. A.: What do you think is right? What do you want your woman to do?

FATHER: I feel that it must be a two-way street.

DR. A.: Do you want her to put you in the mood?

FATHER: Just as much as she would like me to put her in the mood.

The mood between the parents is sharply competitive.

DR. A.: How do you like your love-making?

Therapist again demands specifics.

FATHER: Well, I think if, if instead of getting in bed and having her face the other way, and waiting for me to put my arm around her, if once in a great while she would turn toward me and put her arm around me, and maybe caress me a little bit, uh, it might be a little bit more cheerful.

The question:
  Does husband serve wife?
  Or wife serve husband?

DR. A. (to mother): You make a direct advance to him?

FATHER: Very, very seldom.

DR. A. (to mother): You don't like to make a direct advance to his penis?

MOTHER: I would have no objection to his penis.

FATHER: No, I'm sure she . . .

Here, mother and father cut in on one another.

MOTHER: But I feel bitter in so many ways during the day, that I don't feel that way at night. It isn't that I object to making any direct advances, but I can't do it when my heart isn't in it.

DR. A.: So you're in a double bed and you don't make the move toward him and he doesn't . . .

MOTHER: I wouldn't say that I never do.

Mother cuts in on therapist.

DR. A.: . . . make the move toward you.

FATHER: I didn't say that.

Father tries to get a word in.

MOTHER: And it isn't never, but this is the usual.

Mother dominates conversation.

DR. A.: Tell me, during that period when you had torticollis and your head was turned this way, did you belch?

Torticollis—a condition of chronic spasm of the neck muscles.

MOTHER: . . . that was the same, but that was not . . .

Mother begins another protest.

DR. A. (to father): Which angle was her neck? Did the belch come toward you or away?

MOTHER: My neck was always to the left. My head was always facing the left.

Therapist presses the point of purpose in mother's belching.

DR. A.: Which side does Bill sleep on?

MOTHER: He . . .

FATHER: On the left.

MOTHER: . . . he usually sleeps on my left. But that was . . .

DR. A.: Well, when you had torticollis, if you belched, you belched directly at Bill.

This is direct confrontation. Therapist teases out mother's hidden motive in belching into father's face.

MOTHER: Yes. . . .

DR. A.: It was aimed properly. | The explosion of "gas" was right on target.

MOTHER: (*Laughs.*) Well, don't look for any uh, underhanded reason for this thing, because first of all . . . | Mother's laugh reveals that she catches the point.

DR. A.: You call it underhanded?

MOTHER: (*Laughs.*) You know what I mean. I'm looking for something else. | Yet she again turns evasive.

DR. A.: I'd call that above the belly button. | Therapist uses bluntness to catalyze the release of conflicting emotions.

FATHER: I once heard somebody say something that I think is very true. A woman who makes her livelihood by entertaining men should give a lot of wives lessons. Now, of course, this . . . | Father now turns sharply to the attack.

MOTHER: Such a silly thing to say. | Mother's defense falters.

FATHER: This is a very silly thing to say . . .

MOTHER: Well . . .

FATHER: . . . but maybe by saying it I'm getting a point over.

DR. A.: Let's listen to the man. | Therapist supports father's expression of feeling.

FATHER: Well, I'm finished, I've said my point and I've made the point. Uh, this is something I think most wives don't take into consideration.

MOTHER: I think most wives who honestly are in love and feel their husbands (leave) love them, don't need lessons. I wouldn't need one lesson if I felt inwardly at peace with him. I wouldn't need any lessons at all. | Mother makes a slip of the tongue. She first says "leave" instead of "love."

Mother again refers to "peace."

DR. A.: Well, what do you think he means, that you could learn a trick or two from a professional woman, a prostitute? | Therapist sharpens the issue.

MOTHER: I know what he means. I'm sure that a professional . . .

Mother is very defensive here.

DR. A. (*to father*): Have you ever had a prostitute?

FATHER: Sure, before I was married.

DR. A.: A good one?

FATHER: Well, they, they, they observe certain niceties.

Note the word "niceties."

DR. A.: Like what?

MOTHER: Naturally!

Mother cuts in. She is indignant.

DR. A.: Let's be specific.

FATHER: Well, they make themselves very pleasant, they smile and when you get into bed they don't discuss the problems of the day. I mean I'm sure it's impossible for a wife to disregard these problems of the day. But like women complain about a man bringing his business troubles home and into bed with him, I think a man has the same right to expect that type of thing, too, at night.

Father becomes increasingly vocal in presenting his case.

DR. A.: These girls you knew before you married, they treated you pretty sweet?

In talking with father, therapist is directing meaningful message to mother.

FATHER: Well, I, I guess they did. Yes, sure. But I'm sure that love wasn't involved because there were dollars passing hands.

DR. A.: You mean when the buck comes in the door, love goes out the window?

In this phase, therapist is very direct.

FATHER: No, I don't mean that at all. But this seemed to be the opposite.

DR. A.: Well now, wait a minute. I'm sure that dollars pass between you and your wife.

Another blunt confrontation.

FATHER (*to mother*): I have to pay much more than previously.

DR. A.: Well, you're paying double!

Again, a touch of humor.

FATHER: I'm using that as a figure of speech. I just think that the average wife, no, I shouldn't say the average wife, because I don't know the average wife, but I think that too little thought is given to romancing.

MOTHER: That's true of the husband too. But I don't think the romancing has to be done at night. I think it must start during the day, to have romance at night. . . . That same night we had an argument. I sat there quite peeved. He was reading a magazine in bed. He said, "Why are you, uh, sitting, why are you so quiet?" I said, "Because I'm unhappy." He said, "I know why, because of money. I repeat, and I'll tell you like I told you five, ten, and fifteen years ago, you'll never have enough money. No matter how much I make"—this is a quote—"every dollar I make goes to pay a doctor bill, a dentist bill, re-cover chairs that weren't done for twenty years, pay for a piano." There isn't anything he can point to that's a luxury or something we shouldn't have.

Mother launches a tirade.

Mother's voice turns shrill. Her indignation mounts fiercely.

A quote from her "case record."

DR. A.: Well, he just told you he made a better investment when he passed a few bucks to the girls who catered to him in bed before he married you.

Therapist connects money and sex.

MOTHER: He made a better investment?

DR. A.: Yes, he got more for his "dough."

Another instance of therapist's bluntness, mingled with humor.

MOTHER: Well, that's . . .

FATHER: No, I didn't say I got more, I said I got . . .

MOTHER: I've got a few more quotes for you. Would you like to hear them? I mean I'm giving you specifics. These are the things that gnaw away at me. I'm not the kind of person that you can say something to and I'll forget it.

The pitch of mother's voice becomes sharp and shrill. She is boiling with anger.

DR. A.: Well, what do you say to your husband's charge that you don't give him much fun in bed?

Therapist presses the challenge.

MOTHER: Because I don't feel like it. I'm sincere and when I want to make love in bed, it's because I have my heart full of love, not because I feel that it's the act to do. I want us to love each other, but really love each other.

Mother engages in angry self-justification.

DR. A.: Was there ever a time when you loved one another?

MOTHER: For a very short while.

DR. A.: Did you have any sex before you were married?

MOTHER: Never. I just wish now that I had the guts to indulge in going out with somebody, just to get him riled up. Just to see what would happen. But I'm just not built that way. I could never . . .

This is mother's provocation to father.

DR. A.: You wouldn't dare?

MOTHER: I couldn't. I couldn't live with myself. It isn't that I wouldn't for him, I couldn't for myself. I can't.

This is hardly flattering to her husband!

DR. A.: But the thought of teasing him a little that way is kind of a welcome thought.

MOTHER: It's very welcome and very interesting. And I wish I had the guts to do it.

DR. A.: You don't dare?

MOTHER: I don't dare because I'm just not built that way. But I wish I was.

DR. A.: Bill, how would you feel if she were built that way?

Therapist emphasizes phrase "built that way."

FATHER: I would be very annoyed and upset.

DR. A.: Would you tolerate it?

FATHER: No, I wouldn't tolerate it. Because I have been very true to her, over and above what I think the average man is. Now, maybe this is due to my lack of, uh, requirements, as my wife explains it, but . . .

Again, father backs off.

DR. A.: You're not very sexy?

FATHER: No, I'm not very sexy.

DR. A.: Well, what do you feel about yourself as a man? What kind of man are you? You say you're not very sexy?

FATHER: I would say I was perhaps under the average, as far as sexual requirements go. Now whether this is because of the situation that we're discussing or not, I don't know.

Father "identifies with the enemy." He joins wife's criticism of his masculinity.

DR. A.: How old were you when you were married, Bill?

FATHER: Thirty-one.

DR. A.: And your wife?

FATHER: Twenty . . . two.

DR. A. (to mother): You were a kid when you got married.

Therapist fits his language to the people and their emotions.

MOTHER: Yes, I guess you could call it that.

DR. A.: Did you know the score sexually?

FATHER. No.

MOTHER: No, I really knew very little.

DR. A.: She was very green?

FATHER: She was just as green as the corn.

DR. A.: You married an innocent?

FATHER: I married an innocent that I, well . . . (*Gets lost in laughter.*)

> Father gets a big bang out of mother's naïveté about sex.

DR. A.: But *you* weren't very innocent, were you?

FATHER: No, I was not very innocent.

DR. A.: You had had some experience?

FATHER: Yes, I had had ample experience.

DR. A.: Now, were you "under the average" sexually before you were married?

> Therapist uses father's phrase "under the average."

FATHER: I don't believe so.

DR. A.: Would you say you lost your masculine self after you got married?

> Therapist proceeds to puncture father's denigration of his own masculinity.

FATHER: No.

MOTHER: That's very flattering, I must say.

> Mother now feels challenged.

FATHER: No, it, uh . . .

MOTHER: And the funny part is that I don't think I'm unattractive. I think I'm not bad-looking. And I was always told that I was very good-looking. So if I was a dud or a dog I could understand.

> She reacts indignantly to the implied insult to her feminine worth.

FATHER: I don't think it has anything to do with your physical aspects.

MOTHER: I think it's easier to make love to a good-looking woman than it is to make love to a dog.

> And shows off her physical attributes.

FATHER: Not always. Not always.

MOTHER: I think so.

DR. A.: You're looking at me.

> Therapist catches mother by surprise. She is flirting with him.

DR. A. (*to father*): She wants to know from me if she's attractive. She says it's much nicer . . . to make love to . . .

And seeks his affirmation.

FATHER: I know she's an attractive woman.

DR. A.: . . . a good-looking woman, than a dog. She accuses you of making love with dogs.

The inference is clear. Father would rather make love to prostitutes (dogs).

FATHER: No, we weren't . . .

MOTHER: No, no.

FATHER: Honestly.

MOTHER: You see this is what I think prolongs unpleasantness. Even though it doesn't come out in the open, it seethes within me. I'm angry, we go to bed angry, we get up angry, it, it snowballs. It gets into a proportion that you can't handle quite so well. And I refuse to ignore a problem. If I see a problem, I want to drag it out and cope with it. He, he's just the opposite. He wants to push it away. Whatever problem it is. Whether it's financial or anything else. And this is another thing I have written down here. Until very recently Bill was never truthful with me, which is something that riles me to the point where I could scream.

Mother returns to the attack —another harangue.

She makes a suggestive dragging gesture. Is "the problem" her husband's sex organ?

DR. A.: You didn't know the facts of life. But he was an experienced man. He just said he was a . . . he-man before he married you.

MOTHER: That's what he says!

A high note of sarcasm.

DR. A.: Now he's gotten below average.

FATHER: Well, I don't, I don't mean to state that I was oversexed before we were married.

DR. A.: You were sexed!

Therapist pins father down.

FATHER: I was average. I went out with the boys and we had fun and we had parties. . . .

DR. A.: I don't know what average is; you were sexed. But since you married you've lost your sex?

Another example of the therapist's bluntness.

FATHER: No, no, I don't think I've lost my sex.

The question: Is the father "The Lost Sex"?

DR. A.: Well, what's happened to it?

FATHER: I just think, it hasn't been catered to, that's all, to be honest.

DR. A.: You accuse your wife of not giving you good service?

Who is supposed to serve whom?

FATHER: And I don't think it's because she doesn't want to. I think it's because she doesn't know how.

MOTHER: No, it's because I don't want to.

Now mother says what she really feels.

DR. A.: Because he doesn't romance you during the day?

MOTHER: And by romance I don't mean really romance. I mean to be very careful of what you say, say something pleasant even when you're angry. And when the kids get on each other's nerves, and get on his nerves, why let it out on me?

DR. A. (to father): So you want catering at night and she wants catering during the day.

Therapist puts it squarely.

FATHER: Well, I think this is a matter of being, really, I think the word is, just lazy.

MOTHER: I agree. I am a little lazy at times. . . .

FATHER: I think it's just lazy.

DR. A.: No, no, no, no.

Therapist is emphatic. It is not a question of "lazy."

MOTHER: I am. Physically. But it's the way you say things that I think is more important than what you say.

DR. A.: You're not lazy, you're bossy. You want him to be your "slavey" during the day.

MOTHER: Maybe. Maybe I'm too bossy. But . . .

FATHER: . . . and I resent it. . . .

Mother and father both talk at once. They are very excited.

MOTHER: Wait a minute . . . I swear I wouldn't resent it. If you said it in as nice a way as you know how, "Honey, I don't feel like going out there—you get it yourself." But with a little humor in it, with no malice in it. I wouldn't blame you one single bit. I honestly . . . That's right, he talks down at me.

They interrupt and make menacing gestures at one another.

DR. A. (to mother): Treats you like a dog?

A pointed reference to the emotional equation: dog=prostitute.

MOTHER: Well, I wouldn't say like a dog, but . . .

DR. A.: You feel depreciated, not valued?

MOTHER: That's right. I always . . .

DR. A.: But she thinks she's a wonderful piece . . . good-looking.

Therapist again resorts to plain talk.

FATHER: She is. She's a wonderful . . . I . . .

DR. A.: Wonderful piece?

FATHER: She's a very attractive . . .

DR. A.: You didn't say "piece."

FATHER: Well, I don't like the, the use of the word because I think . . .

DR. A. (as mother giggles): Well, she likes it. Look. . . .

Sharp confrontation.

MOTHER: Well, I think it's a vulgar word, but if it tells you what you want, it's all right.

DR. A.: Did I depreciate you?

Therapist points up mother's interest in sex, and the contrast between her receptivity to husband and to himself.

MOTHER: No, because you're saying it in a humorous way, I didn't mind a bit.

FATHER: Just like a woman likes to have a man that she can look up to and respect, I think a man should respect a woman in certain matters, too.

DR. A.: You talk a big line, you know. You must be a wonderful salesman.

This is said with tongue in cheek.

FATHER: I am a fairly good salesman.

DR. A.: I don't believe what you're saying, though.

A direct challenge to husband's honesty.

FATHER: That's all right, that's your right to disbelieve whatever you feel like. But what I'm saying . . .

DR. A.: But, you don't live that way! Bill, did you ever tell her to get off her fat ass?

Therapist refers here to husband's earlier charge that his wife is lazy.

FATHER: Yes, I . . . No, I, I don't go for that kind of talk and I don't use vulgar language. I'd say "backside" instead. I did that once and she resented it for weeks and weeks afterwards.

He is caught off guard by therapist's directness, and stumbles for words.

MOTHER: Then you didn't say it right. Because I know that I'm lazy . . .

FATHER: I did say it. . . .

DR. A.: You don't mind when I say it?

MOTHER: I don't mind when you say it because you're saying it in a good-natured way.

Mother takes it from therapist, but not from husband.

FATHER: She is next to the laziest woman I know. I know one woman that's lazier [his mother].

MOTHER: And yet nobody works harder than I do all day. From seven o'clock in the morning.

DR. A.: Any woman that talks as fast as your wife can't be lazy.

> Therapist presses the point home.

MOTHER: I'm not lazy.

DR. A.: It takes a lot of energy to . . .

FATHER: Well, she is lazy . . .

DR. A.: . . . to spit out all those words.

FATHER: . . . and I say she's lazy, she's lazy.

MOTHER: I don't sit down from seven o'clock in the morning until three in the afternoon. Not once. I teach every . . .

FATHER: And then from three until eight o'clock, she doesn't get up!

> Father and mother are badgering each other.

DR. A.: Now when your wife had this torticollis, uh . . .

FATHER: She used oil of wintergreen all over her.

MOTHER: Well, that was a horror. Don't . . .

> Note the use of the same term, "horror," that mother applied to son, John.

FATHER: Well, all right, but I'm saying . . .

MOTHER: That time you can just completely discount . . .

FATHER: Well, all right, so there's a year and a half shot to hell.

MOTHER: That was a horror.

FATHER: There's a year and a half shot to hell. You go to bed with a woman . . .

> No sex for a year and a half.

DR. A.: You don't like wintergreen?

FATHER: Well, I like it, but I like to chew on it as gum, but . . .

DR. A.: Don't you want to chew on her?

FATHER: Eh, yes, but I mean . . .

DR. A.: Why don't you like to chew on her?

FATHER: I mean, I mean I think that . . .

DR. A.: Do you take a bite out of her once in a while? (*To mother*) Does he bite or nibble?

Here both parents are caught off guard.

MOTHER: Well, I don't know. I never thought about it that way, but . . .

FATHER: What's the difference between a bite and a nibble?

DR. A.: Well, the one is a teaser . . . and it's fun and the other hurts.

FATHER: No, well, I try not to hurt.

DR. A.: How do you bite?

FATHER: I try not to hurt.

DR. A.: No, no, you're not, you're not telling the truth.

DR. A. (*to mother*): How come that you, you cooperate with me so beautifully? So juicy-like?

This is a reference to wife's warm, flowing response to therapist, but not to husband.

MOTHER: 'Cause I want you to know . . .

DR. A.: And with Bill you don't cooperate?

MOTHER: I do cooperate.

DR. A.: He doesn't cooperate with you?

MOTHER: I'm resentful because I don't feel he uses good judgment. I, honestly, I feel, well, maybe I shouldn't be saying this . . .

DR. A.: To me you're a real pleasing woman.

MOTHER: I think I can be very pleasing.

DR. A.: Well, you are not to him. . . .   Therapist makes the issue
                                          unmistakably clear.

MOTHER: Evidently not.

DR. A.: He rubs you the wrong way?

MOTHER: I think he really is a little   Children return, and arrange-
bit annoyed that he thinks I'm smarter   ments are made for next
than he is. Now I may be. . . .   interview.

This interview shows the therapist in the process of undercutting the tendency of the marital partners to console themselves by engaging in mutual blame and punishment. Ultimately, he stirs hope of something new and better in the relationship. He pierces the misunderstandings, confusions, and distortions, so as to reach a consensus with the partners as to what is really wrong. In working through the conflicts over differences, the frustrations and defeats, and the failure of complementarity, he shakes up the old, deviant patterns of alignment and makes way for new avenues of interaction.

In my earlier book, *The Psychodynamics of Family Life,* I attempted to lay the foundations of a theoretical position. Here my concern is more with the clinical setting and the circular process of evolving theory from the data of actual practice and then again applying that theory in further practice.

In the clinical setting, what is it that we would ask of a comprehensive theory of family? Obviously, we have already limited our problem (but not lowered our sights) by restricting our question to "the clinical setting." The ultimate, universal theory of family must transcend specific purposes and apply to family per se whatever the situation, whatever the environment. Our knowledge is nowhere near the point at which such generalizations are possible, but this need not deter us from working on the problems that face us every day. From our answers to them will come, finally, the psychotherapeutic contribution to the theory.

Now we are concerned with the what, where, how, and why of family life as this relates to the maintenance of emotional health or to the disposition to breakdown. We reach out for a way to describe families, to compare and classify them, to be able to understand the dynamics of the individual's development within the broader frame of the dynamics of family development. What does the group need of the individual? What does the individual need of the group? How do we define the balance? We are impelled to develop criteria to fulfill four main purposes. (1) to define the basic purposes and functions of the family, (2) to identify the mechanisms that control and balance these functions, (3) to delineate the processes of growth and development of the family unit and the patterns of organization that characterize the family at successive stages of its life cycle, and (4) to establish criteria for the functional interrelations of the individual and the family group.

We seek explicit answers to the following questions:

1. What are the functions and activities of family life—that is to say, what is the "work" of the family group?
2. How is the work of the family carried out? How does the family operate and to what ends?
3. How are its multiple functions integrated and balanced?
4. What are the criteria by which to differentiate the organizational pattern of the family, its roles, leadership, and division of labor, its emotional climate, its communication pattern, its sharing of satisfactions and responsibilities?
5. How may we define the complementarity of family role relationships?
6. How do we view the circularity of influence between the inner life of the family and the external adaptation of the family to the wider community?
7. How do we conceive the circularity of influence between the nuclear and the extended family, between the generations?
8. What is our conception of the natural life history of the family, its stages of growth and development? What is the influence of the family on the individual and that of the individual on the family, at each stage?

In evolving a clinical theory of family, we must deal with three main variables: family organization, family role adaptation, and individual personality. Our aim is to illuminate the participation of the family in the emotional health of its members at every stage of the life cycle: infancy, childhood, adolescence, adulthood, and old age.

We seek to define the characteristic conflicts of the family, its resources for coping with them, its mechanisms for restoring balance after an upset. We need to distinguish between healthy and pathological healing of emotional disturbance in the family group. We want to describe a family's capacity to accommodate to new experience, to learn, change, and grow. We are in search of a normative standard for the dynamic evolution of the family group and for the correlation of stages of family and individual development. Within this conceptual framework, it is essential to identify the transitory, reversible disturbances of family life; to identify those forms of disorder that become entrenched, but to which the family achieves a relatively stable internal adjustment; in a further step, to identify those distortions which become irreversible, progressive, and malignant. It is necessary, too, to correlate family type with the tendency of its members toward one or another kind of emotional breakdown. Ultimately, the aim is to design a framework for classifying family types according to mental health potentials.

Along this path lies the challenge to find ways to define particular disorders of growth in the family; to distinguish benign and malignant forms of immaturity; to search out, in the processes of family living, those phenomena that are akin to fixation, regression, progressive deviant development, and disorganization of the family unit.

2

The Question of Cure

Nietzsche once said that no man can see above his own height. In a similar sense, no society sees much beyond its own goals. In our day, a peculiar quality of blindness attaches to the question of cultivating a healthy society. Thus far, the values of Western society have not advanced to the goal of the promotion of well-being. Our society is still directed toward the more limited purpose of relieving distress. It is bogged down in a concern with "freedom from" rather than "freedom to." But it is man's occasional ability to see above his own height and beyond society's goals to catch a glimpse of meanings over the horizon that may open the path to a healthier way of life.

We think we know what a sick person is. We are less sure we know what a well person is. We believe that we can easily recognize a broken, disturbed, or sick family. We are not nearly so certain what a well family is.[1] What, then, is our criterion of cure?

It is surely not enough to seek a cure by getting rid of something "bad," a person's suffering and disablement. It is not possible to expunge the "bad" without being prepared to replace it with something better. Unless the patient is able to envisage a new and better way of living, he will cling to his old way. He will resist exchanging a familiar kind of adaptation for an alternative that he cannot yet perceive or believe in. For a long time psychotherapists

---

[1] Halbert L. Dunn, "Points of Attack for Raising the Levels of Wellness," *Journal of the National Medical Association,* Vol. XLIX, No. 4 (1957).

tended to emphasize the negative aspect of healing, the removal of symptoms and suffering; they evaded the positive side, namely, how to replace a sick way of living with a healthy one.

Health is always relative to a given life situation, and different qualities and degrees of healing and cure fit different persons in different life situations. It is essential to qualify our definition of health—health as related to specific goals, activities, and conditions of living.

Contemporary literature is much concerned with our conceptions of normal and healthy behavior. The definition of mental health seems to have trapped us in endless, circular debate. At one extreme, there are those who say that mental health is a mirage; it is simply not to be found. Everybody is sick, some more, some less. To this contention comes the blithe rejoinder: "Well, if it is true that everybody is sick, then I surely have nothing to worry about!" At the other extreme, some say: Not at all. Most people are well. The only really sick people are the psychotics. Everyone else is more or less normal; it is simply that they express their normality in infinitely diverse ways.

Obviously, these two approaches are fundamentally different. The one is concerned with mental health as an ideal, the other with mental health in terms of customary behavior or as an average standard of behavior, arrived at by statistical means. Neither is wrong; each may be valid in its own separate sphere. The usefulness of either concept rests on its application in an appropriate context. The norm, in the sense of the statistical average, depends on the adequacy of sampling; yet there is no perfect sampling technique for certain broad-scale social studies. In clinical work, on the other hand, a conception of mental health as an ideal is needed. The objection is often raised that this ideal is unreal, romantic, impossible to achieve; that the line between normal and abnormal is arbitrarily drawn. Yet clinicians cannot function without such an ideal; it is indispensable.

Another aspect of the problem must also be taken into account. Under special conditions, certain types of disordered behavior may become quite widespread and therefore may become accepted as a norm. Long ago, Trigant Burrow[2] illuminated the distinction

---

[2] Trigant Burrow, *The Preconscious Foundations of Human Experience,* ed. William E. Galt (New York: Basic Books, 1964).

between normal and healthy. He uncovered the pathology of normality and drew the conclusion that the pathology of the species and the disorder of society are primary; the pathology of the individual is secondary, i.e., the individual neurosis derives from the social neurosis.

Is there a way out of this dilemma? Perhaps so. First, as already suggested, there is the need to suit the standard of normal and healthy to particular problem areas. Second, there is the need in the clinical field for the application of an ideal, a theoretical model of mental health. There are, along this path, relevant concepts: health as the preservation of the capacity to correct disturbance and to maintain the capacity for growth, and health as nature operating toward its end, that is to say, toward the highest excellence of which we are capable. This is the self-actualizing concept of health, the fulfillment of the potentials of being.

In clinical work, every practitioner inevitably judges the level of health of his patients against an inner operational conception of health as an ideal. It is his personal standard based on his experience, training, and accumulated wisdom. Each practitioner builds his own standard empirically, deriving selected elements of ideal health from the individual persons he observes, including himself. He then synthesizes these elements to create for himself an operational conception of health. There is, however, the special difficulty of a lack of consensus among practitioners on this ideal.

Even with the limitations of present-day knowledge, we have learned something about individual personality and something about society and culture. Nevertheless, throughout time, ideas about normal and abnormal have been shaped more strongly by social convention than by scientific study. Social health and mental health have been mainly what people thought they were. In other words, statements on illness and health are normative positions that reflect a prevailing value judgment and thus often echo the vested interests of a given society and culture.

An effect of this molding of the views of sickness and wellness by social forces is revealed by our shifting points of view on the parallelism of physical and mental disease. The equation of mental with physical disease is a loose, inaccurate description. Insofar as we have tended to identify sickness in terms of its end-stages, in terms of pain and disablement, getting well has meant becoming "not sick."[3] It has signified merely the relief of extreme signs and symptoms of sickness. In this sense, the traditional orientation has been mainly toward the negative aspect. Getting well is being relieved of the manifestations of disablement. It is a patching job that allows a person to work again and to carry on his daily living. This result is pointedly illustrated by the attitude of many patients who, when asked by their doctors how they feel, will often reply, "Well, Doctor, I haven't collapsed yet. I'm still functioning." They almost never say, "I feel well and happy; my life is full and exciting."

Thus we are presented with a paradoxical problem. To achieve lasting relief from illness, it is necessary to promote general well-being, in the spheres of both physical medicine and mental medicine. Yet we must confess that we know relatively little as yet about how to promote general well-being.

To get rid of something bad, we must be prepared to replace it with something better—decidedly so in the case of psychotherapeutic healing. The patient clings to a sick condition, to his symptoms and disablement, until convinced he can trade it in for something better. He must develop a true faith that there *is* something better, and he must be able to fit it to his life situation. It is at this level that the psychotherapeutic function reveals a weakness. By tradition, psychotherapists are oriented primarily toward relief of symptoms, not toward the promotion of well-being. They tend to sidestep this aspect of the therapeutic challenge, preferring to believe that the problem of health will somehow take care of itself, that the patient, relieved of his symptoms, will spontaneously achieve well-being. By no means does this regularly follow. The removal of one set of symptoms may merely usher in a new set, sometimes worse than the original. Symptoms, in one sense, represent an effort to wall off the area of sickness, as in the creation of an abscess, to contain pus and prevent it from invading the blood stream; symptoms, in another sense, derive from and reflect the basic character of the person. Character is socially oriented; it is related to other characters. It is this consideration that requires the psychotherapist to consider in depth the individual's adaptive

---

[3] See Mary K. O'Hara, "What Shall Be Called Normal?" *Child and Family,* Vol. III, No. 4 (1964).

relations with his significant human environment, especially that of his family group. The nourishment of general well-being cannot be conceived of except within the matrix of the mutual accommodation of individual and group. Unless an appropriate level of emotional interchange is achieved in these relations, health cannot be maintained. To keep his health, a man must either find or create a healthy family and community. This necessity raises the difficult problem of the relation between well-being and "the good life," the relation between well-being and ethics. In the final analysis, the issue of health embraces the environment as well as the individual. We cannot divorce health from the question of values.

Values are complex phenomena, and they are in no sense static. They are the outcome of unceasing struggle and conflict, the ever-changing product of human evolution within a defined culture. A clear and specific definition of the concept of values is fundamental to the question of healing and cure. Values are life goals that provide an orientation to the relations of individual, family, and society. They are a compass for the expression in action of a person's identity within a complex matrix of social relationships. They connect the person's views of self and world. They are both personal and social. Without socialization there can be no values; without values there can be no socialization. Values by their very essence are shared experiences. Although they do not have a private origin, they become privately treasured. A person may defend his values as he defends his very life.

What about the question of values and health? Surely healthy people often assert healthier values than do sick people. Still, there is the paradox that "normal" people sometimes express sicker values than "sick" people. Generally speaking, mature people hold better values than immature ones, but not always. Parents frequently know better what is good for their children than do the children themselves. Sometimes, however, it is the other way around. Do husbands know better what is good for their wives, or do wives know better what is good for their husbands? Sometimes, as we know, a minority is more correct in its values than the majority. The problem lies in the qualifying word *sometimes*. If the term *value* is to hold meaning, we must scrupulously define the prevailing human conditions.

With impressive frequency certain kinds of sick people choose the better values, despite their sickness. This choice is possible because, although disabled, sick people often preserve islands of health and fight to keep faith with their deepest spiritual yearnings. On the other hand, some persons fall ill mentally *because* they cling to cherished personal values and yet are too weak to defend them; therefore, they break down. In certain human situations this factor is of critical importance.

It is true that neurotics fear exchanging a known way of life for another that is as yet unknown. At another level, however, one sometimes observes neurotic persons experiencing a fierce, agonizing struggle to advance their values in a positive way. Let me illustrate.[4] A man fifty years old is much improved after two years of psychoanalytic therapy. His symptoms, of a rather severe type, have largely abated; they included syphilophobia, an obsessive thought of sticking a penknife into his eye, a fear of blindness, and an addiction to surgery (120 operations). Feeling greatly improved, he belabored the question of terminating psychotherapy. The more he argued that it was time to quit, the longer he hung on. He stayed in analysis for two years more, contentiously debating the issue of value differences between himself and his analyst. He was Christian and an anti-Semite, but he had chosen a Jewish doctor.

He asserted with mounting intensity that there was a barrier to further progress in his therapy. This barrier was an "irreconcilable difference" between his kind of person and the analyst's kind of person. The only thing to do was to agree to disagree. The only standards for analytic cure, he said, were Jewish standards. Analysts advocated humanitarian ideals and social values because they were Jews. The patient is forced to become like the analyst. He must believe in love and friendship. He must believe in freedom, fairness, and justice. He must accept Jews and Negroes. He must want to work for a living. He must be "pink," or at least liberal. He must not worship money or power. He must strive for a better world.

---

[4] Nathan W. Ackerman, "Antisemitic Motivation in a Psychopathic Personality: A Case Study," *The Psychoanalytic Review*, XXXIV (1947), 76–101.

In opposition to these presumed criteria for cure, the patient bitterly asserted his "irreconcilable difference." In a fierce competitive struggle with the analyst, his anti-Semitic feelings emerged in full force. He spit out his violence. But his anxiety caused him to hack, cough, and get red in the face.

"I am a non-Jew. I am too old to change. I don't want to make peace with the world, only with my own needs for pleasure. I have nothing to give anyone. I don't want to work for a living. I will fight to keep my money. I don't want to be a drudge or a slave. It is absurd to think this can ever be a loving world. I hate reformers. You hope for some good out of this world. You are a better person ethically than I. You are gullible because you believe in social reform. You are gullible if you believe you can make me change. The idea of loving people is mystical. I am ferociously hostile to you because you are a Jew and because I imagine you are a fellow traveler. The Jews are righteous. They try to intimidate other people into being good. I don't want to learn to love. In a revolution, I'd fight against you. I'd kill all the Jews and Communists. Can I ever be friendly like a Jew? I don't think so. I just want to hang on to a dear prejudice. The hostility of others brings out the very best in me. I don't want my closed system invaded. Both the old and the new world are dead for me. There is no love in either for me and I feel dead.

"You are Jewish. You want me to swallow the Jews. I gag on it. I refuse. By God, I won't swallow that. When I swallow you I feel bloated. I belch. When I am in a good mood I say: 'Here, take me, I love you.' Then I get scared and draw back on my hate. You are a bad diet. You hurt inside me. That's what I get for trusting anyone. I, the anti-Semite, warm up to you, a Jew. My face and body burn. Affection destroys my defense. You get under my skin. You creep inside me and cause inflammation. I begin to itch and scratch. I've got to grab you out. There's no getting rid of hate. These damn foreigners come here. They sit down to eat with us. They push us away from our own table and food. If I don't want to murder, the only solution is to withdraw. I don't want the hate to chew me up."

From the foregoing quotations it is plain that being cured for this patient meant being Judaized, being converted to the analyst's personal values. It meant being circumcised, being forced to swallow the analyst with all his values; it also meant being eaten by the analyst. This patient feared to be robbed of his sense of self, that self being identified with the power of hate. It is of interest to note that the competitive value struggle with the analyst emerged only in the second half of the analysis, after the patient's symptoms were largely relieved. It took two years more for him to be convinced that it was safe to be a good person. Obviously he was protesting his own basic desire to be converted into a good human being.

Now can it be, as some analysts allege, that a patient can be cured by analysis and still at the point of terminating therapy remain a nasty, destructive person? I do not think so. The patient may be relieved of his symptoms, but he may again fall ill if he does not grow into a better human being.

The basic question is: Does the problem of values belong to the question of psychotherapeutic cure, or doesn't it? I believe firmly that it does. Obviously this rests on how we define psychotherapy, how we conceptualize the goals, the method, and the cure. If we take as a theoretical model Freud's classical description of technique, in which the analyst is not a real person, remains anonymous, and is only a mirror for the patient's fantasies, then surely this process is not a true social interaction and the problem of human values can thus be arbitrarily excluded. If, on the other hand, we conceive of psychotherapy as a genuine social experience involving a circular interchange of emotion between two or more people, then without question the issue of value conflict and value growth must be squarely faced. But this is in no sense a question of the therapist imposing his values, or coercing or converting the patient. It is rather a question of both patient and therapist recognizing explicitly the need to engage in an ongoing struggle with the meaning of value differences, and ultimately reaching a conviction as to which values are on the side of growth and health. If a patient is to become well and stay well, the meaning of human differences and the corresponding clash of values must be clearly faced in the therapeutic experience. Only as the impact of old and new in human experience is sincerely worked through can there occur a true evolution of values toward effective maturity.

According to the World Health Organization's definition, "Health is a state of complete physical, mental and social well-being, and not merely the absence of disease and infirmity."[5] By this definition, relatively few people can be considered healthy. They may not be overtly sick or disabled, but so long as they do not achieve complete well-being, they remain vulnerable in one or another degree to breakdown; they are candidates for sickness.

In the same sense, families may not achieve well-being and yet may not be overtly broken or sick. They are neither purely well nor purely sick, only mainly well or mainly sick. They exhibit healthy and sick tendencies in varying proportions and are, accordingly, more or less susceptible to sickness. The critical feature is, of course, the relative balance that prevails between the health-maintaining forces and the sickness-inducing ones. At any stage of evolution of the family unit, both tendencies coexist, those that maintain health and those that predispose to breakdown and illness. The balance shifts with time and with the vicissitudes of the life situation, both in the inner life of the family and in the adaptation of the family to the surrounding community.

In characterizing families as well or sick, we are reflecting on a way of life. Health and illness are functional aspects of a dynamic, ongoing process of change in the way of life. The way of life affects the balance of health and illness and this balance, in turn, in circular fashion affects the way of life.

To borrow a thought from Dunn,[6] health and illness can be judged in terms of four B's: being, belonging, becoming, and befitting. We can evaluate the level of health of an individual or a family in terms of who they are, where they belong, what they are becoming, and how well their behavior fits with their life situation.

It is not then possible to understand illness without understanding health, nor is it possible to understand health without understanding illness. The value of health relates to the good life in strange ways. A prime characteristic of health is man's unawareness of it. Under ordinary conditions, he takes health for granted. Only as he loses it does he become conscious of its importance. This truth holds for families as well as for individuals. In addition, the health value needs to be understood in relation to other values.

---

[5] From the preamble of the Constitution of the World Health Organization.

[6] *Op. cit.*

The urge of man is not merely to live, but to live better, to live fully and well. His first concern is with what he is able to do in and with life—success or failure in personal, family, and community terms.

Families differ from one another as do individuals. Behavior at both levels is characterized by enormous diversity. Each family has a certain quality of uniqueness, an idiosyncratic pattern. Some families are healthier than others, just as some individuals are healthier than others. It is a relative matter, to be sure. In order to differentiate between well and sick families, we must devise basic standards that can serve as measuring rods for different degrees of the balance of health and illness in the family group.

At the present stage of the emerging science of man, is it possible to derive a theoretical model of a healthy family? Those investigators who say that there is no such thing as mental health, either in the individual or in the family group—that mental health is a value, a dream, a yearning; that we crave it, we reach out toward it, but that it perpetually eludes us—argue that mental health is not *being;* it is *becoming.*

We may surely agree that mental health is relative, as all values are relative. We could go so far as to say that mental health is more of a dream than a fact. Yet, as life goes, the dream has a very real role in human existence. It is exactly the clash between the real and ideal that moves us. Family is both being and becoming. What we must look at is the family on its way from here to there. Who and where is the family and where is it going? That is the question. Can we define the path of the family dynamism? A family group is never static. It moves forward or backward; it is closer to or further from the ideal of mental health.

To this perspective on the concept of health, some may offer the retort, "Maybe so, but mental health is not a question of science." The answer to this rejoinder is easy. It depends on how we choose to define science. If, by a given definition of science, our conception of mental health is excluded, we may offer a twofold reply. There is more to life than science, and some of the most important problems of life are left outside the conventional sphere of science. What we really require here is a broader view. The rules and methods of a science of man are of necessity different in some important respects from the rules and methods of the physical sciences. In the natural life history of man and his relations with other men, we cannot categorically separate what is from what we would like it to be. In a broader, more advanced philosophy of science, questions of health, meaning, and ethics can be included; it is a question of inventing different methods of study to fit the special nature of these problems.

Therefore, when we consider the challenge of healing by means of psychotherapy, we must go beyond the model of "cure" as the relief of distress. We must be concerned with several questions: the relation of cure to our changing conceptions of illness, the nature of partial cure, and complete cure, the quality of cure, the proof of cure, the relation of cure to the specific illness and to the person being treated, the relation of cure to the nature of the curing process itself—the dynamics of the psychotherapeutic relationship—and, finally, the prevailing conditions of life. To bring about lasting therapeutic change requires a testing of new ways of action in social relationships. There is increasing understanding of the criteria by which a true psychotherapeutic change is induced. Such change is expressed as a series of shifts in feeling, in perception, in meaning, in bodily experience, and in the integration of personality into the appropriate role positions in the group. In other words, in the last analysis, cure is measured by the development of a new and more effective set of relationships and corresponding social action.

Psychotherapy itself has achieved a wide range of definitions depending on the differing situational contexts of the relationship between patient and therapist. In a general way, it may be described as a systematic procedure by which one person, professionally trained, seeks to influence through psychological means the emotional functions of another person, the patient, toward health. The task has two facets: the elimination of suffering and disabled functioning, and the enhancement of the patient's ability to fulfill himself as a person and as a member of society. This conception of psychotherapy, limited to the one-to-one relationship between patient and therapist, must be modified when one extends the sphere of therapeutic influence to a group setting, as, for example, in the treatment of a whole family.

It is a widely accepted principle that there are multiple forms of psychotherapy, each specializing in the direction of a different task and intervening in different components of human disturbance. By its very nature, each form of psychotherapy exerts a partial and selective effect on specific levels of disturbed functioning. Two crucial problems must be faced: What are the common denominators in these varied psychotherapeutic methods? What distinguishes good therapy from bad therapy?

It is self-evident that shifts in the theory of behavior and in the theory of social relations influence the changing styles of therapeutic practice. It is also true that the accumulation of empirical knowledge and experience within a range of treatment methods influences the theory of behavior. In other words, a reciprocal influence moves back and forth between the theory of behavior and the theory of therapeutic practice. Within this framework lies the whole principle of the essential interdependence of methods of diagnosis and treatment.

The role of the healer at any given stage in human history is influenced by social and cultural change and by the evolutionary shift in our ideas about illness and health; it is also influenced by historic changes in the concept of the causation of mental illness and in the theory and philosophy of the healing practice itself.

Psychotherapeutic method is influenced by many factors: (1) the personal expectations of the patient, (2) the orientation of the psychotherapist toward his role, (3) the group influence surrounding the patient, which molds his goals and expectations, (4) the group influence surrounding the therapist, which in turn shapes his conception of appropriate therapeutic goals and procedures, (5) further developments in the theory of personality and in the theory of therapeutic method.

The goals of psychotherapy are these: To remove disabling symptoms; to strengthen the patient's personality so that he may not again fall ill, that is to say, to reinforce his immunity against the further invasion of illness; beyond that, to enable the person to realize his potential, to capitalize on his resources, to feel free and happy to satisfy his personal needs and to become an efficient, productive human being. Liberated from crippling anxiety, a person can then unfold his capacity to love others, to share with them both pleasure and responsibility, and to make a positive contribution to the welfare of friends, family, and community, as well as to accept contributions from these sources.

However one defines psychotherapy, it cannot be understood without regard to the relation of the person with his social group. In a basic sense all psychotherapy needs to be understood in the context of the levels of interpersonal support extended to the patient. Psychotherapy needs to be integrated with social treatment. In this larger scheme, psychotherapy becomes psychosocial therapy. Social therapy involves a calculated effort to modify selected elements of the social situation, in order to make possible an improved adaptation of the person to his situation. In addition, in many circumstances that involve a measure of stress or inequality between a person and an environment, one endeavors to make the person more equal to coping with his environment. The process, therefore, entails either a change of the environment or a strengthening of the individual so that he is more equal to it, or both. On the environmental side, there are two facets: a reduction of external danger and an expansion of the range of positive opportunities.

As we survey the field today, a pervasive shift is occurring in attitudes toward the challenge of psychotherapy. The trends toward change can be identified. Psychodynamic science is making room for social science; social science is making room for psychodynamic science. As a broader science of man evolves, a new conception emerges of the responsibilities of the psychotherapeutic specialist. A critical shift is taking place also in the conception of the mental health team and in the rationale that underlies the division of labor among the various members of the team.

In the psychotherapeutic relationship the therapist is less authoritarian. The traditional status differences of patient and therapist are downgraded, and there is a greater sense of mutual respect. The therapist is more humble, more open, more human and spontaneous. He takes the patient as a partner in the healing experience. The relations between patient and therapist are circular, each influencing the other; and the behavior of the therapist is as rigorously examined as is the behavior of the patient. Therapeutic experience is judged as an interactional and transactional process. It is in this context that countertransference is now seen as being fully as important as transference. The emotional attitude of the therapist toward his patient is often viewed as the most important determinant in the outcome of therapy. Coping with conflict and anxiety is seen as a shared interpersonal experience.

Therapy is influenced by a particular coupling of patient and therapist. It is a kind of "marriage." Sometimes the patient is well-motivated, the therapist is competent, and yet the "marriage" does not click. There is a subtle something in the combination that is the deciding factor. In evaluating the dynamics of psychotherapeutic interaction, the value systems and identity connections of both patient and therapist must be taken into account. Social-class belongingness of patient and therapist affects the entire experience of therapy. The group factors are an integral part of the therapeutic process.

The importance of the "here and now" aspect of the patient's struggle with life receives greater appreciation. A one-sided absorption in the conditionings of past experience is outmoded. The determinants of the past are examined in the context of contemporary problems and conflicts. There is no escape from the present by burying oneself in the past. More and more the interaction of patient and therapist comes to be a live, spontaneous one. It cannot be routinized, mechanized, or ritualized. The therapist shows himself as a human being, a real person. The love experience in the relationship is genuine rather than contrived. The therapist uses his own emotions appropriately toward the therapeutic objective. He is active and makes selective use of his personality to bring about the desired therapeutic end. He comes out of hiding. He injects into the emotional interchange the needed kinds of feeling, the needed kinds of imagery of self and others, in order to energize a movement toward health.

The principle of flexibility is increasingly valued in the application of therapeutic process. The method of treatment is freely and fluidly accommodated to the unique nature of the patient's problem and life situation.

A shift of emphasis is taking place away from the traditionally exclusive emphasis on intrapsychic conflict, rooted in the unconscious, to patterns of coping, defense, ego-integration, and social interaction, although integration of unconscious mechanisms is nonetheless accomplished. In effect, the therapist extends his sphere of interest and concern from the entrenched, intrapsychic mecha-

nisms of personality to a systematic evaluation of the total functioning of personality within a range of social situations. He
confronts the patient's merged perception of dangers in the here
and now with dangers coming up out of the past.

The limitations of insight as a therapeutic force are better
recognized. It is now clear that a lasting therapeutic change ne-
cessitates a testing out of new ways of action in the social field.
Therapeutic improvement is measured in a series of shifts in perception, in meaning, in feeling, in body experience, and in the
integration of personality into the appropriate role positions in the
group. Cure is measured by the development of a new, effective
pattern of social action.

Psychotherapy today is approaching a crisis. It is nearing a
fork in the road, and it is confronted by the broad avenue of
psychosocial influence. It must choose one way or the other. Shall
it continue in an exclusive fashion to dig deeper into unconscious
mental mechanisms, or will it transcend this limitation to embrace
the relations of inner and outer experience? Will it join intrapsychic
and interpersonal conflict; or will it join the individual and his
group? The conviction grows that the law of diminishing returns
begins to make itself felt in the traditionally one-sided concentration on the inside of the mind, while ignoring or bypassing the
outside of the mind, the ongoing relations of the individual with
his human surroundings. Unless we develop a parallel concern
with the health of the group, we shall continue to suffer a critical
handicap in helping people to get well and in keeping them well.
The confrontation of this aspect of the problem is the next step
in the evolution of the science of behavior and the science of the
healing arts. It is in this context that we must appraise the potential importance of an emerging method of diagnosing and treating the whole family.

In order to move in this direction, the philosophy of psychotherapy must pay increasing respect to the importance of the role
of values in mental health. The goals of psychotherapy must be
seen in wider perspective. They may be viewed in a hierarchical
series: (1) symptom relief, (2) self-realization, (3) integration of
the individual into his group, which requires an appropriate shift
in personal values. Psychotherapy must encompass the relations
of identity, values, and ethical concern. It must be oriented not

only toward the aim of *freedom from* but also toward the further aim of *freedom for* a set of positive goals in life.

The goals of psychotherapy must be integrated with those of prevention and those of education. With the acceptance of this broader view of the responsibilities of the psychotherapist, the pattern of mental health services in a community must evolve new and different forms. Where mental health services are the responsibility of a professional team, the division of labor must be correspondingly modified. Life is not the individual person; life is the family of man.

Diagnosis and treatment of the whole family are a new challenge in mental health. The challenge is one of mountainous proportions; it frightens us, but the mountain is there to be climbed and there is no turning back.

3

The Family as a Psychosocial Entity

To begin at the beginning, the human family is a unique organization. It is the basic unit of society; it provides for the union of man and woman so that they may create children and assure them nurture and strength. The human being is a true familial animal. The mother's body is structured to carry and to give birth to the child and to nourish him to a condition of healthy growth. The father's body is specialized for strength and potency. He is the protector of mother and young. These are the essential, ever-present features, regardless of the endless variations of family pattern superimposed by contrasting cultures.

The father sows the seed; the mother gives birth to the child. She fulfills this function not only for herself, her husband, and her family, but also for the species and the entire human community. She is able to provide proper care of the infant only with the support of the father and the community. The human infant cannot survive alone. Although the feeding person is literally the mother, the nutritive process and its effects are in the last analysis a function of the supportive characteristics of the parental couple and the family as a whole. Once born, the infant is a physically separate and intact organism. His mind, however, is embryonic and remains profoundly joined for a long time with the parents' minds. The family is literally the cradle for the infant's tender mind as well as for his body.

We sometimes use the phrase "familial organism" to denote the family's qualities of living process and functional unity. The phrase suggests that the family has a natural life history of its own, a period of germination, a birth, a stage of growth and development with a capacity to adapt to progression and change, and finally the passing of the old family and the creation of new ones. There is a useful analogy between the organismic properties of the individual and the vital features of family life, for both entities are characterized by an interdependence of parts and a specialization of functions. Here, however, the analogy ends, for there are crucial differences, too. The individual is characterized by physical unity, but the members of the family do not adhere to each other in the same way as do the organs of the body. The individual organism dies, whereas the family is reborn with each generation.

We speak of the age of the family, which in the course of its life span passes through sequential stages of development. The configuration of the family undergoes significant shifts in each phase of transition. It is one kind of structure in a period of child rearing, another when the children enter puberty and the parents move into their prime, and still another when the children mature, marry, and go their several ways and the parents glide into old age. Just as there are critical turning points in the maturation of the individual, so too are there analogous crises in the life of the family. As the family evolves from one stage to the next, a new and appropriate balance must be discovered for the essential mutuality of man and woman, parent and child.

Thus the family serves biological continuity in providing a socially supported group pattern for the joining of male and female so as to care for the young. The family is a universal design for living. It is the unit of growth and experience, of fulfillment and failure; it is also the unit of health and illness. It does two things: it assures survival, and it molds the essential humaneness of man. Beyond the primary task of protecting the biological integrity of the organism, the main ongoing responsibility of the family is the socialization of its members. Where socialization fails, the human quality of the members also fails, as is dramatically exemplified in those families where the failure of the socializing function results in children who behave like animals, who are brutalized, who turn criminal or pervert, or who become victims of mental illness.

The family is extraordinarily sensitive to the needs of the persons who compose it and to its wider community environment. The bonds of love and loyalty, the reciprocity of need, and the relations of mother, father, and child may be organized in many varying ways depending on social and cultural conditions. The very survival of the family rests on its capacity for flexible adaptation to a changing environment. The complexity and variability of the family constellation in its emergence through history and in the contrasting societies of our own time poignantly reflect the way in which the human community balances man as a social being and man as an individual. It is in the nature of man that his life is continuously intertwined with the lives of other men, and yet he strives to be free.

The family may be regarded as a kind of barter unit. The values exchanged are love, food, protection, material goods, and information. Within the group the parents are in the beginning the prime givers. The children are at first mainly receivers, but, across time, they also make significant returns in kind.

There is a dominant cultural configuration of family, in the form of required role adaptations. The life roles of mother, father, child, and grandparent acquire specific meaning only within a defined family and culture. The family molds the kinds of persons it needs to carry out its functions; the members in turn influence the family toward satisfaction of their personal strivings. The identity of the individual requires support from family identity. In turn, family identity requires support from the surrounding community.

The relations of individual and family are characterized by a delicate interplay of parallel processes of emotional joining and separation. Out of the basic union come individuation and new growth, but each stage of individuation in turn calls for the discovery of new levels of sharing and union. Sharing and cooperation are fundamental principles in family relations. Self-esteem, the satisfaction of emotional need, the control of conflict, and growth and fulfillment in life depend on what is done with elements of sameness and difference in family relations. The qualities of complementarity and conflict in family life rest on the perceptual response of the members to the differences among them.

As the individual matures, marries, and creates a new family, his identity is joined in these relationships, is modified and further differentiated. It is the interaction, merging, and redifferentiation of the individuality of each marital partner that mold the identity of the new family. The offspring epitomizes this new family identity. The psychological identity of the marital and parental pair shapes the child to this identity, but the child, in turn, also shapes the parental pair to his needs. The emotional climate of the family is a continuously evolving one. The identity, values, and expectations of the family change over time, and the family role adaptations shift accordingly. It is within this atmosphere, constantly in flux, that the child's personality and social adaptation emerge.

The emotional give and take of family relationships is the crucial center of forces that make or break mental health. The family determines the emotional fate of the child; it affects the emotional development of the adolescent and adult members as well. The stability of the family hinges on the complicated and sensitive pattern of emotional balance and interchange. The behavior of each member is affected by the behavior of every other member. A shift in the emotional interaction of one pair of persons alters the interactional processes of other family pairs. Thus the interrelations of individual and family behavior need to be scrutinized along three dimensions: (1) the dynamics of the family as a group, (2) the processes of emotional integration of the individual into his family roles and the basic reciprocity of role relationships, (3) the internal organization of individual personality and its historic development.

The organization of society and the patterning of the family are interdependent and interpenetrating. Society shapes the functions of the family to its own historically emerging goals. The family molds the kinds of persons that are required to express these goals. The members themselves, as far as they are able, fit the family entity to their respective individualized needs. In circular fashion, the pattern of the family then exerts an influence on the evolving trends of the wider community.

Specific forms of the family vary with the culture. In our own rapidly changing, heterogeneous culture, there cannot be a clear uniformity of family pattern. There are, rather, many and varied family types, differing in structure, function, and adaptation to the social community. The total configuration of the family molds the forms of behavior that are required in the roles of husband and wife, father and mother, parent and child, child and sibling, and the relation of each of these with their respective families of origin. Each member reacts with a unique balance of tendencies to conform or to rebel, to submit to or actively to alter the family's role expectations.

The specific purposes and functions of the family may be delineated as follows: union and individuation, the care of the young, the cultivation of a bond of affection and identity, reciprocal need satisfaction, training for the tasks of social participation, including the sex role, and the development and creative fulfillment of its members.

The balancing and regulation of these multiple functions constitute a major responsibility. The specific manner in which this responsibility is carried out reflects the organizational pattern, the unique identity, and the value orientation of a given family. This process is a continuously evolving one, influenced by the representations of family moving through three or more generations, molded from within by the strivings of its members and from without by social and cultural pressures. The growth and effective adaptation of the family unit are reflected in its capacity to integrate, harmonize, and balance these multiple functions. The performance of a family at a given time can be assessed in relation to the fulfillment of its aims and values, the regulation of its essential functions, and the resulting balance of health and illness. As the family evolves from one stage to the next, it equilibrates its multiple functions in a special way. Family as family cannot stay the same; it moves forward or backward. As the family moves progressively through each phase of its life cycle, from courtship to early marriage, or to early parenthood, then to advancing stages of parenthood with increasing numbers of children, and finally into maturity and aging, the configuration of family relationships progressively changes. It is the evolutionary development of these complex, interwoven processes that defines the growth and character of a family. It is the efficacy of the family's resources for coping with ever-changing problems and conflicts that influences the relative balance between the tendency to cling to the old and the readiness to receive and adapt to new experience; this is the family's capacity for growth. The family succeeds or fails in accordance with its capacity for achieving an appropriate regulation and balancing of its central functions. It is adaptive if it is able to fulfill and harmonize all essential functions in a manner that is appropriate to the identity and strivings of the family and its members and in a manner that is realistic in relation to both the dangers and the opportunities that prevail in the surrounding environment. It is maladaptive if it suffers a loss of any of its vital functions, if it safeguards some at the cost of others, if it over-asserts some while underestimating others, if it distorts or sacrifices functions indispensable to its own continuity. When such trends appear, the family is out of kilter; it is deficient in its identity representation, in its resources for dealing with conflict, solving problems, and making decisions. It becomes congealed and rigidi-fied; it loses plasticity and its power to learn and grow. In such families one sees increasing fixity, stereotypy, and constriction of behavior; the growth potentials end here.

A distorted balance of family functions is reflected in a dispro-portionate focus on some, while others are rigidified and warped. In the extreme instance, one basic function may be completely sacrificed to another. In some families there is a paramount con-centration on security and survival, or on the acquisition of prop-erty, and a subordination of other essential functions, such as the cultivation of a bond of affection, intimacy, and identity. The needs of one or another family member may be sacrificed to the primacy of economic survival or to the goals of social conformity. In other instances, sexual fulfillment may be sacrificed to child rearing, or vice versa. The development and creative fulfillment of the individual may be subordinated to the need for omnipotent protection and security. Affection, spontaneous expression, and pleasure may be suppressed in the interest of fortifying authority and discipline. Closeness and sharing may be sacrificed to indi-vidual initiative and the striving for self-sufficiency. Essential fam-ily functions may be sacrificed for the aggrandizement of one family member. In some situations, the family preserves an outer shell of success, it acquires security and wealth, but the soul of the family decays. Whatever the pattern of warp, the family has lost its steering power, and its growth potential is impaired. The inevitable consequence is a trend toward recurring crises in family life, an increasing disorder of relationships, and a movement toward disorganization in the family group and the emotional breakdown of some of its members.

In our concern with the family and its health, what is the size of the family we are talking about? What is the dimension, the boundary of the family unit? We may refer exclusively to the nuclear family—mother, father, and children—or we may embrace three or more generations, the families of origin as well as the family of procreation. Do we encompass representations of the extended family—uncles, aunts, and cousins? Do we conceptualize the family group as having but one person who fulfills exclusively the role of mother and one person who fulfills that of father, or do we think of a larger family configuration in which there are multiple representations of parental figures, one in which the responsibilities of child care and training are shared, divided, and diluted?

From the point of view of the relations of family and health, how we define the family may make a crucial difference. In Western society, as a result of urban living and increased social mobility, the main trend is toward a relatively cohesive nuclear family unit, one in which the psychosocial functions tend to become separated from the traditions and standards of the extended family. But this is a question of degree. There are enormous variations in the extent of the connectedness of the nuclear family with the extended family. Also, to whatever extent the nuclear family cuts itself off from the influence of family tradition, it tends to substitute social and emotional connections with a network of peer associations.

For the special problem of the emotional impact of relatives, we must mark out significant points of reference. Relatives are persons occupying specific positions in the family constellation. The emotional expectations attached to a relative depend on the symbolic status and role attributed to that person within the larger image of the family group. The relative has a definitive image of self related to his family position, which in turn is related to the images of him that every other family member molds. There is a continuous interplay between the relative's image of himself and the reciprocal images that other members hold of him. Within this context it is important to know to what extent a relative is perceived as belonging inside or outside the family group, that is to say, as being a member of the in-group or the out-group. Since by definition a relative occupies a fringe position, he may be felt to be inside the family at one time and outside at another time. It is self-evident that a relative living under the same roof may be emotionally excluded or exiled from the family as an influencing agent, whereas a relative living elsewhere may nonetheless be psychically included and may be a potent influencing agent within the nuclear family entity.

How does one approach the question of the emotional impact of relatives? What impact? On whom? The question calls for sharper formulation. One must break it down to the what, where, when, how, and why. It is, of course, not a one-person problem; it is a relationship with two or more people. The emotional influence is circular, not linear. The process moves both ways; the forces are interpenetrating. The relatives and the family members alternate the roles of sender and receiver of influence. The validity of this principle is easily seen in the need to view the mother-child pair as a two-way phenomenon, child influencing mother and mother influencing child, both of them influenced by the role of the father, the family, and the larger community.

The pertinent questions are many. How does the emotional joining and interaction of an individual with a relative affect the role behavior of each partner in the pair? What is the influence of the family group on the emotional identity of the pair? What is the effect of the pair on the identity of the family as a whole? Does it set up conflicting goals and values? Does it set up opposing authority representations? Does it alter the alignment of family relationships? Or is the bond so exploited that hostile emotion against authority representations within the family is displaced to this relative? Does the bond bring about an emotional rift in the family, alter previous relationships, or bring about a new pattern of splits within the group? These are only a few of the relevant problems.

The specific influence exerted by such relationships may be explored within the frame of the group structure of the family and the reciprocal role adaptations within the group. The path and extent of influence vary inevitably with such factors as the status, age, sex, and personality of both the relative and the family member. The effect on family functioning is either toward greater unity or toward deeper disunity. It may produce a positive or a negative influence on family equilibrium and on the evolving patterns of family identity. Of special significance is the potential of a union of member and relative for setting up a pair identity and associated strivings which compete with other partial representations of family identity. The outcome may have integrative or disintegrative consequences. It may undermine the influence of other family representations or serve as a kind of antidote to and controller of the destructive consequences of family conflict. This possibility is especially clear where a family group is threatened by a critical split, such as, for example, a rift down the middle, mother joining son or father joining daughter. In such instances, the link of a family member with a relative may protect the particular family from critical disintegration. A relative may conceivably fulfill the intended or unintended role of therapist for family conflict. The union of a family member with such a relative may act as defense, a neutralizer of a fragmenting trend within the family group. It may also function as a catalyzer of elements moving toward higher levels of personality integration and higher levels of emotional health. On the other hand, such a union may aggravate tendencies toward the breakdown of family unity. In effect, then, the importance of a pairing is that it may influence the homeodynamic equilibrium of the family entity in either a minus or a plus direction. It may serve as an antidote for pathogenic conflict or may aggravate it. The specific effect on an individual family member may be direct or indirect. The relationship of a family member and a relative may play a potent part in determining the ultimate outcome of conflict, both intrapsychic and interpersonal. When one part of the family is set against another, the emotional union of a member with a relative holds the power to make or break the stability and health of the individual family member. It can protect stability or precipitate illness.

For example, in a family where the father is alcoholic and a deserter, the son may form a compensatory attachment to a maternal uncle who provides a more satisfactory paternal image. The relationship of son and uncle, representing a different kind of masculine ideal, may neutralize the harmful influence of the alcoholic father. What is involved is a dynamic and changing equilibrium between the competing emotional forces, the bond of son with father and the bond of son with uncle, both influenced by the quality of the son's attachment to his mother.

At the opposite pole a range of relationships with relatives may exert a negative or injurious influence. For example, a man involved in marital conflict may say: "I love my wife, but I can't stand my mother-in-law." One is reminded of the aphorism, "A mother-in-law who moves inside and takes sides soon finds herself outside."

In clinical practice, the range and complexity of such family problems are legion: a depressive illness in a newly married woman who is excessively dependent upon her mother and rejects her husband; an outbreak of an acute phobic neurosis in a young wife whose husband romances with his attractive mother-in-law; a young woman who develops a postpartum psychosis after disappointing her parents-in-law by giving birth to a girl rather than to a boy.

Today the role of grandparents is especially problematic. The experience and wisdom of grandparents, once respected, are now disparaged. In our time grandparents live longer but frequently tend to be assessed mainly in terms of their nuisance value. Their advice is unwelcome; it is often resented, if not actually condemned. Still, this attitude does not stop young parents from exploiting grandparents as sources of economic assistance or as convenient and unpaid baby-sitters.

Relatives may be used as a source of compensatory love and protection to offset a fear of exposure and injury from some other part of the family, or, at the other end, a relative may be used as a scapegoat, a target for hostility displaced from other family relationships. Sometimes the negative emotional influence of a relative is alluded to euphemistically as part of the "precipitating situation."

In addition, there is often a shift of dependency from extended family and relatives to peer associations. When a pair of young parents moves away from the influence of the older generation, they tend to substitute a network of peer associations. To these the parental partners attach their needs for dependency, intimacy, identity, and guidance, which in other circumstances would be bound to relationships with relatives. Sometimes young parents create in these peer associations the emotional equivalent of an adopted family. Friends are taken into the family nest almost as if they were part of the family. They may be treated as if they were relatives and addressed intimately as "Uncle" and "Aunt." They are taken in as "our very own." Sometimes, in the arrangement of these peer relations, there are peculiar combinations of nuclear families or combinations of husband-and-wife pairs that may culminate in trading or lending wives.

Not infrequently, young parents attach special needs and strivings to employers, community leaders, and educators. This network of relationships in the wider community becomes increasingly significant as a molding influence on family identity, adaptation, and growth. It is one aspect of the striving of young married couples to conform to the community. It is a special expression of the "groupiness" in our present-day community, a factor which tends to suppress individuality.

Elizabeth Bott[1] comes to some interesting conclusions with respect to the influence of the social network as it impinges on the nuclear family. The urban family has a large measure of privacy and freedom to regulate its own affairs. It is not, however, strictly "isolated," since members of the family maintain many outside relationships, but these relationships are more individualized. They constitute a network rather than an organized group. A network is a social configuration in which some but not all of the component external units maintain relationships with one another. The external units do not make up a larger social whole and in this sense do not constitute an organized group. It was Bott's finding that differences in the connectedness of husband and wife with this social network are associated with differences in the segregation of the conjugal roles. Other conclusions are these: If husband and wife come to marriage with close-knit networks that are continued, the marriage is superimposed on previous relationships. Each partner gets satisfactions from outside persons and demands less of the spouse. If husband and wife come to marriage with loose-knit networks, a joint organization is more necessary; the marital partners are more dependent on one another; they draw more from one another and yet are more easily disillusioned. With close-knit networks, husband and wife expect less

---

[1] Elizabeth Bott, *Family and Social Network* (London: Tavistock Publications, 1957) and "Urban Families: Conjugal Roles and Social Networks," *Human Relations,* VIII (1955), 345–384.

from one another and are less likely to be disillusioned, but since they receive less from one another, they may more easily separate.

The fact that urban families are not completely encapsulated by organized groups adds to the responsibility and burden of decision-making. The involvement of husband and wife with an external social network influences the patterning of family life, the choices of role definition, role performance, and related values.

In this context we must give special consideration to the emotional impact of symbolic relatives. A family member may make an attachment to a professional person, for example a psychiatrist or a caseworker, or may depend on a clinic or a hospital in a way that has significance as a transference. The bond with the professional helper may represent a tie to a parent. The therapist functions as surrogate for a relative of good will. He serves as a substitute source of love, or as a mentor or guide. Such a relationship provides emotional support or a channel for the displaced release of hostile emotions. It may set up an influence that competes with that of other family bonds, in this way dividing loyalties. Such competing bonds influence the outcome of personal conflict. The salient question is the extent to which the core conflict expresses itself in varying combinations of dependency, jealousy, hostility, and emotional alienation.

It is clear that such processes are complex and are conditioned by the idiosyncratic characteristics of a particular family group, its internal emotional organization, and its external adaptation to the surrounding community. As the family and the members' positions within it change across time, the emotional impact of a relative or a symbolic substitute also shifts.

The call to explore these questions is a commanding one. The core of the special problem of the emotional impact of a relative or surrogate rests in the vicissitudes of identification and homeo-dynamic control.[2] Such a bond acts as an identity link with a bigger

---

[2] "Homeodynamic" is to the psychosocial as "homeostatic" is to the physical world. A nearly constant condition, such as that resulting from the homeostatic control of temperature within the body, is impossible in the area of interpersonal relations. Therefore, the principle of homeodynamics functions not merely to restore a pre-existing equilibrium; it also makes room for accommodation to new experience, for learning, change, and growth.

world outside. It functions as an agent that connects the homeo-dynamic functions of the inner life of the family with the forces of the larger community, exerting an influence that may be either harmful or healing.

4

The Breakdown of Healthy Process

The indispensability of the human family derives from two basic needs: survival and growth. In providing for these needs, the family group must cope with two fundamental characteristics of man: the incompleteness of the individual and the fact of human differences. Man will forever be incomplete without woman, parent without child; differences are of the essence of man as a familial animal. These factors are here to stay; they are the *sine qua non* of change and growth. They create for the human family the qualities of interdependence and mutuality. For man, self-sufficiency is impossible—only a relative degree of autonomy can exist. In the human family there are male and female, young and old, big and small, tall and short, strong and weak, smart and stupid, light- and dark-skinned, good-looking and plain-looking members, and so forth.

From difference comes union, out of union comes difference, and again new union, on into perpetuity. For the family to be assured of survival and growth, it must deal creatively with the ever-present qualities of incompleteness and difference. This is the principle of complementarity of family relationships, the merging and emerging of family members. It is the joining, sharing, and co-operating of family members that make way for change and growth, for the cultivation of individuality and the fulfillment of human goals.

Complementarity: Conflict and Coping

Complementarity of need is a central feature of family life. Affection, caring, loyalty—these are the hallmarks of family unity. Without shared concern for one another's welfare, a family becomes a mere shell. "When in need, look to your family. . . . If your family doesn't care about you, nobody else will." The family shapes the individual; the individual shapes the family. Each needs the other; each is part of the other. By the phrase "complementarity of family relationships," we mean a quality of circular support, interdependence, and intimacy molded by the need to understand and care for other family members.

Complementarity in family relationships can be examined at five levels: (1) the support of self-esteem, (2) cooperation in the quest for solutions to conflict, (3) the satisfaction of needs, (4) the support of needed defenses against anxiety, and (5) support for the development and creative fulfillment of the individual family member.

Complementarity and conflict of needs are, however, twin processes: there cannot be one without the other. In the dynamics of family living, an understanding of the vicissitudes of conflict is of the essence. Difference may lead to merging or to conflict. From birth to death, the human being moves, changes, and grows in accordance with his way of adapting to difference. At some points in time, conflict is inevitable: it is intrinsic to the struggle of life, intrinsic to the process of change and growth.

The vicissitudes of conflict are complex. Conflict can be catalytic or paralytic; it can integrate or disintegrate human experience. It may enhance human growth and adaptation, or it may induce its arrest or distortion or both. Under one aspect, conflict is a functional expression of growth in a changing constellation of adaptive needs; under another, conflict, in its vicissitudes, its control, and its ultimate fate, molds the processes of growth. Viewed in this way, human conflict becomes a main point of reference for understanding the forces of adaptation to life and the associated tendencies to health and illness.

The epitome of all human conflict is conflict within the family. It is within the day-by-day intimacies of the family group that conflict exerts its deepest molding force on growth and development and on the related disposition to health and illness. Conflict in family relations expresses a conflict over difference, a clash of values with regard to the goals and functions of family life. It is manifested in competing images and expectations concerning the organization and carrying out of essential family purposes. Conflict in family relations expresses what the family is or ought to be, how it may or may not serve the needs of its members and fortify their role competence both within the family and in the wider community. What the family does or ought to do for its members, male and female, young and old, and what they in turn do for family and community are reflected in the patterns of complementarity of role relations of husband and wife, parent and child, parent and grandparent, child and sibling. Such complementarity reflects in action the implicit identity and value orientation of the given family.

Competition and cooperation in family relations are not necessarily opposites, however. The true opposite of cooperation is not competition but apathy or indifference. Under favorable conditions certain competitive trends may mark the transition to the achievement of new levels of union and cooperation. The ultimate success of a family's capacity to integrate, harmonize, and balance its varied functions rests on the dominance of a spirit of acceptance, empathic understanding, and cooperation. Competition can have healthy or pathogenic effects. It can lead to new levels of identification and sharing in family relations, or it can aggravate a tendency toward emotional alienation and fragmentation of relationships. The outcome depends on the dynamic context of a particular set of conflicts within the larger frame of the dynamic evolution of the family as a whole. In the larger concatenation of family events, what is competition at one phase in the development of the relations of husband and wife or parent and child may become cooperation in a later phase, and vice versa.

When differences within the family group are felt as a menace instead of being prized, conflict brings a rift. Conflict in family life occurs at many levels. From the outside inward, there may be conflict between the family and the surrounding community. There may be conflict between the nuclear family unit and representations of the extended family entity. There may be conflict between one segment of the nuclear family and another. There may be conflict between particular family members. Finally, there may be conflict within the mind of an individual member. Insofar as the family is an open behavior system, conflict constitutes a potent contagious force. It invades and pervades every aspect of family experience. Conflict at any one level influences conflict at every other. The feedback of influence among these several levels of conflict is circular and interpenetrating.

Conflict and the means of coping with it constitute a single dynamic process. One cannot talk of the one without referring to the other. The end results with respect to adaptation and the vicissitudes of health and sickness depend fully as much on the means of control as on the content of conflict itself. The organization of the family resources for the control of conflict, both conscious and unconscious, expresses an unceasing struggle to enhance complementarity of family roles. The process involves an interplay between the image of self and the image of family, an accommodation of the needs of individual and group, an interplay between individual defense against anxiety and group defense against a threat to the continuity, stability, and growth of the family.

Conflict in family relations may be resolved or at least contained; it may be compensated for or the attempt at compensation may fail. The possible outcomes of the struggle for control may be stated thus:

1. The conflict is correctly perceived and an early and rational solution is found.

2. The conflict is correctly perceived and is contained while an effective solution, not immediately available, is being sought.

3. The conflict is misperceived or distorted; it is not adequately compromised; it is not adequately contained and spills over into irrational acting out.

4. The control of conflict fails and leads to progressive disorganization in family relations.

In the long view, the effectiveness of the control of conflict rests on a clear and correct perception of its nature. This perception is a shared function, an expression of a particular quality of complementarity of role relations in the family. In the last analysis, valid and appropriate perception of conflict is a function of family interaction and consensual validation; no one person by himself can achieve the needed clarity of perception, nor can he alone inaugurate effective control.

A pattern of conflict and coping may be appropriate or inappropriate to the prevailing family problems. It may be rational or irrational. It may hold a central or a peripheral significance for the inner life of the family. It may be dormant or overt, conscious or unconscious, diffuse or circumscribed; it may be benign or malignant, reversible or irreversible. In family process, one conflict may be substituted for another, or the pathogenic focus of conflict may be displaced from one part of the family to another, from one function to another. Parallel with such a shift, an attempt at control may be appropriate or inappropriate, rational or irrational, strong or weak. The dominant pattern of the family's role complementarity influences the individual member's reliance on such defenses as denial, projection, displacement, or withdrawal. At the level of group defense, there may be an increased rigidification of role patterns, an exaggerated loosening, a mechanization and routinization of family relations, an increase in emotional distance, a thinning and distortion of communication, a recourse to diversion and escape, or an indulgence in prejudicial scapegoating and acting out, in which all or several members of the family may participate.

Adaptive attempts to contain and control the effects of conflict often take the form of compromise. Such compromise may be either rational or irrational. Irrational compromise fosters acting out. The greater the irrationality, the greater the cost in terms of the fit of family roles and the emotional health of the family members. An irrational compromise that favors one part of the family imposes harm on another part. The result is further distortion of the emotional life of the family and new conflicts superimposed on old ones.

Conflict between the minds of family members and conflict within the mind of any one member stand in reciprocal relation to one another. The two levels constitute a circular feedback system. Interpersonal conflict affects intrapsychic conflict, and vice versa. Generally speaking, interpersonal conflict in the family group precedes the establishment of fixed patterns of intrapsychic conflict. Psychopathic distortion and symptom formation are late products of the processes of internalization of persistent and pathogenic forms of family conflict. Potentially, these disturbances are reversible if the intrapsychic and symptom-producing conflict can once more be externalized, that is to say, can be reprojected into the field of family interaction where a new solution can be found.

For the clinician, the relations between the interpersonal conflict and the intrapersonal conflict are a central concern. When family conflict is sopped up and internalized, when it becomes locked inside the mind of one member, it cannot be solved. The pathological consequences become progressively more fixed. If a useful and healthy solution is to be found, intrapsychic conflict must be activated and reprojected into the field of family interaction. Otherwise, the submerged conflict becomes entrenched and isolated, and leads progressively to distortion and to malignant intensification of conflict. In other words, the longer the delay, and the longer the period of intrapsychic containment and isolation from the field of active interpersonal interchange, the less chance is there to reverse the sick process.

The complementarity of family relationships supports unity; it supports joining and sharing. Conflict deriving from differences among the family members and competing needs and interests may be a creative force in the emotional development of family and its members, or it may be a divisive force. On the negative side, certain pairs and threesomes in the group may ally themselves and split off from the larger entity. Some of these alignments and splits are reversible, others irreversible. Some are long-standing and persistent, others have an evanescent character. Some alignments and splits are appropriate, others inappropriate. Some are benign, others are malignant. Some, in the long view, are on the side of growth and health, others on the side of disordered functioning and sickness. The patterning of these subgroups is also affected by the network of relationships of the family members with persons and groups in the wider community.

Allegiance to a particular set of identity and value representations forms the pattern for the family's structure, its functions, its role adaptation and the corresponding family alignments. A conflict of identities, values, and strivings splits the family group; it mobilizes one segment against another. Such splits may be horizontal, vertical, or diagonal. They may set male against female, mother and son against father and daughter, the younger generation against the older one. The competing factions may be relatively equal or severely unequal in power and in composition. It may be two against two, three against one, or one against all. It is almost never "all for one and one for all." Occasionally, the fragmentation extends to the extreme of each man for himself. Beyond a certain critical point, the breaking up of the family unit into these warring factions distorts the balance of family functions. In a selective manner it favors some family functions while it disables and warps others. What the family does or ought to do for its members, male and female, young and old, and what they in turn do for the family and the community are reflected in the patterns of complementarity of family relationships, in the patterns of alignments and splits, and in the patterns of individuation. A healthy family provides the needed elements of nourishment, union, and cooperation, maximizing the creative potential of differences, whereas in a broken or sick family, differences become felt as an invasive, disruptive threat.

Prejudicial Scapegoating

Among the specific emotional mechanisms of family living, there are some that are brought sharply into focus in clinical work and in the study of the breakdown of healthy process. Some families, for example, centrally organize their emotional life, or a part of it, around a family idol, a family pet, a family troublemaker, a sick member, or a family "whipping boy." Others build a myth around one member as the family genius, while another member fills the part of family dunce and a third that of family clown. In still other families, sentiment focuses on the "doll baby" of the family or on the "ugly duckling," or the group splits its allegiances between "Little Miss Sunshine" and the family "kill-joy."

With respect to these special patternings, some significant questions arise. Under what circumstances is integration into these roles protective, and for whom? Under what other conditions does it intensify susceptibility to family and individual breakdown? In some families the balance works out so that no one member suffers severe and irreparable emotional damage, each member achieving sufficient compensation to counteract any negative effects of the situation. In others, however, where a particular family member or a special activity is aggrandized, another member or activity is disparaged. Only too often, in disturbed families, the positive factors do not weigh heavily enough to prevent the foisting of emotional injury onto one or another member.

In examining the relations of family process and psychopathology, can we perhaps trace some specific correlations between types of family, types of prejudicial scapegoating, and types of emotional breakdown? Is it possible to discover in a range of family types idiosyncratic emotional allergies, specific intolerances of symbolically perceived qualities in the offspring that lead to scapegoating and breakdown?

The questions posed here need to be conceptualized in a wider framework. In the relations of family and individual, the family seeking to rid itself of a felt threat inflicts emotional damage on a member, but this member retaliates and also damages the family. Each defends himself against the other's urge to blame and punish. Something is known of the means by which the family damages the individual. Less is known, however, of the other side of the question, how the individual damages the family. Clinicians are familiar with the many ways in which a patient tries to make his family over or wreaks a bitter vengeance. We have felt in rare instances the dramatic impact of a psychotic patient's killing a parent. Thus far, however, the circular interactions of patient and family, emphasizing at one pole reciprocal punitive injury or withdrawal and at the opposite pole the reciprocal effort to promote change and healing, have been seriously neglected as an area of investigation.

Since people make one another sick, they may also make one another well again. In this context, we may pose a broad question: What is the balance of forces in the relations of family and individual between destructive scapegoating and compensatory healing? How is it that in one family a given member breaks down when the effort to heal what ails the family fails? How is it that in another family the members integrate emotionally into particular roles by which they shield themselves from or avert a breakdown?

It is commonly observed in troubled families that one child is made a scapegoat and becomes susceptible to a breakdown. But there is a broader process that needs to be defined: how parents divide their traits, conflicts, fears, and prejudices among their brood of children in a special way.

In a family group of three daughters, for example, the eldest is assigned and accepts the role of the "brain of the family." She becomes a lawyer, following in the path of her father, who was a judge. The middle daughter is the "body beautiful," destined to a "successful marriage" with a rich man; she fulfills this part. The youngest is the family renegade, the Bohemian artist who lives in Greenwich Village with a series of men. The mother of these three daughters suffered a depressive psychosis and committed suicide. The three girls developed obvious character disorders but escaped major mental collapse.

There is still another angle of the problem that should be explicitly considered. If, in a given family, one member is made a scapegoat, caused to suffer, and driven "crazy," the emotions of the other members are inevitably deeply stirred. A contagion of guilt and fear fans out to affect every part of the family. First comes a secret feeling—better it should happen to someone else, not me. Second comes a surging wave of guilt and fear: if one has witnessed the mutilation of another member of the family, then one feels that in some way one is accessory to the crime. There follows a spreading, guilty fear that sooner or later, in retribution, one will suffer the same fate, that is to say, will be driven insane.

In this situation, the mental breakdown of one member is not felt to be an accident of life, but rather as having been caused by some malevolent force within the family group. The conviction is that the victim was purposely persecuted and pushed into a breakdown. Always the question comes up: Who did it? Who is to blame and who must pay the penalty for the crime?

If the victim happens to be a child, the defense against guilt and blame, the self-justifications, the projective accusations become all the more intense. When a helpless child is psychically maimed and hurt, whom shall we blame and punish, the child himself, the mother, the family, or society?

History reveals to us the universality of the device of scapegoating, the offering of sacrifice to appease the fates. In times past, society has excluded and made scapegoats of its worst offenders, the lepers, the victims of pestilence, the poor, the vagabonds, the criminals, and the insane. Society imposed on these unfortunates such punishments as exile, whipping, and enforced labor in the sewers. In our age, the criminals and the mad inherit the domain of the lepers of earlier times.

Surely, therefore, it is no surprise that the family group cultivates its own special devices of scapegoating and of exiling its offenders. One must consider, too, the dynamic interplay between scapegoating in society and scapegoating within the family.

To represent this set of interrelated role functions, we offer here a theoretical model. Stated in overly simple terms, the punisher, destroyer, or persecutor uses a special prejudice as the vehicle of his attack. Another member of the family becomes the object of this attack, the victim of scapegoating; he may be selectively rewarded for adapting to this role; he may sustain an emotional injury that renders him susceptible to breakdown. The "family healer" or "doctor" intervenes to neutralize the destructive powers of this attack and thereby, in some measure, rescues the scapegoat. The enactment of these reciprocal role behaviors may be overt or covert, simple or complex, sharply outlined or relatively amorphous. These processes may occur at multiple levels of family interaction. They may change as the family moves from one stage of adaptation to another or otherwise undergoes change in its organization. We suggest that a specific patterning of these emotional mechanisms offers a useful diagnostic clue to the psychosocial identity and emotional health of a given family.

Close study of family interaction suggests that specific kinds of prejudicial scapegoating are characteristic of a given family and become organized in an irrational way around special meanings that are attached to differences among the family members. Prejudice of this kind is of a distinct and private nature. It differs from the common stereotypes of prejudice in the wider community. Insofar as it is a recurrent, idiosyncratic, and predictable manifestation, it provides a specific diagnostic clue to the emotional organization and functioning of a special kind of family.

From this hypothesis arise several problems: What is the special role of prejudicial scapegoating in the life history of a given family? How are the role functions of attacker, victim, and healer organized within such a family? What is the significance of these processes for the emotional health of the family and its members? What is the relation between this kind of social disorder and susceptibility to specific mental disorder?

Before amplifying these questions, we must first make clear our conception of the phenomenon of family prejudice. We distinguish here two categories of prejudice, private and public. They are different and yet related. Prejudice within the private life of the family assumes a form manifestly unlike that encountered in public life, where we see the familiar antagonisms based on differences of color, religion, or ethnic origin. Private intrafamilial prejudice is of another kind, so subtly different that it is often not recognized as prejudice at all, yet it is there just the same—real, abundant, intense, far-reaching in its effects. It attaches to differences, both real and unreal, among family members. Private prejudice may become displaced and translated into public forms of prejudice. Public forms of prejudice may in circular fashion aggravate the tendency to private prejudice.

In a basic sense the members of one family may be viewed as being the same kind of people. They are, in fact, related by blood. They resemble one another; they have much in common; they share the same way of life. In view of this sameness, one might expect an absence of prejudice among the insiders and the concentration of prejudice against outsiders. This is not the case, however. The emotional life of the family is such that some members are felt as inside, others as outside. Among members of the same family group there are elements of difference as well as sameness, difference in appearance, mood, attitudes, traits, strivings, and values. Depending on the idiosyncratic emotional structure of a particular family, symbolic meanings are attached to these differences. One side of the difference is felt to be right, the other wrong. The difference may be perceived and reacted to as a distinct danger. The person showing the difference is felt to be the alien, the invasive stranger who threatens the security, the needs, and the values of other members of the group. Sharing this sense of threat, several or most members of the family form an alliance to attack the source of the difference.

In the inner life of the family, prejudice becomes organized around a range of differences: the battle between the sexes—male vs. female; money and power vs. a passive way of life; control vs.

spontaneity and pleasure; obedience vs. defiance; a liberal vs. a conservative political ideology. At other levels, prejudice becomes attached to such qualities as fat or skinny, tall or short, smart or stupid, light or dark skin, smooth or hairy skin. Still other prejudices of this kind attach to such matters as habits of eating and dressing or cleanliness and orderliness.

A question may promptly be raised: Why do we call this prejudice? Are there not valid reactions to difference, legitimate likes and dislikes, preferences and aversions that may not constitute true prejudice? Certainly it is true that people who achieve sound health have a full measure of likes and dislikes, attractions and repulsions. Such attitudes become transformed into true prejudice, however, to whatever extent they become rigid, fixed, or automatized, and walled off from the tempering and corrective influence of the prevailing realities. Furthermore, such prejudice may be mild or intense, benign or malignant. In its benign form, such prejudice need not extend to the compulsive urge to hold the self together by breaking someone else down. In point of fact, however, the more disturbed the family becomes, the more do the members lean toward the organization of malignant forms of prejudice. The significant feature is its very contagion. Some, or even all, members of the family become bound in its organization. While contagious, the tendency toward prejudicial organization is also selective in its influence. It aggravates prejudice in some members, while fortifying the immunity of others against it.

Prejudice and mental illness have something in common. Both have to do with human relations and are affected by the struggle to reconcile human differences. Both impair a person's ability to perform his tasks in life, especially the task of getting along with other people. The ultimate source of both conditions is the intimate emotional exchange within the family group, which is the prime training ground for learning to get along with other people. It is the striving within the family to establish one's position, and to win the reward of affection and respect for one's unique quality, that affects the proneness to prejudice as well as to mental illness.

Nevertheless, in some crucial respects, the two forms of behavior are distinct. They evidence themselves in a different life context, and yet between them there is a significant dynamic connection. A person moving toward an emotional breakdown frequently leans on prejudice as a defense. To save himself, to stave off the threat of his own breakdown, he is motivated to break down another member of the family. The question is: Who drives whom crazy? There is convincing force in such remarks as "My mother is driving me crazy"; "She'll be the death of me yet"; "Twenty-four hours in my home, and I go batty."

Our immediate concern is with these private family prejudices, both as individual defenses against the fright of dangerous exposure and as family defenses of the continuity of family functions. To the degree to which an individual feels incomplete, weak, exposed, and vulnerable, the difference of another can become magnified, symbolically, to the dimensions of a penetrating threat. In analogous fashion, to the degree to which the family as a group fails to integrate an effective identity and value orientation, or suffers a split of identity, the assertion of difference in one part of the family may be felt as a menace to the unity and continuity of the family as a whole.

To return to the questions posed earlier, when a clinician trains his eye on a troubled family, he is immediately struck by the division of the group into competing emotional alliances. Each member identifies with particular component representations of family identity, expressed in terms of what he or she wants the family to be or do. A competing faction wages its battle around the felt threat of these differences. Around these differences, there is the patterning of specific family prejudices. In the unfolding of such emotional mechanisms, we believe we can identify the three main patterns already mentioned, the roles of the attacker, the victim, and the healer. At a given point in time, these roles are filled by particular members; with the passage of time they are filled by other members. Each of these persons is selected for his respective role by shared unconscious emotional processes within the group. The family destroyer punishes the member whose difference is felt as an offense and as a menace to family continuity. The member who is chosen as scapegoat suffers an emotional injury and is thus rendered vulnerable to mental breakdown. Still another family member takes on the role of peacemaker, protector, healer, or, if you like, "family doctor," rising to the rescue of the victim of the punishing attack. To the degree to which the rescuing member holds the capacity to neutralize the destructive force of the prejudicial assault, he offers to the scapegoat some immunity against breakdown. At times, the member who starts out in the role of persecutor or destroyer may shift to the role of victim or healer, or vice versa. Each of these functional roles may be filled at various times by a member of the nuclear family, by a relative, by a delegate of the extended family, or, by symbolic extension, by a psychotherapist. Again it is to be emphasized that this is a theoretical model rather than an actuality; in the clinical observation of family life these patterns may be complex, disguised, and difficult to identify.

Further developments must be considered. In the unfolding of critical family conflict, a primary prejudice attaching to the conspicuous and threatening difference of one member may evoke a counterprejudice. In this case, the emotional sequence is attack, defense, and counterattack. Thus the emergence of one pattern of scapegoating evokes the emergence of an opposite pattern of attack and scapegoating. Ultimately, reciprocal patterns of attack and scapegoating appear on the scene. The role of family healer then becomes progressively more complicated and may be filled in sequence by different members of the group. In this context, one direction of scapegoating may be counterbalanced by another. The scapegoating may occur also at multiple levels and in a circular pattern. We must also bear in mind here that the experience of scapegoating in extrafamilial relationships may provoke scapegoating within the family. If a boss makes a scapegoat of his subordinate, the man may go home and beat his wife. A pair of parents may make a scapegoat of a teenager, the teenager a scapegoat of a younger sibling, the sibling a scapegoat of the dog. All of them together may then make a scapegoat of a grandparent. Or the scapegoating theme may unfold in a different way. In a conflict between a pair of parents, a teenager may at one point in time enter into the role of healer of the war between the parents and at a later stage shift to the role of destroyer.

Temporarily this process may serve to bind the family closer together, but at another stage it may be critically divisive in its effects. The less rational the prejudice, the more does it lead to the progressive distortion of the family's role relationships and the impairment of essential family functions. Although it may serve temporarily as a means of support for one or another partial family alliance and the corresponding family identity and value orientation, at its core the mechanism becomes progressively less rational, fragments family relationships, and alienates its members.

In this concatenation of events, several other developments are possible, contingent on the emotional condition of the family. If that condition favors it, there may be a movement toward resolution of the primary prejudice and, with it, an easing of the scapegoating assault; or, if the emotional matrix so disposes, a counterprejudice may emerge. Beyond that a range of efforts unfold, the intent of which is to neutralize and assuage the harm inflicted upon the victim of family scapegoating.

If the movement is toward the resolution of the primary prejudice, and the pressure toward splitting the family and setting up competing alliances is reduced, the family members reach out for an improved quality of union and love. On the other hand, if this movement is blocked, the primary prejudice evokes a counterprejudice and the family healer is stirred to action; his function becomes, in fact, an urgent necessity. But one must bear other alternatives in mind. The prejudicial attack may shift from its original object to another member of the family. One prejudice may be substituted for another. The attack may be displaced from the family scapegoat to a new target outside the family.

The vicissitudes of control of intrafamilial prejudice are the paths along which the emotional split of the family group achieves a specific pattern; one part of the family pits itself against another. Therefore, prejudice and counterprejudice need to be correlated with the split of the family into warring segments, the conflict over differences, the method of coping, and the unconscious selection of particular family members as scapegoats and others as rescuers or healers.

If, on occasion, a member tries to avoid being sucked into the family conflict and for his own safety seeks to remain unaligned, he achieves, at best, merely a temporary and precarious protection. Over a stretch of time, such an attempt at noninvolvement is short-lived and must fail. Often such a gesture of noninvolvement is patently false; in fact, it conceals a movement into a compensatory alliance with some other part of the nuclear family or the extended family, or it reflects a flight for protection into alliance with a peer group. It is of the very essence of the emotional life of the family that there is no such thing as nonintervention. At the very most it is a protest, a dramatic gesture. Even so, it cannot be sustained because it disconnects the member's feeding line to the family and ultimately ends in alienation. In occasional instances, it appears superficially that a family member has succeeded in achieving noninvolvement. If so, the isolation of the member is achieved at cost to himself. What it really cloaks is a hidden tendency to fickleness and betrayal and the urge to find compensatory belongingness and protection elsewhere. A member of the family behaving in this way may erratically juggle his alliances from one side of the family to another. In such a setting, acting out becomes not merely a unit of experience in which one member lives out the unconscious urges of another, but also a vehicle for the discharge of shared aggressions as one part of the family does battle with another part.

It is, therefore, essential to identify specific forms of family prejudice, the roles of persecutor, scapegoat, and healer, the competing family alliances, the specific conflicts around which the battle rages, and the types of group defense and individual defense that are mobilized to neutralize the destructive results of scapegoating.

Symptom, Defense, and Growth

The concepts of complementarity, conflict, and scapegoating as we have outlined them point up with special force the nature of the family approach to diagnosis and treatment and its differences from the individual approach. In the sphere of individual psychology, behavior is examined as a function of the internal organization of personality. Personality is viewed predominantly as an autonomous entity, a closed system of behavior. The characteristic modes of behavior are formulated in the abstract, unrelated to a particular social situation. Formulations concerning intrapsychic organization are not paralleled by corresponding formulations regarding the mode of interpersonal adaptation.

In the sphere of social psychology, personality is defined within the matrix of a social group. The main point of reference is the dominant mode of interpersonal adaptation, the integration of the person into specific social roles. The characteristic role adaptations within the group may or may not be correlated with the intra-psychic organization of the individual. In effect, then, the first frame of reference places the emphasis on the inside of the mind; the second places the emphasis on the outside of the mind, and the two are not adequately correlated.

Symptom, defense, and growth carry different connotations when they are referred on the one hand to the internal mechanisms of individual personality and on the other hand to the family group. Within the frame of reference of individual psychology, the terms may have one set of meanings; within the frame of reference of family behavior, they may take on modified meanings. In other words, the human context molds the connotations of these basic terms. Symptom, defense, and growth refer to partial processes. It is self-evident that each partial process must be related to every other and to the whole as well. Conflict, anxiety, symptom, and defense are indivisible. The symptom is the minus aspect of adaptation; growth is the plus aspect; conflict, anxiety, and defense may mold behavior in either direction.

In the context of individual psychology, a *symptom* refers to a unit of behavior that is patently nonrational and maladaptive. It indicates that a derailment has occurred in the course of healthy development. The symptom is incongruous with the total personality and with the requirements for adaptation to the surrounding environment. It is a unit of behavior that is disassociated, ego-alien; it is not only lacking in adaptive usefulness here and now but also impairs the efficiency of other more appropriate, more adaptive components of the personality. A symptom tends to become rigid, automatized, and repetitive, inappropriate to the total pattern of emotional reactivity and inappropriate also to the requirements of the individual's position in his surrounding group. The sole qualification to be entered here concerns those secondary and compensatory gains which pivot about the core of illness and disabled functioning and further mold the relations of the person with his surrounding group. We refer here to the adaptive value of the secondary gains of illness.

If, fundamentally, a symptom is adaptively useless, burdensome, and incapacitating, what keeps it alive? The answer is conflict. The symptom is a way of compromising conflicting drives. Each of the opposed elements of drive presses for expression but neither is completed. A symptom thus represents the paralysis of movement that results from the encapsulation within the psyche of unresolved conflict. A selective influence is present, however, in that some areas of personality functioning are more severely disabled than others. Some areas of adaptation are relatively immune to the disintegrating effect of anxiety precisely because other areas are incapacitated. Processes of secondary emotional gain, the advantages of sickness, emerge as the struggle with illness begins to fail.

The concept of *defense* refers to a psychic means for the control of endogenous sources of anxiety. In effect, defense is a protective wall that safeguards the ongoing adaptive operations of personality from being overrun and disorganized by an excess of anxiety. Defense serves the function of preserving the continuity of the struggle for adaptation and is therefore related to the maintenance of a degree of intactness and integrity of the self. Defensive operations need to be differentiated in terms of whether they are healthy or pathogenic, and to what degrees. They may also be distinguished according to their rigidity or flexibility, their value for maintaining old static forms of adaptive stability or their relative receptivity to change through new experience—in effect, the issue is one of stasis or homeostasis.

Resistance is a special form of defense. It is a protection for the continuity of the self while the patient is undergoing therapeutic influence. It reflects a patient's need to place a fence around the most vulnerable areas of self in an attempt to immunize the self against the danger of reopening old psychic wounds. The common forms of defense that are implemented as resistance are avoidance, opposition, denial, repression, rejection, displacement, condensation, substitution of aggression for anxiety, magic omniscient thinking, and magical undoing.

The term *growth* refers to those vital forces in the personality which facilitate the maturing process. The growth of personality is viewed as a progressive movement through the finite stages of development and fulfillment. Each stage signifies a new integration of the forces of personality, new personal and social achievements. Growth is expressed in the progressive differentiation of personality, in the achievement of autonomy and creative realization in society. Movement from one stage of growth to the next implies successful resolution of the conflicts and adaptive problems of the previous stage. Symptom, defense, and growth are differently represented in structural and functional terms within the context of each stage of development. The stages of the unfolding of personality may be conceptualized within the scheme of Freud's system of psychosexual development, or within an adaptive frame of reference such as is epitomized in the following sequence: (1) the magical symbiotic union of infant and mother, (2) interdependence and intimacy, with progressive differentiation of the child's individuality, (3) the achievement of autonomy, self-sufficiency, mastery of the environment, and personal initiative, and (4) the creative, expansive fulfillment of the self in wider society.

As we shift our frame of reference from that of individual psychology to the dynamics of the family group, correlating intrapersonal and interpersonal patterns, our interpretations of both diagnosis and therapy must be modified. In the group setting we must consider three phenomenological levels: the group, the individual, and the zone of contact and interchange between them. This combination of factors introduces the concept of role adaptation, which requires consideration of the phenomenon of the reciprocity or complementarity of role relations within the family group.

Within the context of family interaction, the partial processes of symptom, defense, and growth become interrelated parts of a unified experience; disorders of behavior become something more than phobias, hysterical symptoms, or obsessive ideas. Conflict, symptom, and defense assume the form of certain unreal, inappropriate feelings and patterns of action within the group. They assume significance as automatized, static, repetitive forms of role relationships in the family, inappropriate to the prevailing social realities. Intended to assure security and stability, they are revealed as narrowing the potential for homeodynamic change and growth. Within the family it is possible to examine these processes by characterizing the balance of family functions, the pattern of role complementarity, the conflict and the coping, the interplay of family defense and individual defense. and the discrepancy between family performance and family ideal.

One may observe two extremes: either a progressive constriction and rigidification of potentials for family role adaptation, or an unstable, uncontrolled fluidity of role relations that threatens confusion or loss of identity for both family and member. At one pole, the progressive rigidification lowers receptivity to new social learning; it reduces the range of exploration of new alternatives of role complementarity. At the other extreme, the shift toward excessively rapid, loose, unstable role relations leaves the members pathologically open and exposed to invasion by outside influence. In this setting, it is difficult to preserve continuity in the identity relations of individual and family. Healthy role adaptation lies somewhere between these two extremes. It is the optimal balance between continuity of the old and openness to new experience. In other words, processes of growth can be impaired either by changing too slowly or by changing too rapidly. In family processes these extremes of role adaptation are reflected either in narrow, rigid pairings of the self-image and the image of other family members or in a continuously changing self-image and image of others even to the point of the clouding of the perceptual processes. Therefore, in family process we may arbitrarily define a symptom as a unit of relational adaptation that is irrational, inappropriate, automatized, and repetitive, one that restricts the range of new levels of interpersonal adaptation. Or we may define a symptom as a set of pathologically loose, rapidly changing role relations that leads by stages to the disintegration of the family and to a fragmentation of the identity relations of individual and family. It is to be borne in mind, always, that the interrelationships of individual and group, the operation of family defenses, exert a selective influence on the choice of individual defenses against anxiety and also determine the degree to which these defenses are operable or inoperable, compensated or decompensated.

In family process, growth is forward movement. It is embodied in a progressive shift of the dynamics of family role adaptation. It is the ability to accommodate to new experience, to cultivate new levels of complementarity in family role relationships, to find avenues for the solution of conflict, to build a favorable self-image, to buttress critical forms of defense against anxiety, and to provide support for further creative development. The whole issue rests on the quality, the appropriateness, and the pace of change. In the psychotherapeutic situation, it is this capacity for change that must be mobilized and channeled into growth in the direction of health.

5

The Functions of the Family Therapist

The vivid impact of face-to-face interchange, the opportunity to correlate directly intrapsychic and interpersonal processes, is one of the major assets of the family therapeutic interview. The therapist moves quickly into the living space of the family group. The members draw him into the whirlpool of their anxiety-ridden struggle as a participant, a surrogate for a parent or grandparent. His primary responsibility is to mobilize a useful quality of empathy and communication, to arouse and enhance a live and meaningful emotional interchange. Figuratively speaking, he strives to lend to the contact the quality of a touching experience, a spontaneous and deeply genuine kind of communion. As the members feel in touch with the therapist, they come into better touch with one another. Through the quality of the therapist's use of self, his open, earnest sharing of his own feelings and attitudes, he sets an example for the needed sincerity of interaction among the family members.

Sometimes the whole family is pervaded by a mood of disillusionment, defeat, and depression. Even so, there is always a flicker of hope. It is the therapist's responsibility to nourish this hope and to build faith that the family may achieve something better.

In the evolution of this method, several distinct emphases have emerged which are not mutually exclusive: (1) re-education of the family through guidance, (2) reorganization through a change in the patterns of family communication, and (3) resolution of pathogenic conflict and induction of change and growth by means of a dynamic approach in depth to the affective currents of family life. It is the last of these, the dynamically oriented depth therapy of the emotional life of the family, that we shall consider here.

Diagnosis and treatment of the family are interwoven and parallel activities. Diagnosis qualifies the choice of therapeutic goals and the specific techniques of intervention. At the same time, the therapeutically oriented, exploratory interview with the whole family is the pathway to diagnosis. The clinical interview is the main instrument for obtaining relevant information. The kind of information we get depends on how we get it. Each level of entry into the inner life of the family offers selective access to some components of family experience while for the moment obscuring others.

In a first contact with a troubled family, a formal procedure for intake and diagnosis is disadvantageous. It is preferable to initiate the process in a fresh, unprejudiced way, without historical data obtained separately and at different times from one or another member of the family. As the group wrestles with its immediate distress, a live type of history emerges that is apt to be more relevant and accurate than traditional history-taking. As the members become engaged in the therapeutic struggle, selected fragments of background are tossed out and subjected promptly to a process of consensual validation among the family members. For the clinician the live, pungent, and dramatic quality of spontaneous historical disclosures is a convincing experience. After all, history, in the best sense, is contemporary. Its importance and relevance hinge on its being a vital part of the here and now. Factors of pathogenic influence that have come up out of the past can be traced in the contemporary emotional events of the family, though they may now be organized and expressed in a different way. This is the "live past," not the "dead past," of family life.

Whatever the presenting complaint, and regardless of which member is labeled the "sick one," the whole family is invited to come in and talk it over. The number of persons involved varies; at some stages, it is the larger family entity, stretching across three generations; at other stages, when limitation is clinically useful, the therapist may concentrate on the parent-child interaction or excuse the children and focus on the husband-wife pair.

Therapeutic interviews with the family group may be conducted either in the office or in the home. Home visits are of great value but are insufficiently used.[1] Families are usually seen once a week, though occasionally more often, for about an hour. Significant therapeutic change is often achieved within a period of six months to two years.

At the outset, the family is troubled and perplexed, sometimes frantic and panicky. The members know that something is deeply wrong, but they do not know how or why, nor do they know what to do about it. By tradition, the family pushes one member forward as the sick, disabled one. Yet, in actuality, often several and sometimes all of the members are disturbed, although in different ways and to different depths. What the psychiatrist faces is a cluster of interrelated processes of illness, not a "single patient."

In many families, regardless of the symptoms, there is no urge for psychiatric referral as long as the family role relationships are held in tolerable balance. The timing of the demand for professional help strongly coincides with the immediate, dramatic impact of a decompensation of the previous state of balance, which then brings in its wake a distressing family conflict. Critical upsets of the emotional equilibrium of a family group thus become a significant health phenomenon. It is natural as an initial step, therefore, to ask the entire family to come in and talk things over.

In family interviewing, what one parent conceals, the other reveals. What the parents together hide, the child blurts out. What one member expresses in a twisted, prejudiced way is corrected by another. When certain anxiety-filled material is touched on, the family may engage in a silent pact to avoid these areas. Sooner or later such denials are broken through. Family life by its very nature is inimical to the guarding of personal secrets. Such secrets exist, but they are difficult to preserve. Sooner or later "the cat is let out of the bag." It is the clinician's responsibility to distinguish true and valid secrets from false, pathogenic ones. He respects the former while supporting the family in piercing the latter.

In this process, the clinician integrates his knowledge and his use of self in a special way. He is participant-observer; he is active, open, fluid, forthright, and at times blunt. He moves directly into the family conflict to energize and influence the interactional proc-

---

[1] Marjorie L. Behrens and Nathan W. Ackerman, "The Home Visit as an Aid in Family Diagnosis and Therapy," *Social Casework,* January 1956.

esses; he withdraws to objectify his experiences, to survey and assess significant events; then he moves back in again. Weighing and balancing the healthy and sick emotional forces, he supports health and counteracts sickness by shifting his function at changing stages of family process.

His responsibilities are many and complex; they require a flexible, open, and undefensive use of self. The family and its parts interact with, absorb, and use his influence in a variety of ways. Depending on the shifting foci of conflict and anxiety, one or another member joins with and separates from particular elements of the therapist's identity. These partial joinings and separations reflect elements of both transference fantasy and realism.

The processes of transference, countertransference, and reality testing must be specially conceptualized in the matrix of face-to-face family interaction. These processes emerge spontaneously among the family members and with the therapist. The potentials for effectively testing the reality of distorted expectations in this special setting are enormously enhanced.

The therapist must move his influence from one part of the family to another, following the shifting core of most destructive conflict. In this way he stimulates an expanding awareness of the true nature of the emotional and social disorders of the family unit and engages the members in a progressive process of working through the related conflicts.

Family therapy begins promptly with the first face-to-face contact. The therapist makes instantaneous observations of the personalities of the family members, their ways of interacting, their adaptation to family roles. How do they enter, who sits next to whom, who looks toward whom, who away from whom? Who speaks? Who listens? Who smiles? Who frowns? At a typical session the family arrives in a state of pent-up anger, pain, fright, and thwarted need. The therapist quickly senses the emotional climate. He observes the quality of appeal that the members project to one another and to himself. Who wants what from whom? Do they deny and disguise their needs or express them in urgent, frantic, coercive ways? Do they simply give up and, in a mood of resigned apathy, cease to ask and expect anything? He notes the existing confusion, distrust, and hostile fragmentation of family relationships.

In an over-all view, the therapeutic orientation may be characterized thus: the therapist discovers the idiosyncratic language of the family, how the members talk, what they choose to talk about, and, very importantly, what they tacitly avoid. He makes rapid note of what is felt and communicated below the level of words in bodily stances, facial expressions, inarticulate gestures, and postural avoidances. He evaluates the outer face of the family, its protective mask. He perceives and assesses the deeper currents of emotion that the family members fear and inhibit, the fright, mistrust, and despair, the bitterness and vindictiveness. He identifies those forces of conflict and anxiety which freeze the reaching out of the members, the asking for closeness and understanding, each with the therapist and with one another. He defines for himself the levels of the struggle to cope that characterize the particular family. He assays the interplay between the preferred defensive operations of the family group and the individual defenses against anxiety. In a continuous process of communion with self, he brings to his awareness the emotions stirred in him by the deeper streams of feeling moving among the family members and toward himself. He uses his disciplined insights into his personal emotions as a diagnostic yardstick for what is being experienced by the family. In so doing, he develops a series of clinical hunches which he progressively tests as he builds his diagnostic image of the group. This image includes the family's patterns of functioning, complementarity, conflict and coping; the interplay of family and individual defenses; and, finally, the family's struggles with conflicting representations of family identity, values, and patterns of action. In a selective, sequential manner, he penetrates the family façade, the patterns of complicity in denying and disguising the deeper currents of feeling, conflict, and fear.

Now let us depict the process in sharper detail. Stage by stage, as the therapist strips away denials, displacements, rationalizations, and other disguises, the essential conflicts between and within family members come into clearer perspective. Acting as a catalyst, the therapist provokes increasingly candid disclosures of underlying currents of interpersonal conflict. He lifts intrapersonal conflicts to the level of interpersonal process. In a progressive working through of the elements of conflict, and through a process of consensual validation, significant connections can be traced be-

tween the family's disorder and the intrapsychic anxieties and dis-
ablements of its individual members. A further function of the
family therapist is to neutralize prejudicial assault and scapegoating. Through this mechanism, one part of the family armors itself
and prejudicially attacks and sacrifices another part. When necessary, the therapist intervenes to neutralize these sick patterns of
attack. By counteracting scapegoating as a special defense against
anxiety, the therapist can retranspose the underlying conflict to
its place of origin in the family group; that is to say, the conflict
can be moved back to its primary source. In this phase of therapy,
it becomes possible to identify the organization of the family roles
of persecutor, victim, and rescuer or healer of family conflict.
Often, the therapist joins hands with the member who takes on
the role of "family healer."

As family and therapist together define the main trends of conflict and coping, it becomes necessary to mark out the interplay
between the family's group defenses of its continuity and functions
and the members' individual defenses against anxiety. Toward this
end, the therapist makes free use of the device of confrontation.
By a variety of interventions, he penetrates and undermines the
pathogenic patterns of coping and defense. He calls attention to the
inefficiency, inappropriateness, and harmfulness of certain sickness-
inducing defenses, and he fosters the substitution of healthier ones.

To stir movement, the therapist pierces pathogenic operations
by a device that I call "tickling the defenses." This is a tactic of
catching the family members by surprise, by exposing dramatic
discrepancies between their self-justifying rationalizations and
their subverbal attitudes. He challenges empty clichés and static
or pat formulae for meeting the problems of family living. He
halts fruitless bickering over routine, external, or unimportant
matters. Watchful for each cue, he reaches out for more honest
and meaningful kinds of communication. In the service of this
effort he may make effective use of certain forms of "body talk."
He confronts the members forthrightly with the meaning of certain
units of nonverbal communication as reflected in mood, expression,
posture, gesture, and movement. To counteract the tendency to
substitute empty verbalisms for genuine emotional interchange,
he catalyzes in the members the urge to explore these dramatic
contradictions between verbal utterances and bodily expression.

As therapy proceeds, the sense of tension and danger often mounts. The family experiences an increasing threat of loss of control. To deal with this fear, the therapist steers a path between the extremes of a rigid avoidance of the dangers of closeness and an uncontrolled explosion of rage that might lead to panic and disorganization. His calm, firm presence must offer the needed assurance against family catastrophe.

The family therapist's function as a controller of interpersonal danger is but one phase of his role as a true parent figure. In this position, he executes other functions: he offers security, emotional support, acceptance, understanding, affirmation of worth, and direct satisfaction of valid emotional needs; he catalyzes the interchanges among the family members toward cooperation in the quest for solution to conflict or toward finding more appropriate compromises. Along this path he activates a shift toward improved mutual complementing of needs.

As a true parent figure, the family therapist offers emotional support on a selective basis, now to one part of the family, now to another. He may, in all honesty and with considerable effectiveness, support a weaker member of the group against the attack of a stronger one. In the long view, the genuineness of the therapist's concern, his fairness, and the manner in which, from time to time, he shifts support from one part of the family to another, minimize destructive rivalry.

At still another level, the family therapist provides support through a kind of substitutive gratification; that is to say, he supplies the family with elements of emotion and imagery of self and others in which the family had before been lacking.

A crucial function is the family therapist's use of self as an instrument of reality testing. The social structuring of the family interview, the face-to-face interactions, the increasing depth and honesty of the quality of the interchange, offer a fertile matrix for the reality testing of warped images of self and others, of twisted perceptions of conflict, and of the threat of punishment. In this sense, reality testing, fortified by the therapist's activity, begins at the outset. In the spontaneous give and take among the family members, each has the opportunity to offer a reality check for the fantasies and anxieties of other members. What one member hides is revealed by another. What one expresses in a twisted, prejudiced way may be counterbalanced by another. By testing against the therapist's more objective perceptions, each family member has the opportunity to experience every other member without the felt dangers of their distorted imagery. Each member takes a second look at every other member and at the therapist and re-adapts toward more realistic images of self and other members of the group.

Finally, the family therapist serves as an educator in the problems of family living and as a person who represents in his own being a range of models of family health. As the family members work through what they feel, think, and do, the therapist stirs in them an expanded awareness of alternative patterns of family relationships. He shakes up the pre-existing alignments and splits; he opens the way to new designs for family living that offer more mutual satisfaction and a greater potential for growth to the family as a whole. In a shared way, the family members are able to find constructive solutions or compromises for conflict and to discover new levels of intimacy, sharing, and identification.

In a troubled family group, there is an aggravated clash of competing identities and values. This competition is expressed in an ongoing contest of needs, identities, and value representations between parental partners, which in turn can be traced to the links of identity and values of each parent with the respective family of origin. In this clash, the offspring are forced to take sides, and thus the nuclear family is split into contesting factions. In such family warfare, each faction competes with every other faction to push change toward what it wants the family to be and to do for the family members.

In this setting, family study and therapy have a dual orientation, the aim of which is the dissolution of pathogenic conflict and fear and the support of residual forces toward health. The therapist fosters the internalization of his influence to support change in the direction of health. He awakens respect for individual differences and affirms foundations for sharing and identification in family relationships. He facilitates the efforts of the group to balance sameness and difference, joining and individuation. He energizes and enriches the processes of critical reassessment of family identities, goals, and values, especially those that pertain to essential family functions—the relations of husband and wife, father and mother, parent and child, child and sibling, parent and grand-parent. Crucial to the entire effort is the breaking down of anxiety-ridden taboos against the discussion and sharing of basic family problems and conflicts. The changing processes of complementarity of the family's role relationships must be judged in the larger context of the total organization of the family group. By the merging of these many functions, as activator, challenger, supporter, interpreter, and reintegrator, the therapist shakes up pre-existing pathogenic relationships, alignments, and equilibria and opens the way to the discovery of healthier family bonds.

In summary form, the therapist's functions may be itemized as follows:

1. The family therapist establishes a useful rapport: empathy and communication among family members and between them and himself.

2. He uses this rapport to evoke the expression of major conflicts and ways of coping. He clarifies conflict by dissolving barriers, defensive disguises, confusions, and misunderstandings. By stages he attempts to bring to the family a mutual and more accurate understanding of what is really wrong. This aim he achieves through a series of partial interventions, which include

   (a) counteracting inappropriate denials, displacements, and rationalizations of conflict;

   (b) transforming dormant or concealed interpersonal conflicts into open interactional expression;

   (c) lifting hidden intrapersonal conflict to the level of interpersonal interaction;

   (d) neutralizing patterns of prejudicial scapegoating that fortify one part of the family while victimizing another part.

3. The therapist fulfills in part the role of a true parent figure—a controller of danger and a source of emotional support and satisfaction-supplying elements that the family needs but lacks. His emotional nurturing of the family is a kind of substitutive therapy. He introduces more appropriate attitudes, emotions, and images of family relations than the family has ever had.

4. The therapist works toward penetrating and undermining resistances and reducing the intensity of shared currents of

conflict, guilt, and fear. He accomplishes these aims mainly by the use of confrontation and interpretation.

5. The therapist serves as a personal instrument of reality testing for the family.
6. The therapist serves as an educator and a personifier of useful models of family health.

In carrying out these functions, the family therapist must fit himself into a wide range of roles, as activator, challenger, supporter, confronter, interpreter, and reintegrator. The challenge is great, but the end results are exciting and rewarding.

The treatment of families is a natural kind of therapeutic influence. It has a fascination uniquely its own. It gives one the conviction of getting close to the heart of the matter, of seeing the real thing, alive and whole. It is a method that hits home, both literally and figuratively. One sees things firsthand in the family interview, things that one cannot see in any other way. The family method opens up a new vista, a new path of entry into the phenomena of illness and health. It is a potent therapeutic instrument.

Meanwhile, practical problems remain. For those trained in the specific skill of individual therapy, it is difficult to adapt to and adopt another mode of treatment. The art of mental healing in general is not easily taught, but in the case of family psychotherapy, even the opportunities for training are sorely lacking.

The differences between family therapy and individual therapy are obviously many, but one of the most striking lies in the relationship between the therapist and his patient. To exemplify the critical developments that have been occurring in this area, it is useful to re-examine the issues of transference and countertransference.

In the original Freudian model, the analyst is anonymous, a mirror for the patient's inner mental life. The analyst hides his face. He reflects "only what is shown to him." As a "blank screen," he receives the imprint of the patient's projected fantasies but withholds the usual social cues. He does not fulfill the part of a real person. The patient on the couch is left in the dark concerning the real qualities of the analyst. The Freudian model, therefore, does not provide the architecture for a true social experience.

The analyst activates the patient's explorations of his inner and past life. Conflict with the analyst is reinterpreted in terms of conflict with the older parts of self, linked to childhood condition- ings through significant figures like mother, father, and siblings. The primary focus is on disturbed and conflict-ridden orientation to past experience. Intrinsic to the process is the temporary sub- ordination of reality. Transference achieves not only a position of prominence, but one of dominance over existing realities. Ulti- mately comes the task of working through by way of interpreta- tion and reality testing. The analyst personifies objective reality. But the check with this representation of reality is delayed. For the patient, there is not one reality, there are many realities. The power of the analyst to test these is in some ways limited. Often the analyst lacks definitive information about the prevailing inter- personal realities, or he is deficient in his capacity for translating them to the patient. Insofar as the analyst has no face and no identity and shows no emotion, this relation, I repeat, is not a true social experience.

The classical analytic process favors a reliving of the symbiotic component of conflict in the original child-parent unit. It reactivates the craving for magic omnipotence. It propels into the foreground the autistic, magic core of the psyche. As defined, this process lends access to the egocentric, symbiotic nucleus of intrapsychic pathology which contains the distorted percepts of the joined in- fant-parent image and the patient's own body. The analyst does not intrude his personality and emotions. Such emotions are con- ceived of as a contamination, an impurity injected into the patient's expressions of primary process. Here, in Freud's view, the primi- tive expressions of the patient's unconscious may dangerously contaminate the analyst's mind.

The patient projects his irrational, conflict-ridden emotions, fantasies, and magic expectations—the "primary process"; the analyst injects the modifying, organizing, and disciplining effects of the "secondary process." As the patient brings into awareness his unconscious, the analyst contributes insight, reason, reality, and conscious control. Between them they make up the functions of one mind.

What happens the moment we join, conceptually, transference to countertransference? Just as soon as we view them as reciprocal processes, the head and tail of a single phenomenological entity, we have, in effect, executed a shift from a theoretical model of analysis as a "one person" process to a two-or-more-person phenomenon. Immediately, as we admit countertransference into the conceptual framework, we are compelled to envisage the interaction of two or more minds, two or more persons. The relationship is now a twosome, but a twosome that leaves room for the influence of third parties and more—family and community. The relationship now involves a circular interchange of emotion. We must then be concerned with the balance between real and unreal, between appropriate emotions and pathological, inappropriate ones. The shift to a two-person model now provides the potential for a true social interaction and requires the redefinition of all partial processes. Each part must be interrelated with every other, and with the whole. Transference is then conceived of as a failure of social learning and must be tested against the backdrop of existing reality and against the potentials for new social learning. In order to achieve internal consistency in such a framework, we require an expanded foundation for the dynamics of personality, namely, a biopsychosocial model. Intrapsychic events must be matched against the corresponding interpersonal events; the unconscious must be paralleled by a definition of the conscious organization of experience and the related modes of social adaptation. The unreal must be matched against the real. The essential continuity of past, present, and future must be respected; a person's behavior may be molded by his view of the future as well as by his view of the past. The theoretical and clinical significance of this shift in conceptualization is enormous. Transference, countertransference, free association, resistance, working through, interpretation, reality testing, and new learning all become interrelated parts of a unified process.

Freud[2] characterized countertransference as the influence of the patient on the analyst's unconscious. The analyst receives and interprets these messages from his own unconscious. But he must exclude them from the analytic process; they are an impurity, a contamination. In contrast, Benedek[3] asserts that the therapeutic

---

[2] Sigmund Freud, "Analysis Terminable and Interminable," *International Journal of Psychoanalysis,* Vol. XXIII (1937).

[3] T. Benedek, "Dynamics of the Counter-transference," *Bulletin of the Menninger Clinic,* Vol. XVII (1953).

personality is the most important agent in the therapeutic process. Clara Thompson[4] highlights the significance of the analyst as a real person. Reich,[5] Weigert,[6] Fromm-Reichmann,[7] and Tauber[8] mention deliberate use of countertransference. Tower[9] hypothesizes a regular and inevitable emergence of a countertransference neurosis in the analyst.

In the light of present-day knowledge, can we not say that the real issue is not whether the analyst has or shows emotions, but rather, which emotions are right and which are wrong for the healing of a given patient? Just here there emerges the critical importance of the subverbal components of communication. In my opinion, true healing does not take place unless the understanding of emotion goes both ways. It is necessary not only that the analyst understand the patient's emotions, but also that the patient understand the analyst's emotions. The analyst must sift out his own emotions and selectively inject those which the patient needs to experience in order to become well. Freud stated that analysis takes something away, a pathogenic idea; it does not add anything new. As I see it, were this literally correct, there could be no reality testing and no new social learning. Since transference is a failure of social learning, the analyst, to accomplish its resolution, *must* inject something new, namely, the right images and emotions to neutralize the patient's wrong ones.

Is there a risk in the analyst's use of his own sense of self, and in the injection into the process of certain selected emotions? Certainly there is. But nothing ventured, nothing gained. Risk is inherent in omission as well as in commission. There is certainly no magic erasure of danger in the principle that the analyst shows

[4] Clara Thompson, "The Role of the Analyst's Personality in Therapy," *American Journal of Psychotherapy,* Vol. X.

[5] A. Reich, "On Counter-transference in Psychoanalysis," *International Journal of Psychoanalysis,* Vol. XXXII (1951).

[6] E. Weigert, "The Importance of Flexibility in Psychoanalytic Technique," *Journal of the American Psychoanalytic Association* (1954).

[7] Frieda Fromm-Reichmann, *Psychoanalysis and Psychotherapy,* ed. Dexter M. Bullard (Chicago: University of Chicago Press, 1959).

[8] E. Tauber, "Exploring the Therapeutic Use of Counter-transference," *Psychiatry* (1954).

[9] L. Tower, "The Counter-transference," address to the Chicago meeting of the International Psychoanalytic Society, Spring 1955.

no face, no identity, and no emotions. That principle, in my opinion, represents an understandable caution on the analyst's part, but also a questionable one. Such caution may lead to stasis. Certainly analysis holds dangers for both the patient and the analyst. Life itself holds danger, but also the thrill and adventure of expanding experience and new growth. Nothing in life stands still; life is never safe. We must take a calculated risk, but we must know clearly what we are doing.

The withholding of emotion on the analyst's part, therefore, the hiding of the analyst's real self, is no answer to the dangers of emotional contamination. These dangers are there, for both participants. To play it too safe, however, is to sterilize the potential of analysis as a therapeutic instrument. The sheer avoidance of emotional engagement with the patient may protect a cautious analyst, but it will not heal anyone. Is it not true that some analysts are overprotective of a patient's anxieties? This attitude may be, in fact, not a genuine protection of the patient against psychic pain, but rather a cautious protection of the analyst's own anxieties from exposure to the public eye. In such instances, the analyst is hiding himself. He is giving himself immunity against possible criticism rather than assuring the well-being and growth of his patient.

It is my conviction that people can tolerate emotional upset and psychic pain much better than we give them credit for. Basically, a patient's need to be deeply understood is a far more potent force than his fear of personal exposure and psychic pain. In other words, if the patient is given his choice between exposing his psychic wounds or losing the opportunity to be understood, he will decisively choose to be understood and will take his chances with the pain. On the other hand, if the analyst hides his emotions, the patient will surely find him out and will indict him for being insincere and self-protective. It is my belief, therefore, that there is only one right choice for the psychotherapist, and that is to face squarely the possible dangers of emotional contagion in a close relationship, but to use to the best of his knowledge the right emotions and to take maximal advantage of the potential for inducing change and new learning.

A closely related question is what criteria should be used in assessing change in a patient's behavior. Some analysts have stressed the use of dreams as the index of change; others have emphasized insight; still others, a diminution of anxiety. It seems likely, however, that no one of these indices is adequate by itself. What we seek is real change, certainly not mere intellectual insight which fails to be translated into life action. The only dependable evidence for change is a shift toward integration of previously dissociated elements of the personality, a change best expressed as the ability to pull oneself together into one piece. This kind of change is reflected in a growing harmony of expression in words, feelings, and bodily movements, and an integration of oneself into social roles. Ultimately, the movement is toward the creation of a new identity and a changed value orientation.

Our perspective toward change in a patient undergoing analytic therapy confronts us with a critical problem: How shall we judge the issues of decision making and action in real life? The dangers of irrational decisions and actions during psychotherapy are self-evident. Here lies the origin of the Freudian principle of postponing critical life decisions until the completion of treatment. But decision making is of the essence of life; it means action. Without decision and action, there is no movement, no life. There arises, then, a crucial value judgment: the distinction between action—appropriate, rational action—and acting out—inappropriate, irrational, dangerous action. Then, too, there is, to coin a new phrase, "acting in." "Acting in" may be viewed as those forms of acting out in the therapeutic relationship which may be tested against reality. Many forms of "acting in" are benign and spur a piece of learning. Freud himself distinguished between mild, harmless forms of acting out and dangerous forms. Often there is only a hairline difference between appropriate action and acting out. I suggest that the issue in psychotherapy is not at all to discourage action, but rather to promote progressively more effective reality testing of specific kinds of action, those that may stimulate personal and social development.

In a basic sense, all action in all places represents a varying mixture of appropriate and inappropriate, rational and irrational experience. In this view, some forms of "acting in" provide a possible solution of conflict and the promotion of new learning and growth. By a similar token, some, though only *some,* forms of acting out in real life may also offer avenues for solution of conflict and for new growth, depending on the character and involvement of the persons who are the partners in the acting out. There can be no acting out without the complicity of one or more partners. There tends to be a bias here toward the view that "acting in," which is acting out in the therapeutic relationship, is a desirable experience, whereas acting out in real life is an undesirable and dangerous experience. Instead of arbitrarily entrenching this distinction, however, we must more carefully differentiate benign and malignant forms of such action. The problem lies ultimately in the emotional complementarity of the patient's personality and the therapist's personality; also, in the complementarity of the patient's personality and the personalities of other significant individuals with whom the patient is emotionally engaged in a close way.

In this context, other questions arise: Why do we prize the irrationality of transference neurosis? Why do we enhance the value of "acting in" and arbitrarily indict acting out in other relationships? The patient is supposed to be as "normal" as possible in real life, reserving his "sick" behavior for the treatment session. Is the therapist's role the opposite? Is he expected to be "normal" during the psychotherapeutic session and to reserve his "sick" behavior for real life outside? With respect to solving conflict and achieving new learning, varying combinations of the real and the unreal present a certain danger, but they may also afford opportunities in action for the solution of conflict, for learning, and for further development.

Psychotherapists deeply conditioned to the one-to-one secret relationship of patient and therapist often react with a profound sense of surprise and shock to the impact of their first experience with family therapy. They raise many questions. Is this emphasis on family really old or new? Does the family interview invade personal privacy? Is there a traumatic effect in dealing with personal matters in this open way? How can a therapist intervene on a whole family and talk meaningfully at the same time to child, adolescent, and adult? Is it not true that each of these age groupings calls for a different level of language? How can a family therapist bridge the gap between the generations? The difference between the sexes? Do not the members vie for the favor of the therapist? How can the therapist remain neutral, avoid taking sides? Does the therapist stir up feelings among family members that hang over and cause a later disturbance at home? Do the members lose control at home? Does the family interview critically upset personal defenses and leave the members emotionally naked with one another? How can a therapist observe so many multiple events at once? How can he deal with them simultaneously? Is it true that the family interview method is inherently superficial, incapable of access to depth material?

Like transference and countertransference, this question of depth may seem critically important to the psychotherapist accustomed to treating individuals, but it should be made clear that although family therapy may begin on the surface, it need not stay there. It can move from the outside inward or from the inside outward. A competent therapist can achieve access to any emotional depth he may require in meeting the problems of a particular family. The challenge of reaching, as and when needed, selected components of the depth experience of the family group rests, in the ultimate, on therapeutic talent, including know-how, clarity, appropriateness of goals, and confidence in action. Real difficulties are encountered, to be sure, but more often than not they are the consequence of inexperience, insecurity, and the inadequate use of the therapist's self in this special role. They are not, in a primary sense, the fault of the family treatment method itself.

A family has body, mind, and spirit. It has a heart; it throbs with the pulse of life. Like the individual, it has both depth and surface expression, an inner face and an outer face. It builds a façade, a mask. If we strip away the mask, we can glimpse the inner being; we enter the stream of conflict experience of the family in depth. What do we mean, in this special context, by "depth material"? What does it mean with respect to the individual? What does it mean in a family? What does the therapist do to mobilize access to depth material in a family interview? What special insights and skills can he bring to bear on this challenge?

In psychoanalytic terms, depth material is material which derives from the unconscious psyche, from buried conflicts, feelings, and fantasies; in essence, it is a motivating force that is defensively excluded from awareness. It is repressed, denied, displaced, projected.

But how, at the level of family living, shall we conceive of depth material? Are there processes in the emotional life of the family group analogous to depth experience in the individual? Are there perhaps shared currents of conflict, feeling, and fantasy that are excluded from clear awareness, yet which constitute significant molding forces both of the development of the family and of its individual members? In my view, the answer is yes. There are emotional forces in the life of the family that are embodied in its imagery, its dreams, its deepest strivings and conflicts. In the same sense that we refer to an individual unconscious, we may also speak of something like a shared, interpersonal unconscious in the family group. Significant elements of the family unconscious may be reflected in a disguised form in the carry-over of components of conflicted, projected, introjected images of the families of origin. In essence they might be thought of as fragments of transference projection from the old families to the new, partly shared by the members, partly caught in conflict. It is true that we do not have the words or language for this kind of experience—we are plagued here by a semantic problem—but this complication is surely not greater in the case of a concept of "family unconscious" than it is for the term "individual unconscious."

From another point of view, however, the contrast between depth and surface experience in family process may be reflected in the polarities of important vs. trivial, relevant vs. irrelevant, central vs. peripheral. Some types of unconscious material and childhood conditioning may be of little relevance, whereas other kinds of conflict, conscious conflict in the here and now, may be more important. Often, things that are consciously felt but that the members tacitly conspire not to talk about are of the essence in family interaction.

Let us exemplify this point of view in a particular direction, again by way of analogy. The emotional life of some individuals seems shallow, thin, lacking in depth. But such people are not always as they look. The apparent shallowness is a protective disguise, a shield against hurt. By penetrating or circumventing the shield, we expose the hidden depths, the concealed emotions. The situation is similar in the case of troubled families. The emotional life of the group may appear thin, superficial, lacking in depth, but here, too, the appearance may be a protective camouflage. Initially, such a family appears apathetic, unresponsive; it seems sleepy. In fact, it is depressed; it has lost heart; it is affectively dead. Has the deadening gone too far? Is it too late to attempt revival? Experience demonstrates that it is often possible to pierce the mask of deadness, to bring the depths to the surface, to stir the family to breathe, feel, and act—to come to life again.

To achieve access in depth, the therapist uses as an instrument his own being, his own emotions as he experiences them. The emotions stirred in a therapist facing a family group are diagnostic, provided that the therapist can correctly read his own emotions. The thesis is a simple one. The emotions aroused in a therapist as he confronts a troubled family offer specific clues to the shared currents of feeling among the family members. That part of the therapist's own depth experience that pertains to his family feeling is especially relevant. He must be able to distinguish clearly which of his inner responses are his own private emotions toward family and which others are specifically induced by the unspoken, conflict-ridden feelings of the family sitting before him. What is of diagnostic import is the clash between the family's image of itself and the therapist's image of the family. The therapist needs merely to make a correct and appropriate reading of the meaning of these very differences, but *merely* is the heart and core of the problem. The task is by no means easy, nor is every therapist able to perform it. Still, here is the essence of depth therapy, whether it be with an individual patient or with a whole family.

Inevitably, the principles of the family method must be differently expressed by contrasting types of therapeutic personality. The personal equation, the art and style of a given therapist, will always be with us. This is an asset, not a liability. The subtleties of psychotherapeutic relationships are infinite. The challenge is to discover a good fit between the style of a given family and the style of a particular therapist. It is the idiosyncratic quality of this relationship that shapes the final outcome. The issue of personal style ought not to be confused with the question of multiple types of family therapy. The basic theory of therapy must remain problem-oriented; it ought not become lost in endless debate over styles of execution.

In general terms, family psychotherapy may be the method of choice, the sole method of treatment, or may be combined with other forms of therapy. It can be employed in phases of critical change in family relationships. It can be used together with the individual therapy of one or another family member. It can be helpful or even indispensable for engaging a sick member in a therapeutic program. It can be of value at selected phases of the individual psychotherapy of a family member; here it is viewed as a complementary influence. It is frequently a useful form of intervention when a member has bogged down in his individual therapy. It can break the impact of resistance to progress, influenced by the secondary gains of illness. It can be helpful in the reintegration of a patient with his family group in the final phase of personal therapy.

Family psychotherapy can appropriately be applied to a wide range of behavior disorders, but it must be flexibly accommodated to the specific and unique features of each of these conditions. It can be useful in the treatment of neuroses, psychoses, and character disorders, especially those that show acting out, and, in some instances, in the special problems of addiction. It is especially helpful in those conditions in which the here-and-now struggle with the interpersonal conflicts of the family potently affects the outcome of coping with intrapsychic conflicts. As already suggested, family psychotherapy is an effective means of penetrating and reducing the secondary gains of emotional illness. It can be of value for disturbances at all stages of the life cycle: childhood, adolescence, adulthood, and old age. It is, however, uniquely effective with marital disorders and with disturbances involving the relations of children or adolescents with the family.

There are, of course, situations in which family therapy is contraindicated; they may be summed up as follows: (1) The presence of a malignant, irreversible trend toward breakup of the family, which may mean that it is too late to reverse the process of fragmentation. (2) The dominance within the group of a concentrated focus of malignant, destructive motivation. (3) One parent who is afflicted with an organized, progressive paranoid condition, or with incorrigible psychopathic destructiveness, or who is a confirmed criminal or pervert. (4) Parents, one or both, who are unable to be sufficiently honest; lying and deceitfulness that are deeply rooted in the group negate the potential usefulness of family therapy. (5) The existence of a certain kind of valid family secret. (6) The existence of an unyielding cultural, religious, or economic prejudice against this form of intervention. (7) The existence in some members of extremely rigid defenses which, if broken, might induce a psychosis, a psychosomatic crisis or physical assault. (8) Finally, the presence of organic disease or other disablement of a progressive nature that precludes the participation of one or more members.

In assessing these considerations, the psychotherapist must explicitly consider an ever-present force—ambivalence. Lay persons unabashedly exhibit this emotion toward mental healing. Psychotherapists, however, also feel ambivalent about what they do; the only difference lies in the increased subtlety with which therapists hide and disguise such feelings. The basic force of ambivalence attaches to all forms of psychotherapy, and family therapy is no exception. If anything, the challenge of treating a whole family arouses a fiercer ambivalence than any other form of treatment. The very image of the family stirs a rush of such feeling; after all, the family is the very cradle of ambivalence. It is surely not an accident of history that Freud himself issued his dire warnings against involvement with relatives.

The therapist himself may be affected in his view of family psychotherapy by a personal disillusionment with the image and value of the family, a feeling that the importance of the family is on the decline, that family relationships move toward spiritual bankruptcy. Does he tend preferentially to value the individual and to set him against the family? Insofar as some therapists are tempted to cross off the family as a lost cause, they push psychotherapeutic responsibility toward a position of ethical nihilism.

Looking to the future, it becomes important to strip away the emotional bias that contaminates the arguments of some who are opposed to the family-centered approach, and at the same time to temper the prejudice of those who show an ardent but uncritical support of it. The irrationalism of both the optimists and the pessimists runs counter to progress. In the meantime, the challenge is not to deny and dissolve the feelings of the therapist toward the family, but rather to receive from them the message and meaning that will enhance our understanding of this new method.

6

Treating Husband and Wife

Marriage is more than sex; it is a whole way of life. It is a joining in the work, joys, and sadnesses of life. Disorders of the marital relationship cannot be understood in a social vacuum, because of the influence of the past family groups of each partner and their current family situation. The fit or lack of fit of the partners can be properly appraised only within the framework of the family viewed as an integrated behavior system with dominant values and a definable organizational pattern. The marital adaptation needs to be seen within that larger network of relationships that reflects the identity connections of each partner with his respective family of origin and with the larger community. Relevant beyond sexual union are the basic functions of family that have to do with security, child rearing, social training, and the development of the marriage partners both as a joined couple and as individuals.

Because the family begins with marriage, disorders of marital interaction hold a place of focal importance in family dynamics and development. The goals of the therapy of marital disorders are to relieve the distress and the disabled functioning of the relationship, to strengthen the shared resources for problem solving, to reduce conflict while improving the level of coping, to encourage substitution of more appropriate controls and defenses for pathogenic ones, to enhance the complementarity of relationships at the sexual, emotional, and social levels, to bolster immunity against the disintegrative effects of emotional upset, to promote the growth of the relationship and of each partner as an individual, and to fit

113

the pattern of the marriage to the needs of further family growth.

Therapy begins with the exploration of salient problems. Only as the therapist becomes engaged in the ongoing process of treatment does he achieve, step by step, the needed understanding of the specific content of the marital disorder.

It is advantageous at the outset to see the couple within the matrix of the family group, including all those who play a part in the ongoing struggle—children, grandparents, and even more distant relatives. Afterward, at a suitable stage, the therapist can concentrate on the marital pair to the exclusion of other family members. Appointments may be arranged once or twice a week. Frequently, the true nature of the marital conflict is denied, concealed, or rationalized behind displacements and projections onto other relationships, like parent-child and parent-grandparent. Marital partners who are caught in conflicts that they cannot resolve often maintain a defensive distance by putting other family members between them. Sometimes each parent establishes protective alliances with one or another relative. This device is silently yet eloquently dramatized by the manner in which parents arrange to seat their children or one or another grandparent between them— tacit testimony to the marital barrier.

How is the marital trouble viewed? How does each partner see the problem? What do other family members say and feel about it? What is the child's version, the grandparents', the in-laws'? What are the views of neighboring families? What is the same and what is different in these several views? The therapist must assess what each partner wants of the other, of the family, of the community. Do they get it? If not, why not? Do they continue to try to find satisfaction in one another? What is each willing to do for the other? What has the couple tried? What have they not tried? Have they perhaps tried in a wrong and self-defeating way? Are they now discouraged, beaten down? Have they surrendered hope? Have they given way to disillusionment and despair? Do they console themselves with mutual accusation and punishment? What do other family members want of the married couple? What does the community expect? Finally, what is the orientation of the therapist? How does he see the situation? What does he, in turn, propose to do?

In the therapy of marital disorders, the therapist must know what he stands for, what he is trying to do. He must also know what he can and cannot do. He must have explicit awareness of his own ideology concerning marriage and family life. In his own mind, he must sharply define whatever discrepancy prevails between his personal family values and those of the marital couple.

Having established rapport, he implements many of the therapeutic interventions already described. He moves by stages toward a common understanding with the partners as to what is really wrong. He mobilizes in the partners the needed depth of emotional honesty. He clarifies the real nature of conflicts by dissolving barriers and defensive disguises and by stripping away confusion and misunderstanding.

He explores the here-and-now situation, the current conflicts, their origin, the clash between real and ideal in the relation of the partners, the disillusionment, the bitterness, and the mutual urge to punish and make a scapegoat of the partner. He deals with the projections of transference from one partner to the other, and to the therapist. He promotes reality testing, openly using his own self as the instrument of such testing. As each partner projects unfulfilled needs onto the marital relationship, the therapist receives them empathically, supportively. This procedure raises each partner's hope of finding satisfaction in the other.

A crucial therapeutic task is dealing with the competitive tendency that is so often a central feature of marital disorder. Each partner engages in ploys in order to be "one up" on the other. Each seeks to get the better of the other. It is as if the business ethic of profit and loss has invaded the inner life of the married couple. Neither is convinced of a gain unless he imposes upon the partner a loss, a semblance of sacrifice. Here, the therapist must expose the utter futility of the game of "one-upmanship" in marriage and family. He must knowingly enter into a struggle with the couple in which the meaning of the clash of values between the partners, and between them and the therapist, is explored.

He points up the self-defeating and futile nature of inappropriate family values. He punctures the delusion that the expansion and well-being of one partner come only with a measure of surrender and sacrifice by the other. He opens the way to the discovery of healthier values, to the recognition that, often in the long view, what is good for one partner is also good for the other, that the survival, continuity, and growth of marriage hinge on love, sharing, and cooperation.

To illustrate the family approach to the basic problems hidden behind an obvious marital disorder, we present here verbatim excerpts involving a couple who, after six years, had not yet consummated their marriage. Two years after marriage, the wife was shocked to discover that her husband had been arrested for exhibiting himself sexually. This was the problem that they presented when they came to Dr. D. In the following interview, at which both Dr. D. and I were present, these problems are clarified. (In this particular case, the author served as consultant and supervisor to Dr. D. In the procedure called "live supervision," the therapist sits with the supervisor during the interview.)

Verbatim Record	**Interpretive Comment**
MRS. P.: Dr. D. was telling me that one impression *you* got was that (*clears throat*), excuse me, about my being so frightened . . . you know, as far as intercourse and . . . pregnancy, that I was very frightened about the whole thing. Well, I think I *am* more frightened, I *would* be more frightened than most people. But don't you think that other women must be a little frightened, too?	Wife seeks reassurance that she is not different, that other women also fear sex and pregnancy.
DR. A.: Well . . . what other women are you talking about?	
MRS. P.: Women in general. I'm sure they don't go into it . . .	
DR. A.: I don't know any women in general.	
MRS. P.: I . . . I think that each woman is a little fearful of, uh, you know, becoming pregnant. . . .	
DR. A.: Let's talk about you. We can't talk about . . . the idea "woman."	Therapist presses wife to be more specific.
MRS. P.: I think I would be . . . I think I would be a little more frightened . . . due to my background, but	

on the other hand I think I would be *elated.* . . .

DR. A.: What scared you about getting pregnant? Tell me.

MRS. P.: Well, because of my childhood.

DR. A.: Be specific.

MRS. P.: Well, the way I was brought up without a father . . . and my mother had it very difficult, she had a very hard time, and we were told about this, quite often. . . .

Wife now refers to her special family background and to having had no father.

Wife's mother, as a lone parent, had a difficult struggle.

DR. A.: You were told *what,* by Mom?

Again, therapist presses for a specific response, not vague generalizations.

MRS. P.: How hard it was for her. And . . .

DR. A.: That you as a baby were a great burden to your mama?

MRS. P. (*softly*): That's right.

Now wife's voice drops and she begins to cry softly. The question: Was she loved and wanted as a child—or was she a burden to her mother?

DR. A.: It makes you cry. Mm . . . It almost makes you feel like maybe you shouldn't have been born?

Therapist recognizes her pain.

MRS. P.: (*Pause.*) No. (*In tears.*)

DR. A.: That hurts? (*Pause.*) Did you ever feel that . . . that with no father your mother might've at such moments felt sorry she had all those children?

MRS. P.: Yes.

Wife feels her mother resented the burden of the children.

DR. A.: There were five, too. (*To Mr. P.*) Do you want to comfort May?

MRS. P.: Yes.

Therapist invites husband's response to wife's pain.

DR. A.: You don't like to see her cry.

MR. P.: No, I don't. Because it also makes *me* sad.

Husband feels empathic with her sadness. He feels like crying with her.

DR. A.: Are you afraid you might cry with her? Huh?

MR. P.: I suppose so. It doesn't bring out the best feelings in me. To see her cry. (*Softly.*)

DR. A.: So you give her your handkerchief to hush the tears lest you start crying yourself with her.

Therapist makes articulate the urge to inhibit the crying, for fear of loss of control.

MR. P.: I . . . never looked at it that way.

This is a vivid illustration of a contagion of sad feeling, and a contagion of anxiety about loss of control.

MRS. P.: It's a good way of putting it, though, I guess.

DR. A.: See, you've already hushed her tears. Look.

MR. P.: (*Laughs.*)

DR. A.: She's drying up right way.

MRS. P.: Well, I can't talk if I'm crying.

DR. A.: Yes, you can. I think you talk even when you cry.

Therapist expands awareness of the flow of emotion, below the level of words.

MR. P.: . . . Expresses . . .

MRS. P.: (*Sobs.*)

DR. A.: From the heart.

He is receptive to the deeper sources of this feeling. He makes a quip which eases tension and at the same time communicates his sympathy.

MRS. P.: Oh.

DR. A.: When you get ready I'll give you my handkerchief.

The injection of a light, bantering touch of humor is supportive and helpful.

MR. and MRS. P.: (*Laugh.*)

DR. A.: As a matter of fact I've got three of them; they're all set. One, two, another one is three. (*Produces handkerchiefs.*)

MRS. P.: (*Laughing and crying all at once.*) Might need them. You might need them, Dr. A. (*Laughs loudly.*)

Wife wants therapist also to cry with her. (Is this urge a touch of empathy, hostility, or both?)

DR. A.: I might cry, too?

MR. P.: One for show and one for blow. (*Laughs.*)

MRS. P.: (*Laughs and blows her nose.*) Well, this is why I feel the way I do, because it wasn't easy and, I guess being the youngest one, I don't know . . . in a way I *did* have it better than my sisters did. They were older and they . . . I guess they *pam*pered me a little. And, uh . . . I guess I did have it easier in a way. But (*pause*) it's just that I never knew my father. (*Tearfully.*)

Wife was the youngest of five girls, the baby pampered by her older sisters.

Here, she is sorry for herself in having been denied a father.

DR. A.: You were two when he died?

MRS. P.: (*Crying.*) About a year and a half.

DR. A.: A year and a half. Mm. Did your mother or older sisters talk about your father, the kind of man he was?

She was too young to know her father.

MRS. P.: I know that he was . . .

DR. A.: Did you get an image of him?

MRS. P.: Not too good.

DR. A.: He was what?

MRS. P.: (*Crying.*) Excuse me. I know that he was a good man. And I know that he worked hard. (*Pause.*) And he was very much like an uncle I had. In other words, my mother's sister-in-law's husband. And I understand that he looked very much like him; we didn't have a picture of my father or

Her uncle replaced her father. Note here that she defines in female terms—not "my father's brother."

anything. But I never thought I had any feelings for him.

Wife discovers feelings for father she never knew.

DR. A.: They're coming out right now.

Therapist encourages release of feeling.

MRS. P.: (*After a long pause.*) Because I never knew him.

The long pause suggests a welling-up of intense emotion.

DR. A.: How could you help but have feelings for your father? He brought you into the world.

MRS. P.: How can you have feelings if you . . . if you never knew a person?

Here again, wife attempts to deny feeling, to restore a sense of control.

DR. A.: Didn't you think about your dead father?

Therapist counteracts effort to suppress feeling.

MRS. P.: Maybe I did. I didn't realize it though. Most of my life was without him.

DR. A.: You mention you often heard he was a good man, he worked hard for his family. Didn't Mother ever say anything about Father? Why he left her alone with all five little children? Why he died?

In fantasy and retrospectively, wife makes her dead father into a good man. Therapist challenges this view with a pointed question as to a feeling of desertion by her father.

MRS. P.: He died of pneumonia. That I know. At that time pneumonia was a very serious thing. They didn't have such marvellous drugs as they do to-day.

DR. A.: Your mother never showed any feeling of resentment, any feeling of irritation about when he died and left her with five babies?

Therapist stirs admission of conflict between wife's parents.

MRS. P.: Oh, I guess she may have, I can't remember very clearly. I think she did feel that it was my *father* who wanted a large family and she never did. And . . .

Father wanted children. Mother did not, and if she had had her way, the patient would not have been born.

DR. A.: Aha. You hear that.

MRS. P.: . . . and she said that as a matter of fact, if he was still living they probably most likely would have had more children.

DR. A.: So your mother *was* angry.

Wife now admits mother's anger at father.

MRS. P.: I guess so.

DR. A.: She didn't want this . . . big brood of children. He wanted it . . .

MRS. P.: No, my father wanted a boy, she said.

Now comes the crucial confession. Father wanted boy, not girl.

DR. A.: And he was going to go on making her pregnant until he got a *boy*. He didn't want five girls.

MRS. P.: I don't blame him.

DR. A.: You don't blame him? You don't *like* girls. You looked at John. (*To Mr. P.*) Is it true? She doesn't like girls?

Therapist teases out wife's rejection of self as girl.

MRS. P.: I think a mixed family is nicer. . . .

MR. P.: Well, I think May would like a mixed family. I think she feels she would have liked to have a brother besides just having four sisters. For a little change. To get accustomed to living with somebody else, because they had for a while her grandfather, an elderly man, who used to visit and be with the girls, and he more or less took over the male symbol in the family.

Husband refers to the need of a "male symbol" in wife's family.

DR. A.: Mmhmm. Mmhmm. He took over the "male symbol." And you?

MR. P.: I'm speaking about May's family at that time. I certainly hope I take over the male symbol.

He is not at all sure he can fill the role of "male symbol."

DR. A.: You hope you have what it takes? To be a male symbol?

MR. P.: Yes. I always thought I did have what it takes.

Does he have what it takes?

DR. A.: Do you have it?

MR. P.: I think so.

DR. A.: You're sure?

Therapist dramatizes husband's doubt.

MR. P.: (*Laughs.*) I hope so. I . . . if . . .

DR. A.: You hope so. That isn't feeling sure.

MR. P.: Huh? I . . . I always thought so, but I suppose if I was a hundred per cent correct I wouldn't be sitting in this chair right now. (*Pause.*) I never . . . I never had any doubts in my mind that . . .

Again husband vacillates. He wishes he could be the "male symbol," *but!*

DR. A.: Oh, you must have, because after all . . . what I'm thinking about is your . . . urge to display your penis, to exhibit yourself. Why would you do that if you were sure you had one? You want everybody else to convince you that you have one. By looking at it, by admiring it. You're reassuring yourself against your own doubts, somehow, that you have what it takes. After all, your father was a very violent man, a very severe man. In your family, your father didn't *allow* any other male symbol. Only himself.

Here therapist introduces husband's exhibitionism, and his doubt of having a penis.

Therapist now refers to husband's experience of emasculation by his father.

MR. P.: And my older brother. My *oldest* brother . . . would share the symbol with him.

Husband's oldest brother was identified with father's masculinity.

DR. A.: Did your father have a big symbol? You know what I mean? Did he have a big one or a little one?

This is an example of the therapist's way of "tickling the defenses," stirring the patient's fuller awareness of experience at the bodily level.

MRS. P.: (*Laughs.*)

MR. P.: I don't know. (*Laughs.*)

Both wife and husband echo this greater awareness with a knowing laugh.

DR. A.: You never looked at him?

In the light of husband's exhibitionism, did he have the urge to look at and admire his father's penis?

MR. P.: Never.

DR. A.: Honest?

MR. P.: I would . . . I'd . . . always shy away, because I think anything . . . I would feel as if there was a guillotine over my neck, was the impression that was, or the environment that was created, around something that would be so sacred as sex, in my . . . in the household that I was brought up in.

Husband's response to this challenge is a faltering, confused one, but his guilt and dread of punishment come through unmistakably.

DR. A.: You weren't allowed to peek, huh? You were scared to death to take a look.

Therapist heightens husband's awareness of his fright.

MR. P.: I wouldn't say that it was ever put to me in those terms, but, uh . . .

DR. A.: I mean you're not that short-sighted, are you?

Again, therapist injects a touch of humor. Husband wears strong optical lenses.

MRS. P.: (*Laughs.*)

MR. P.: (*Laughs.*) I don't think so. I'm very, I'm very myopic, but, uh, not that bad. . . .

DR. A.: With your glasses you could snatch a look, you know?

Therapist offers some affirmative support for husband's competitive curiosity.

MRS. P.: (*Laughs.*)

MR. P.: (*Laughs.*) I guess I could always strain my eyes.

MRS. P.: But I think that John exhibited himself also to get attention. I think this is very . . .

Wife turns subject back to husband's exhibitionism.

DR. A.: What kind of attention?

MRS. P.: Any kind of attention. Because he didn't get enough attention at home.

DR. A.: Did he exhibit it to you?

Therapist makes the issue a personal one. He asks for particulars.

MRS. P.: Yes.

DR. A.: Tell me how. Give me a . . . picture. How did he do it to you? How did he show off?

MRS. P.: Well, I hope by attempting to have a sexual relationship with one another.

This is again an attempt to cover up the sexual deviation.

DR. A.: Did he want you to look at it? With or without glasses?

MRS. P.: It was so *natural* that I . . . I did look. It was such a natural occurrence . . .

Wife admits urge to look.

DR. A.: How did you feel when you took a look?

MRS. P.: I liked what I saw.

DR. A.: You did?

MRS. P.: I was a little frightened, I guess, at the beginning. But you know it was such a natural thing that . . . I don't know. When you ask a question like that it sort of puts you off, because to me it was just natural.

It was just a "natural" curiosity. Wife's repetitive emphasis on sex as "natural" is suspect.

DR. A.: Well, after all, you were sick and tired of the girls in your family.

Therapist again emphasizes the lack of a "male symbol" in wife's family.

MRS. P.: That's true.

DR. A.: You couldn't wait to get a look at a boy. Here's the boy.

Therapist points to husband.

MRS. P.: Well, I *had* got a look before John.

Wife now admits prior curiosity with men.

DR. A.: You had?

MRS. P.: Yes, I had.

DR. A.: Where did you snatch a look before that?

MRS. P.: (*Laughs.*) At another boy. But I had never had relations because, I guess, I don't know, maybe I wasn't *able* to, or . . . I didn't think it was the right thing to do.

Note the anxious, indecisive quality of wife's attitude.

DR. A.: What happened with that boy?

MRS. P.: That was just nothing.

Wife backtracks, becomes evasive.

DR. A.: Now, now, now. Look, you were raised in a very strict way . . . sexually.

MRS. P.: That's true.

DR. A.: You felt it was wrong to go all the way, but . . .

MRS. P.: That's right.

DR. A.: That didn't stop you from taking a peek.

MRS. P.: That's true.

DR. A.: Was that wrong? To take a peek?

Therapist challenges wife to be more open and honest.

MRS. P.: No. I don't think so.

DR. A.: You've got to peek.

MRS. P.: Because I felt I didn't do anything wrong. I wasn't *doing* anything wrong.

Wife defends against sex guilt by distinguishing between peeking and doing.

DR. A.: Well, then, you can't say the relationship was nothing. You got a *look*.

MRS. P.: Mmhmm.

DR. A.: Was that your first look at a boy child?

MRS. P.: No. A *baby* boy child I had seen before.

It is not sinful to peek at a baby boy.

DR. A.: You had? When?

MRS. P.: When I was young. I used to baby-sit.

DR. A.: Ooh.

MRS. P.: (*Laughs.*)

DR. A.: So you were a very curious young lady?

MRS. P.: I don't know. . . .

DR. A.: You took a peek when you baby-sat.

MRS. P.: I guess I had to. (*Laughs.*)

DR. A.: (*Laughs.*) What did you feel when you took a peek at the boy baby?

MRS. P.: I thought that life was . . . well . . . it was kind of amazing, in a way, that little boys were made one way, and little girls another way. And I thought it was . . . it was a wonderful thing. I . . .

> Here wife communicates her feeling of awesome attraction to the differences of boy and girl.

DR. A.: Did you feel it was cute?

MRS. P.: I thought it was cute and I thought that . . . I don't know . . . it's hard to explain . . . uh . . . that this was what God had created. But . . .

> It is the miracle of God.

DR. A.: But did you feel you could look but not touch?

MRS. P.: You mean at a boy baby?

DR. A.: Mmhmm. Did you only look? Was there some sort of a mental sign in your mind: "Look but don't touch"?

> Again, the emphasis on the difference between thought and deed.

MRS. P.: Well, I don't think I *did* touch. As I remember.

DR. A.: You didn't touch. You didn't have any feeling about *handling* the little boy's penis. . . .

MRS. P.: No, I didn't think of it.

DR. A.: You just took a peek.

MRS. P.: I looked. Yes.

DR. A.: Mmhmm. That was a little one.

MRS. P.: That was all. That's right.

Here it is as if the wife herself is as pure and innocent as a baby (no sex).

DR. A.: Cute little one.

MRS. P.: The boy baby, that's right. (*Laughs.*)

DR. A.: You continued to be curious, yes? So after that, you got a peek at a bigger one.

MRS. P.: (*After a pause.*) Yes.

The long pause is significant of conflict and fear.

DR. A.: Well, I'm interested in the chronology. What was the next step? You were growing up, you were curious. . . .

MRS. P.: There was no next step because I felt it wasn't . . . it wasn't the right thing for me to *do*.

Again, the guilt is connected with doing, not just peeking.

DR. A.: No next step till your boy friend? Before John, is that it?

MRS. P.: Well, there were a few boys. But I guess I made sure that . . . they were always the type I couldn't marry.

This is a meaningful confession of avoidance of sex.

DR. A.: Mmhmm. It was still "look but don't touch," in other words.

MRS. P.: Well, I did touch, but I didn't . . . We didn't go *all the way*. That's right, this is the way I was brought up. . . .

DR. A.: Mmhmm . . . you did touch.

MRS. P.: Yes.

DR. A.: How did it feel?

MRS. P.: Good.

DR. A.: You're thinking . . .

MRS. P.: Yes. (*Laughs.*) I wanted to say something, but I refrained from saying it. (*Laughs.*)

DR. A.: Well, looking at your eyes I felt that; I couldn't help but feel it. What are you hiding?

Therapist confronts wife with the look in her eyes. What is she hiding? Another illustration of the device of "tickling the defenses."

MRS. P.: (*Continues to laugh.*)

DR. A.: You looked at your husband. . . . Do you want to refrain from sharing that with us in front of John?

The same device again. Therapist brings husband into the picture.

MRS. P.: Mmhmm. Uh . . . I don't know.

DR. A.: Will you share it with me privately?

MRS. P.: (*Laughs.*) Probably.

DR. A.: Not with John here?

MRS. P.: Uh, not . . . not excluding John, I didn't mean that.

Here wife contradicts self. She is anxious and evasive. Husband feels he is in the way, and makes an insincere offer of a graceful exit. Therapist lets husband know he doesn't really mean it.

MR. P.: If you'd want me to walk out, I'd walk out. . . .

MRS. P.: No.

DR. A.: You're so obliging, John.

MRS. P.: (*Laughs.*)

MR. P.: Well, the feeling in a way has come over to me, I mean, May is my wife and we have to, uh, learn to be frank with one another. And when we were together the last time, if you recall, and I felt very bad about it because I was holding my [sexual] exposure *from* her, and May thought that this was the most terrible thing in the world. But about these impressions that she's giving you now, this is the first I've ever heard of them. I mean I wouldn't think it was bad, but

Here emerges husband's resentment of wife. He compares his sexual exhibitionism with his wife's peeking. If it's all right for her, then why not for him, too? He uses her disclosures to ease his own guilt.

I think . . . it would be bad of her to condemn me, and in a way, this is . . . *I* feel . . . that this is a similar instance. I . . .

DR. A.: I see.

MR. P.: That's the way I feel.

DR. A.: Mmhmm.

MR. P.: And I don't feel like . . . that . . . I would condemn May for these feelings, but I feel if she would withhold them from me, why hold it against me because I withheld anything from her?

He defends self against wife's reproach for concealing his exhibitionism.

MRS. P.: But I don't think this is any comparison at *all*.

MR. P.: Well, this would be an . . .

MRS. P.: I think mine is just a natural thing.

Wife justifies self. What she did was "natural." What he did was not.

MR. P.: This is a thing for every person to think in their own way.

MRS. P.: But I can't see any comparison at all. It's a completely different level, John.

DR. A.: You were very hurt when she threatened to leave you after discovering you were an exhibitionist— that you were arrested for exposing your penis.

MR. P.: Yes.

DR. A.: You were very hurt when she threatened to leave you?

Therapist sharpens the issue.

MR. P.: Yes, I was. I felt that May was . . . the one thing I loved in life. That . . . so many things I grasped for to hold dear to me, and I felt that I reached this . . . person in life that would like whatever I do in life, share whatever the outcome would be with her . . . whether it be pleasant . . .

DR. A.: You were willing to feel that through her *love* of you . . .

MR. P.: Yes.

DR. A.: If she accepted you and loved you and married you, for better or worse, then she should accept the worst as well as the best part of you.

Husband declares his love— "for better or for worse."

MR. P.: That's right.

DR. A.: At least tolerate this . . . thing.

MR. P.: I don't know about tolerate, but at least try to . . . understand, and have a little love at the moment I needed love most.

Husband demands wife's understanding and forgiveness.

DR. A.: Well, your husband makes a very feeling appeal to you, May. How about it?

MRS. P.: How about what?

Wife is again evasive.

DR. A.: You listened very carefully. You know very well what he's asking you.

MRS. P.: Well, I'm *here*.

When pressed, wife justifies self. After all, she hasn't abandoned her husband.

DR. A.: That's your answer. You haven't left him.

MRS. P.: That's right.

DR. A.: You still love him. And you're trying to understand his difficulty with exposing his penis. . . .

MRS. P.: Mmhmm.

DR. A.: Mmhmm. John, did you sort of imagine what perhaps May was holding back . . . a few minutes ago when she said she would refrain from sharing with me some memories of these early experiences with young boys? Did you imagine what she was . . .

Therapist puts wife on spot. Challenges her self-righteousness and hiding attitude.

MRS. P.: (*Blows nose loudly.*)

DR. A.: . . . what she was hiding?

MR. P.: Not particularly. Not particularly.

DR. A.: Mm. Do you imagine *now* what it might be? Because I imagined right away.

Therapist uses his feeling and clinical hunch to sharpen the issue.

MR. P.: I don't really know what particular . . . It isn't so much . . .

Again husband falters. This may be in collusion with wife's hiding.

DR. A.: She was sharing with you . . .

MR. P.: Yes . . . yes.

DR. A.: . . . how she grew up as a little girl.

Therapist presents a quick recap of wife's sexual anxieties.

MR. P.: Yes.

DR. A.: First she looked. She took a peek.

MR. P.: Yes.

DR. A.: And the feeling was, look but don't touch. By and by, she dared touch. She also said, she was trained very strictly. She wouldn't go all the way. There was a next step. May?

MRS. P.: Well, the only (*clears throat*), the next, what *I* considered the next step, would be to have intercourse and I didn't. So to me that would be the next and final step. Which I didn't do.

Again, wife makes a formal denial of wrongdoing.

DR. A.: There are other things in between.

Therapist undercuts this denial.

MRS. P.: Uh, yes.

DR. A.: You know.

MRS. P.: Yes.

DR. A.: Is that what you held back?

MRS. P.: (*Pause.*) To a certain extent.

DR. A. (*to Mr. P.*): Now can you imagine?

MR. P.: Yes.

DR. A.: What do you imagine?

MR. P.: I could imagine that she mas-turbated her boy friend.

Husband uncovers wife.

DR. A.: Is that what you held back?

MRS. P.: (*Long pause.*) Yes.

DR. A.: Some feeling of shyness about the boy "coming"?

MRS. P.: (*Clears throat.*)

DR. A.: . . . having a climax?

Therapist stirs a deeper, more honest sharing of experiences.

MRS. P.: No, not really. If I can think of it. . . . It seems so far away now.

DR. A.: Was that a good feeling? Hold-ing a boy's penis until he came?

MRS. P.: Yes.

DR. A.: Do you think that's wrong, John?

His purpose here is to ease the shared guilt and shame of both husband and wife.

MR. P.: Do I think what's wrong?

DR. A.: Do you think that's wrong?

MR. P.: Now, I don't think that's wrong.

Husband indicates his atti-tude is changing.

MRS. P.: That's just what I was going to say.

MR. P.: However, at the time I first met May, I would have thought it was wrong.

DR. A.: So you have both changed your feelings about some of these matters.

MRS. P.: Because I thought that John was very narrow-minded.

Wife returns to the attack.

DR. A.: Tell me about that.

MRS. P.: And (*laughs*) . . . and he had such a very strict upbringing. He was completely different from what I had gone out with. . . . (*Pause.*)

DR. A.: You mean he wouldn't let you hold his?

Again, therapist places the issue in terms of bodily ex-perience.

MRS. P.: (*Laughs.*) I don't think I did. I don't remember. But he . . .

Wife ridicules husband with laughter.

MR. P.: I mean, I was fairly free with you for a while. . . .

Husband defends self.

MRS. P.: But he just . . . he just seemed so . . . I can't think of the right word, offhand. He just seemed very distant. . . .

MR. P.: I was like a stuffed shirt, right?

Husband admits his inhibition.

MRS. P.: Yes, yes, he was.

DR. A.: You get a bang out of that. . . .

Therapist makes explicit wife's gleeful triumph in her husband's fright.

MR. P.: Not really, but sometimes when you reflect on certain of the attitudes in your background, sometimes you, it reminds you of the way you were, and you . . . and things, you know, perhaps weren't correct but it's the way you were; you wish to change.

Husband again refers to his willingness to change.

MRS. P.: And he had a very poor sense of humor, Dr. A., when I first married him. A very poor sense of humor. If I would tease him or something, he would say, "I don't have time for that," and I thought that was horrible. . . .

Wife resumes attack.

MR. P.: It depends. . . .

DR. A.: (*Laughs.*)

MRS. P.: I . . . I couldn't figure that out. I thought that was a terrible thing for him to say, "I don't have time." (*Laughs.*)

DR. A.: So in those days you were a stuffed shirt.

MRS. P.: Very strait-laced.

DR. A.: A terrible prude.

MRS. P.: He was.

MR. P.: Very much a prude.

Husband admits he was a prude.

DR. A.: But May is playful. She wanted to play with you, and you didn't want to play with her.

MRS. P.: I didn't have a playmate. (*Laughs.*)

Wife feels triumphant; she is safe as long as her husband is dominated by fright.

MR. P.: Yeah, well . . . I didn't know whether she wanted to play or not.

MRS. P.: Oh, John. Nonsense. (*Laughs.*) I don't know . . . Even if an off-color joke was told, John would step on my foot. As a matter of fact, before we were *engaged,* we were at a night club and I think we were with my sister and her boy friend at the time, and it's the show people's code to be suggestive, and I think I must have chuckled, and the next thing I knew . . . I think I had a new pair of shoes on . . . and John had stepped on my *foot,* and I thought that was terrible.

For wife, sex is an off-color joke. She likes that, but fears the real thing.

DR. A.: Mmhmm.

MRS. P.: And I thought he had a very poor sense of humor. And he stepped on my foot very hard, Dr. A., it was paining me. It wasn't just a light, *soft* touch, like a loving touch.

MR. P.: (*Inaudible mumble.*)

MRS. P.: Do you remember that?

MR. P.: (*Inaudible again.*)

DR. A.: So you're like your "old man." She likes a little sex play, and you crush her foot. Your father crushed you and then you stepped on her foot. Huh?

Therapist identifies husband with his father.

MRS. P.: I think it's unfortunate that I never knew John's father. Don't you think? I didn't know anybody's father,

I didn't know my own, and I didn't know . . .

DR. A.: That's just what I was thinking. . . .

MRS. P.: . . . John's father, I didn't know *anybody's* father, I never had a brother. . . . I was so completely isolated from the *male* world that it's . . . pretty horrible. You know?

Again wife refers to her having been deprived of a male figure.

DR. A.: I feel pretty much that way, but here's your chance now, you've got three [men]. Not just one.

Referring to husband and two therapists, therapist lays down the gauntlet.

MRS. P.: And I think you're *all* wonderful.

Wife feels flattered by the attention of three men.

DR. A.: I think you're blossoming out with the three of us.

MRS. P.: I hope so.

DR. A.: You sound like you'd like to be a *real . . . woman.*

MRS. P.: I would. Very much.

DR. A.: You would. Well, now, does John let you play with him now?

Therapist turns back to the exclusive relation of wife and husband.

MRS. P.: Yes, he does. He's really quite changed now. As a matter of fact, last night after we had seen Dr. D., I said to John, I don't remember what we had said taking the subway home, but I said to John, "Your sense of humor certainly has improved." I don't remember what it was, it was something very small, very insignificant, it doesn't really bear repeating, I don't know what it was, do you, John? I don't know. And he sort of smiled and . . . I mean, he took . . . can take it now. Before he was terrible. He just had no sense of *humor,* he was just . . . a real sour grape. He was a real bookworm. . . .

Wife says: husband is now more playful, shows a sense of humor. But she then reverts to her old complaints about him. One may ask here: Is she playing up to male therapists rather than appreciating her husband?

DR. A.: A sour puss. . . .

MRS. P.: And . . . I mean, I think it's very, very nice, I always admired an intelligent man. I think it's . . .

DR. A.: But at least he should learn . . .

MRS. P.: But I think you have to have a little sense of humor. I think this is very important to survive, for life. You can't get through all of your life just sticking your nose in a book. Because this isn't all of life, and this is what's happened with John, I think he's . . .

DR. A.: Sex wasn't even an off-color *joke,* for John.

MRS. P.: That's right. It wasn't even in the books he had *read*. I wish he had read them. But he didn't read that kind of book, you know?

Again, wife sounds sad.

DR. A.: Well, it was also due perhaps to . . . limited acquaintanceship with people.

This is a vague allusion to husband's fear of people, his tendency to withdraw.

MRS. P.: That's right.

MR. P.: And that . . . whenever . . .

DR. A.: Tell me, did you get a look at anybody else's penis besides your own? You say you didn't dare take a peek at your father's.

Therapist now turns to husband.

MR. P.: Only at times in showers, at the beach, or something of that nature, but . . . I mean, I wouldn't stare . . . just what comes in the periphery of my eye vision, you know?

DR. A.: Would you like to have stared?

MRS. P.: (*Laughs.*)

MR. P.: I mean, I wouldn't probe with my eyeball.

In the previous interview, husband referred to his anxiety about probing aggressively with his eyeballs and suffering a detached retina. He spoke, also, of a terrible burning in the foreskin of his penis.

DR. A.: You would put the penis in the periphery of your vision. In the edge of your eye?

MRS. P.: (*Laughs.*) See what I mean?

MR. P.: In fact this was . . . this wasn't something that was a goal to attain at the particular time. I mean, if it was in the periphery of the eye, I wasn't going to jump out of the window, but certainly I wouldn't walk ten blocks just so I could go into the shower so . . .

This is a defense against the guilt of peeking.

DR. A.: You know, I don't believe you. I just don't believe you.

MRS. P.: (*Laughs loudly.*)

DR. A.: I think you'd walk *twenty* blocks.

MR. P.: (*Laughs.*)

DR. A.: If you could look it straight in the eye. How about that? I challenged you.

MR. P.: Maybe . . . I would walk twenty blocks into a *female* shower, perhaps. But I wasn't prone to, uh, walking into a *male* shower.

Husband tries hard to appear normally heterosexual, to deny his sex deviation.

DR. A.: Are you sure about that?

MR. P.: Positive. Very positive. I think that's probably one of the reasons why I was exposing myself while I was . . .

DR. A.: You want to persuade me you'd rather look at a woman's breast than a man's penis.

Therapist challenges defensiveness.

MR. P.: There's no doubt in my . . .

DR. A.: No question.

MR. P.: No question.

DR. A.: You'd swear it on a stack of Bibles.

MRS. P.: (*Laughs.*)

MR. P.: I'd swear if I had them in front of me. (*Laughs.*)

DR. A.: Well, is a woman's breast in the very *center* of your visual field? Is that in the center? You say a man's penis is on the edge, on the outside. . . .

Therapist pushes the point.

MRS. P.: (*Laughs.*)

MR. P.: No, well, if it comes within, I'll try to do without it, too.

DR. A.: You could do without sex? That's how your father trained you. To do without that.

MRS. P.: That's right. That's right.

DR. A.: But you weren't *able* to do without it. That's why you got into trouble.

Therapist interprets connection between husband's emasculation by his father and husband's tendency to exhibitionism.

MRS. P.: How come parents don't realize that? In other words, it would seem to me that parents that aren't intelligent shouldn't have children, then.

DR. A.: Mm.

MRS. P.: I think it's a very cruel thing to say, but I think there's a lot of truth in it. I think that if you bring a child or children into the world, it's your obligation to see that they have as normal a childhood as possible. . . .

Wife expresses her indignation and begins a preachment about child bearing and sex education.

DR. A.: And he got gypped and *you* got gypped. . . .

Therapist points out that both husband and wife have felt cheated in this regard.

MRS. P.: That's *true.*

DR. A.: *Both* of you.

MRS. P.: That's true. And I'm very annoyed and I'm very hurt and I'm angry.

Wife is now diffusely angry at all parents.

DR. A.: You're angry.

MRS. P.: I *am.* And I'm angry at my mother *too,* because I think where she did a good job, she did in a way, we were fed and we were clothed, and she kept us very clean and all that, and . . .

DR. A.: Too clean?

> Now emerges the connection between dirt and sex.

MRS. P.: Possibly. She was a fanatic. Because this is what she did twenty-four hours a day, Dr. A. She . . . didn't have much of a life, I mean, she had friends, but she wasn't the type that would . . .

DR. A.: Don't you think that in a sense, because your ma was a kind of fanatic about cleanliness, she was a dirt-chaser, that you got very curious about a little dirt?

> Therapist interprets wife's covert defiance of mother's strict standards.

MRS. P.: Well, I'm not that way now.

DR. A.: Well, you were brought up to feel that sex was *dirty.*

MRS. P.: Uh, no . . . you mean, about sex? No, I don't, because I think that if you're married this is what marriage *is.* It's part of . . .

DR. A.: When you want to play with a little dirt . . . You like an off-color joke . . . That's playing with a little dirt. . . .

> Wife is secretly attracted to sex and dirty jokes.

MRS. P.: Yes, I think this is what makes life a little more interesting.

DR. A.: Hm. She wants a little excitement, John.

> Therapist invites husband to respond to wife's craving for excitement.

MRS. P.: (*Laughs.*)

MR. P.: Yes. (*Laughs.*) I . . .

MRS. P.: I found John to be very prudish. Very prudish.

> Wife promptly devalues husband as lover. He, like her mother, is too clean.

MR. P.: Well, I *was* prudish.

DR. A.: Was he a dirt-chaser too?

MRS. P.: (*Laughs.*)

MR. P.: Am I a dirt-chaser? Well, I think in the proper . . . in the proper environment, I think that's the one thing that . . . also made me prudish. . . . Any off-color jokes that I heard in my childhood came from people that I couldn't respect or I thought very lowly of. Naturally, even if you get it in a proper context . . .

Husband stumbles, gets lost in the problem. Admits he's a prude.

DR. A.: You mean that's why you crushed her foot? You stepped on her foot.

Therapist reminds husband of punishing wife for a slight sexual transgression.

MRS. P.: Yes.

MR. P.: I didn't want her to think . . .

MRS. P.: He thought it was terrible. He really did.

DR. A.: She likes to play with a little dirt. How about you?

MR. P.: I . . . I do now. But there was a time that it . . . it was a sacrilege in my life that, uh . . . that I would play around with dirt. I was led . . . led to believe beyond the question of any *doubt* that, uh, such was the . . . case. Because I was cornered off from females in my life. . . .

Husband once again connects his sexual guilts and fears with his father's severe prohibitions. Note the phrase: "cornered off from females."

DR. A.: But you know, when you exhibited your penis, you were playing around with something a little dirty.

MR. P.: But I never looked at it that way. You can look at it *now,* that way, but I didn't *feel* it that way.

DR. A.: The women to whom you exposed your penis felt that way.

Therapist returns to question of husband's exhibitionism.

MR. P.: I'm sure they did, but I didn't feel they should at that time.

MRS. P.: And they were *right*.

Wife identifies with husband's victims. She gets angry and accusatory.

DR. A.: They were right?

MRS. P.: And they were *right*.

MR. P.: I wasn't in any condition to determine what was right and wrong.

Husband comes to own defense.

MRS. P.: Well, that was *your* side of the story, but as far as the women were . . .

MR. P.: Well, I can't look at it at that time from their side of the story.

MRS. P.: Because to them you're just a stranger in the street. . . .

DR. A.: You were doing something dirty, huh? Hm?

MRS. P.: That's right. I say, John was out in the street and they were, and . . . it wasn't the time or the *place*, and to those women you were just a stranger. And not a very nice one at that.

Wife allies with other female victims against husband.

DR. A.: And that comes when you don't feel you can play with a little dirt at all.

MRS. P.: That's true.

DR. A.: So you go out on the street and play dirty.

MRS. P.: That's right. It's just like children that are . . . that are kept very strict at home. When they go out, they go . . . haywire. It's just like keeping a dog in an apartment, where they don't belong to begin with. Then they go outside, and they . . . they go *wild*. They're all over the place.

She compares husband with a dog too long confined.

DR. A.: You see, John, May is trying to bring you up all over again. . . .

MRS. P.: Competing with a dog. (*Laughs.*)

DR. A.: Bring you up *right* this time. She wants you to learn how to play a little dirty at home.

MR. P.: Either that or train me as a dog. (*Laughs.*)

Who is the dog now, husband or wife?

MRS. P.: There must be a similarity along these lines.

DR. A.: You see, you may make an insult out of that, but she's talking about a cute little hot dog you've got.

Therapist alludes to the symbolic equation, dog equals penis.

MRS. P.: (*Laughs.*)

DR. A.: She's not insulting your dog. She *likes* it. Is that right, May?

Therapist puts the partners to a test. Do they now want to come together, to have intercourse (for the first time in their lives)?

MRS. P.: Yes, I do.

DR. A.: You play with it now?

MRS. P.: Yes, I do. I was just thinking, Dr. A., that . . .

MR. P.: She has to be invited, though at times, too, I'm thinking of . . . going to a printing press and printing cards to invite her at times to do this. Sometimes she feels like doing it voluntarily and sometimes not, you know.

Now, husband turns angry and reproachful to wife. When he's ready, she's not. They don't get there at the same time.

MRS. P.: (*Laughs.*) But Dr. A., just to get serious again, I was just . . . the pity of the whole thing is, you know, we're not very young. That's the unfortunate part, we're, you know, we're not 18, 19, or 20.

Here they use a small disagreement to quarrel again and distance themselves.

MR. P.: We're not ready to go out with a cane, either, May.

MRS. P.: No, but we're not that young either, John. And this is the very unfortunate part about the whole thing. I think that . . . You know what I mean?

DR. A.: I understand, but you're crying about spilled milk. All the fun you missed all these years. I think you're angry about that.

Therapist again tries to bring them together.

MRS. P.: Well, I think I did have fun.

MR. P.: And I think it's probably a feeling of mine, too, and . . .

MRS. P.: Yes.

DR. A.: You felt cheated.

MR. P.: But . . . why must the future be spoiled because of the past, and, uh, I don't want to look at it that way. I feel that . . .

Again, the temptation to engage in mutual blame, the game "If it weren't for you."

MRS. P.: But a lot of the future depends on the past, John. Doesn't it?

MR. P.: You're getting old before you're looking at it.

DR. A.: You want to spank him? For what you missed? Is it all his fault, all the fun you missed?

MRS. P.: No, I don't think it's John's fault. I think it's my home life, too. I don't think it's completely John's fault.

DR. A.: Are you inviting her to hit you?

Therapist teases out the preoccupation of both partners with the theme of punishment.

MR. P.: Well, if she would *feel* better, I don't care. (*Laughs.*)

MRS. P.: (*Laughs.*)

DR. A.: Where? Where? Where did you get all the spankings?

MRS. P.: He got . . .

MR. P.: On the backside.

MRS. P.: He's got fat all over, Dr. A.

DR. A.: Do you want her to smack your backside?

MRS. P.: (*Laughs.*)

DR. A.: She's talking about playing with your *front* side.

Therapist makes another reverse. Can husband and wife really join?

MR. P.: If she wants to hit . . .

DR. A.: She's very interested in a man, but also very angry, disappointed, and angry. She got cheated.

MRS. P.: It's true. It's *true*. I did, Dr. A.

DR. A.: All right, what are you doing about it now?

Therapist neutralizes wife's attack on husband. Challenges her to do her part in really getting married.

MRS. P.: I think that we *are* trying to get together.

DR. A.: Are you going to take it [husband's penis] in?

MRS. P.: I would like to.

DR. A.: That doesn't quite answer my question. I *know* you'd like to.

MRS. P.: What should I say? Yes?

DR. A.: Is it [wife's vagina] *itching* to graduate to womanhood?

Therapist pointedly refers to her resistance to vaginal penetration.

MRS. P.: (*Laughs.*) Yes.

DR. A.: To have intercourse for the first time in your life?

MRS. P.: That's right.

DR. A.: Go all the way? You're still scared to go all the way. Married six years, and you haven't yet gone all the way.

MRS. P.: I think it's John's fault. (*Laughs.*)

Wife reverts to attack.

DR. A.: You can't lead it in?

MRS. P.: I've tried.

DR. A.: What happens?

MRS. P.: And I will continue to try. I don't know. It's a funny thing . . . It just doesn't go *in*. (*Laughs.*)

DR. A.: I don't understand. I don't understand. It has a mind all its own?

An example of therapist's use of a light touch of humor.

MR. P.: (*Laughs.*) I hope not.

DR. A.: What has he got? A self-directed penis?

MRS. P.: (*Laughs loudly.*)

DR. A.: You've got to keep track of your penis?

MR. P.: (*Laughs.*) No. I was thinking about when you said "Do you lead it in?" About the only thing May does to help me is that she's like a radar station and tells me that I am off course but does nothing to correct the course. (*Laughs.*)

Husband follows therapist's example and exhibits his wit.

MRS. P.: (*Has been laughing violently throughout.*) John, you'll pay for this.

This is no small threat on wife's part.

DR. A.: You've got me laughing to tears about this.

MRS. P.: I told you you'd use your handkerchief. (*Laughs.*)

DR. A.: I'm busting out all over again. She's got a little radar signal, which always tells you your penis is going in the wrong direction. But never . . .

Therapist plays out more fully the husband's message about wife.

MR. P.: But never . . . directs it in the *right* direction.

MRS. P.: Because this is the way it *feels,* Dr. A. Seriously.

DR. A.: What does he do? Bump the wrong places?

MRS. P.: It seems like it's just not going in the right place.

DR. A.: Is it stiff? Is it erect?

MRS. P.: Yes.

DR. A.: Well, where does it go? Where does it want to go instead of inside you?

Therapist presses wife.

MRS. P.: I just feel that it's just not going in the right place. . . .

DR. A.: Where does it *go?*

MRS. P.: I can't explain it.

DR. A.: What's the wrong place?

MRS. P.: The wrong place is not the *right* place.

MR. P.: (*Laughs loudly.*)

MRS. P.: You ask a question like that, how else can I answer except that way?

DR. A.: Is he bumping you in the hip joint?

Again, a light vein of humor to ease the tension.

MRS. P.: No, not in the *hip,* that's way off course, Dr. A. (*Laughs.*)

MR. P.: (*Laughs.*)

DR. A.: Well, where does he bump you then? You have a collision.

MR. P.: That's what I ask her, where am I *going?* She can't answer me.

Husband allies with therapist. Feels his sympathy and support.

MRS. P.: (*Sighs.*) Well, a man's supposed to know. Isn't he, Dr. A.?

MR. P.: But she isn't allowed to know.

MRS. P.: A man is supposed to be the leader. You read that in all the books ever since you went to school.

DR. A.: Nobody knows, nobody really knows, you feel your way, but you don't feel your way the same way.

MRS. P.: You mean I don't feel my way?

DR. A.: You bump. Now how does he bump? He made the story clear.

The sexual "bumping" epitomizes the unconscious collusion between the partners to avoid the completing of the act.

MRS. P.: Yes.

DR. A.: You *bump.*

MRS. P.: That's right.

DR. A.: Now where does he bump you and where do you bump back?

MRS. P.: It just doesn't go *in*. I guess it just stays in one spot and he's making an attempt to go in.

DR. A.: What spot?

MRS. P.: I guess close to the vagina but not in.

DR. A.: You mean he collides with a wall, he runs right into the curbstone?

Therapist teases out the imagery of sexual collision. Is the obstruction to penile penetration on the side or in the middle?

MRS. P.: I guess so. (*Pause.*) Isn't that so? Am I giving a . . .

DR. A.: Well, have you got a wall in the middle, too? I know you've got walls on the side. . . .

MRS. P.: I hope not, Dr. A.

DR. A.: I'm not sure you haven't got a middle wall, too.

MRS. P.: I don't know. I've been examined, and they say I'm okay.

DR. A.: I understand that. But you know, if you tense up, without being conscious of it, you can make a wall right in the center.

MRS. P.: Well, I try not to, though. I try very hard to, and, uh, I try to be relaxed and have nothing on my mind, and I want John.

Wife is evasive, pleads her innocence.

DR. A.: When you say you try to be relaxed, you were just confessing to me you are very tense. . . .

MRS. P.: I try to be as relaxed as I can, because I feel we haven't been successful, that's why.

DR. A. (*to Mr. P.*): Do you feel like you hit a wall?

MR. P.: I . . . I do, and I can't imagine, I go through the pains of spreading her lips apart, and I place my penis right up against the orifice to the vagina and I'm all ready to push and then I can't feel anything, except like, uh, a wall, uh . . .

DR. A.: Like the gates are locked and you can't get in.

Wife locks husband out.

MR. P.: That's right. And sometimes I feel that, uh, placing my penis up against the orifice, all kinds of reactions happen. Either *she's* not comfortable, *I'm* not comfortable, everybody . . . *constant* movement going on, there, I just . . .

MRS. P.: Not all the time, John. Not all the time.

Wife is again defensive.

MR. P.: Yes . . . and, uh . . . very rare that May would do anything to come, to keep my penis . . .

MRS. P.: Well, Dr. D. told me once that I shouldn't move around so much, so I try not to move.

MR. P.: Well, this was something else. . . .

MRS. P.: Remember? So . . .

MR. P.: You . . . pick what suits you now. He also told you that you should try to help me to get in, to guide me, too.

Husband pins her down.

MRS. P.: That's true. That's true.

DR. A.: May . . . there's something amiss with your part. We agreed . . . There's some kind of emotional conspiracy . . . and some kind of collusion, to make sure it never happens.

MRS. P.: Well, I have to be that way. Because I'm frustrated.

DR. A.: Yes, but you . . .

MRS. P.: And I'm very concerned.

DR. A.: You are very . . . You must be very tense, and John says you used to squirm a lot and move a lot and . . .

MRS. P.: Well, I don't any more. I I don't think I do. Not as much.

DR. A.: He squirms, you squirm, we all squirm, I . . .

MR. P.: But at the time Dr. D. told her to contain herself a little. We had nicknamed her the kangaroo because she was hopping from . . . we have a king-sized bed and she was hopping from one side to the other side. (*Laughs.*)

This is a truly funny analogy.

MRS. P.: Well, I . . .

MR. P.: And I'm following her, you know. (*Laughs.*)

MRS. P.: I didn't mean that particular time, John. We're all having a good laugh on me. Go ahead, I'll get back at you. (*Laughs.*)

Again, wife promises to punish husband for exposing her to the doctor.

MR. P.: I'm not doing this with any malice or . . . I'm doing it so we can get some . . . help. . . .

DR. A.: You complained a moment ago he hasn't got a sense of humor. . . . He's got a sense of humor now. He's not insulting you.

MRS. P.: It didn't have to be *that* improved. (*Laughs.*)

DR. A.: Well, he says you leap around the bed like a kangaroo. How's he going to get in?

Therapist presses point.

MRS. P.: That's true. But I haven't lately, though. Not that I can think of.

DR. A.: What do you do lately?

MRS. P.: I try to stay as still as I can. And I'm trying to help. And I'm very frustrated, Dr. A. And I'm concerned, too. It's serious, very serious.

DR. A.: I smiled about it. But I'm concerned, too. It's serious. Very serious.

MRS. P.: And I'm . . . very serious about it, and I think about it a lot. And . . . I know many times Dr. D. will say something . . . "You're smiling, I don't know what you're smiling about," you know? And this is true, because sometimes I'm smiling, but I'm very hurt. And I'm very serious.

Wife is evasive, feels threatened, covers up anxiety with a smile.

DR. A.: Well, May, I'm very serious. I'm quite sure that even though you now can constrain yourself from leaping around the bed . . . like a kangaroo . . . that you must still anyhow be very tense, very tight, and somewhere underneath, you are still frightened to death of letting him *in*.

Therapist recognizes her fright.

MRS. P.: So what can I do about it?

DR. A.: Let's get to your fright.

MRS. P.: Well, I don't think I'm that frightened any more. I might still be a little.

DR. A.: Well, let's get to the "little," then. Whether it's a little, or a little more than a little, you're still . . .

MRS. P.: And I'm thinking that I'm not, but I guess I am. I don't really feel that I'm relaxed. Because I want John very badly and I don't think that I *am* tense.

DR. A.: As far as you're aware, I'm sure that's so. You want to complete the act. . . .

MRS. P.: I do. I do.

DR. A.: You've been stumbling around there for six years.

MRS. P.: For too long.

DR. A.: You want to get it over with.

MRS. P.: That's right. That's right.

DR. A.: Quick.

MRS. P.: That's right.

DR. A.: But something else happens between your legs.

MRS. P.: (*After an extended silence.*) I don't know. (*Another silence.*) I don't think I'm as frightened as I used to be.

DR. A.: I think you're better, I'm convinced you're better, but you're not better enough, you're still *bumping* him away.

Therapist holds wife to the problem.

MRS. P.: Because I feel it's not the right place.

DR. A.: That's what you *think*.

MRS. P.: That's true.

DR. A.: Well, now, we've all agreed that John grew up not being sure he had a penis; so I begin to wonder whether you grew up not being sure you had a hole there.

Therapist opens up a new angle.

MRS. P.: That's true.

DR. A.: Tell me some more about that.

MRS. P.: Well, I mean like even now when, you know, before he makes the attempt to get in, I feel that maybe . . . I feel that there's just no opening there and I feel . . . I'm very frustrated and . . . I don't know how to explain it, how else, but it's very . . . You know . . .

In fantasy, wife erases her vagina.

DR. A.: Something happens subconsciously with your fright so that you do away with the hole.

MRS. P.: That's true.

DR. A.: You feel like you haven't got an opening.

MRS. P.: That's true. That's true.

DR. A.: And you must imagine you've got something in place of the opening.

MRS. P.: Well, I never thought of it that way. But I just feel . . . That's right, just like you said. But I don't know, in place of . . .

DR. A.: Did you ever imagine—as a little girl or *any* time—did you imagine what it might be like to have a penis there instead of a vagina?

Does wife have an imaginary penis?

MRS. P.: No, I don't think so. No.

DR. A.: You don't like girls. You didn't like being a girl.

MRS. P.: I never thought of it that way. But I just didn't like having so many sisters because I . . . You know, we were all the same sex.

DR. A.: And after your father tried five times, if you'd been born with a little penis, a cute little penis . . .

MRS. P.: Well, my mother always said they were both disappointed when I came along . . . because they were hoping that the fifth one would be a *boy*. And she even had blue clothes in the drawer, and she said when I came along, she said, "Oh, another girl."

Her parents wanted her to be a boy.

DR. A.: She should have had a little . . .

MRS. P.: That's right. That's right. So I was, you know . . . the one that shouldn't have been there.

DR. A.: Well, who knows—maybe you've got a little "dog" there.

In place of her vagina, there ought to have been a penis, to please her father.

MRS. P.: No, I don't. (*Laughs.*)

DR. A.: You're sure?

MRS. P.: Positive. (*Laughs.*)

DR. A.: You're not sure. You haven't opened it.

MRS. P.: (*Laughs loudly.*) That's true. I never thought of it that way. But shouldn't this be a . . . *natural* thing, though, Dr. A.?

DR. A.: There you go. Talking about how it *ought* to be.

MRS. P.: Shouldn't it be *natural,* though?

MR. P.: But it doesn't happen by osmosis. . . .

DR. A.: We're trying to help you to be more natural, but you aren't natural. You're like this, see? It's as though you're colliding with his penis with something hard—like a wall or a penis —you don't provide an opening. . . .

Therapist draws a visual image of the sexual collision.

MRS. P.: That's true. It's true.

DR. A.: You have a little collision with his thing.

MRS. P.: Well, why do I do that, though . . . besides being frightened? Why do I *do* it?

DR. A.: It seems you're less scared of bumping him back than you are of letting him in. You're afraid to believe you have an opening.

MRS. P.: That's true. I never thought of it that way.

DR. A.: You're scared of your own opening. Do you ever look at it?

MRS. P.: Yes.

DR. A.: What did it look like? You made a face. . . .

MRS. P.: Just like pictures. (*Laughs.*)

Wife feels aversion for her vagina.

DR. A.: You made a face.

This is a clear example of the catalytic use of mood and facial expression.

MRS. P.: Just like you see in the books. (*Laughs.*)

DR. A.: May, you made a wry face. As if you didn't like it.

MRS. P.: I don't think it's the most *beautiful* thing. It's, uh, . . . yech . . . I don't know. (*Laughs.*)

DR. A.: It's "yech"?

MRS. P.: Just like in the *books,* Dr. A. (*Laughs.*)

DR. A.: Were your feelings . . . a little bit disgusted?

Is it ugly and disgusting?

MRS. P.: I don't know, it's just . . . It's funny. You know. It's funny. Just like . . . you see in the books.

DR. A.: You mean strange. You can't believe your eyes.

Wife has a sense of unrealness about the sexual parts. Therapist counters with a bantering joke which strengthens the realness of her femininity.

MRS. P.: (*Laughs.*) That's true. Just like in the books. (*Laughs.*)

DR. A.: You know . . . maybe she isn't a girl after all.

This remark is pointed to husband.

MR. P.: (*Laughs.*)

MRS. P.: (*Laughs.*) I'd rather not answer that.

DR. A.: I can't be sure, can I? She felt not sure. How can I be sure?

MRS. P.: I don't blame you for saying that. I'm really ashamed of myself. I sometimes wish that I could . . . take a tranquilizer or something. Would that help me? Maybe it would be the easy way, but at least, you know . . .

Wife's mood shifts. Perhaps she can still complete the sex act and become a woman.

DR. A.: You mean a pill? Or a couple of drinks?

MRS. P.: Yes . . . anything that would help.

DR. A.: Is this an invitation for John to get you drunk? So you can . . .

MRS. P.: We've had a few drinks. But I think when we drink we get sleepy.

DR. A.: So you forget you've got an opening?

MRS. P.: That doesn't even work with us, Dr. A. I guess so. I guess so.

DR. A.: You just don't like having an opening there.

MRS. P.: But at least I feel that, you know, we could be successful at least the first time.

DR. A.: You'd break the ice.

MRS. P.: That's right. I even suggested hypnosis to Dr. D. And he sort of looked at me.

Wife turns to therapist to dissolve her fright and teach her sex, not to her husband.

DR. A.: What kind of look did he give you?

MRS. P.: (*Laughs.*)

MR. P.: (*Laughs loudly.*) I don't think it's so funny, really.

DR. A.: Well, I understand his look. It's as though you were appealing to him to get your *head* out of the way. You're too worried about that ugly-looking spot there. . . . You think it's ugly.

The image of getting the head out of the way refers to the removal of intellectual resistance and conscious constraint.

MRS. P.: Well, I don't think it's so pretty. I never really gave it much thought that way, Dr. A. I guess I . . . did think it was ugly.

DR. A.: Yes, you did.

MRS. P.: Yes.

DR. A.: You *still* do.

MRS. P.: Well, does anybody think it's so beautiful?

DR. A.: I do.

Therapist deliberately uses own feeling to reinforce a more natural response.

MRS. P.: Well, you're a *man*. I mean as far as women are concerned. That shows you're *normal,* Dr. A. I mean, as normal as you *can* be.

DR. A.: I hope so.

MR. and MRS. P.: (*Laugh.*)

MRS. P.: But I mean as far as women, I'm sure they don't all think that way.

DR. A.: Let's not talk about other women. . . .

MRS. P.: Okay. I know.

DR. A.: We have in this room one lady and three boys. . . .

The presence of three males dilutes the danger of sexual attack by one man. The use of the phrase "one lady and three boys" is deliberate.

MRS. P.: Which is another problem . . .

DR. A.: That's right. You don't like to look at it, you make a *face,* as if it spoils your appetite, you feel it's . . . dirty.

MRS. P.: I guess so. Never . . . not really *dirty,* but I . . . I guess dirty, too. I don't know, I'm not too sure.

DR. A.: Well, those two bumpers are very close . . . ugly and dirty. Very close.

MRS. P.: It's just like something that . . . You know, I was going to say something that shouldn't be there. I mean I feel that, you know, it can't be but it is.

DR. A.: You can't take anything away from it unless you put something in

Therapist makes interpretation: if she had been a boy

its place. You want to get rid of it. You don't like it. Now you must have wanted to put a little "hot dog" in its place. You must have wanted to . . .

MRS. P.: I never thought of it. . . .

DR. A.: . . . fulfill your daddy's wish that you should have a little "hot dog."

MRS. P.: Oh, I see what you mean. I never thought of it that way. You mean if my mother hadn't said that, then things wouldn't have been this way? To a certain extent?

DR. A.: Oh, maybe something like that. Like your father couldn't possibly like it down there. He wanted a little "dog," not a dark, dirty-looking space. Maybe he had a prejudice: he liked the boys and he didn't like the girls.

MRS. P.: Well, no. I think he *did* like girls, but . . . after having so many . . .

DR. A.: How do you know he liked girls?

MRS. P.: Well, uh . . .

DR. A.: You never knew the man. How do you know he liked girls?

MRS. P.: Don't they say usually that a father likes to have a little girl, you know, opposites attract?

DR. A.: There you go . . . "usually." You know . . . theorizing.

MRS. P.: But isn't that so? That a mother likes a boy, a son? Usually?

DR. A.: What? You read that in the Bible?

MRS. P.: No.

DR. A.: I don't know about these rules. We don't go by the rules.

perhaps father would not have become ill and died.

Therapist refers again to father's prejudice for boys, against girls.

Again, a general form of resistance.

Wife hits therapist with Freud's oedipal complex.
Therapist makes a quip, implying the equation of Freud with God and His prophets.

MRS. P.: No. Psychology books. Opposites, you know?

DR. A.: They're all wrong. That's why I decided, in my old age, to write books.

Therapist acts the part of a professional maverick, but adopts a humble position.

MRS. P.: (*Laughs.*) What makes you so sure *yours* won't be wrong, Dr. A.?

MR. P.: (*Laughs loudly.*)

MRS. P.: So why bother writing them? (*Laughs.*) Why bother?

DR. A.: I get a kick out of it.

MRS. P.: I was going to say something else, but . . .

DR. A.: Let's hear.

MRS. P.: I was going to say, it might even be *profi*table, I was going to say. Isn't that why people usually write books?

DR. A.: There are easier ways to make money, believe you me.

MRS. P.: I guess so.

DR. A.: Not for money. For love. I get a love-kick out of writing.

Is there a hidden symbolic equation of the therapist's book and penis?

MRS. P.: Well, I think if you write books, if they help just one person, it's a wonderful thing.

DR. A.: Well, now, I'm trying to help you, but not with my book.

MRS. P.: I want to be helped.

DR. A.: So . . . you need to do something about your bad feeling about what you've got down there. I repeat, I would *guess* that your father had a prejudice.

A reference to the mechanism of prejudicial scapegoating in family life.

MRS. P.: I think I *do* remember my mother saying that he, you know, maybe he wanted boys. He was disappointed he had so many girls. And I always remember her saying, "If your father was still alive, I probably would have had seven or eight, or more, because he wanted a boy, he wanted a son."

DR. A.: So you're still trying to be a good girl for your father. Obeying his wish that you should be a boy.

A repeat of wife's repressed wish to be a boy to please her father so as to keep him from dying.

MRS. P.: But how can I obey his wish if I never spoke with him?

DR. A.: In your heart, you can still be trying to obey. You want to give him what he wants. I'll even guess that . . . I'm *guessing* . . . maybe your ma imagined, or you yourself imagined, that if you'd been born a boy . . . with a little thing between your legs instead of an opening . . . that maybe your father wouldn't have died of pneumonia.

MRS. P.: Mmhmm.

DR. A.: He'd have been so happy with a little boy. . . .

MRS. P.: He wouldn't have died.

DR. A.: He wouldn't have caught pneumonia.

MRS. P.: You know, Dr. A., I was telling Dr. D. once that, going to see my father in the cemetery, and I think I just went once or twice . . . I hardly remember. And I didn't have any feelings. And I was very concerned.

DR. A.: Over what? That you'd have plenty of feelings if you were a little boy . . . going to the cemetery? You must have felt you would want to bring to his grave what he wished for. (*Long silence. Wife is crying again.*) Very sad. You feel bad now? What do you feel?

MRS. P.: And I always felt that, well, how could I have any feelings if I never knew him?

Once again, a show of resistance.

DR. A.: You know me. I'm here. Do I want you to be a boy or a girl?

MRS. P.: I guess . . . a girl.

DR. A.: You guess? You're never sure, hm?

MRS. P.: How can I be sure of anything?

DR. A.: You're looking me in the eye?

MRS. P.: (*Laughs and cries simultaneously.*) I don't think I ever cried so much as now. I think Dr. D. started the whole thing. (*Laughs.*)

A mixture of sadness, a sense of loss, and flirtatiousness.

MR. P.: (*Laughs.*)

DR. A.: But you know, I think you're really glad he started it. You appreciate what he started.

MRS. P.: Yes, I do.

DR. A.: Are you supposed to start it and me finish it?

Finish what? The sex act?

MR. P.: Well, I think the three of us can finish it. It's a good thing. . . .

DR. A.: Let me in on the party.

MRS. P.: You know, Dr. A., John said something about vacation, and I said something about . . . something about Dr. D., uh, going on vacation soon, or something like that, uh, and I said to John, "I think that Dr. D. will need a vacation, especially after the both of us." I said he'll need at least a two-month vacation.

DR. A.: What did you do—wear him down to a frazzle?

The effect of wife's resistance on Dr. D.

MRS. P.: Yes, we did.

DR. A. (*to Dr. D.*): Did she reduce your potency all the way down to the floor? Did she step on it?

MRS. P.: (*Laughs.*) We'd given him some very trying times.

DR. A.: You bumped him too, then.

Therapist interprets the sexual collision with Dr. D.

MRS. P.: (*Laughs.*) I think so. (*Pause.*) You know what I said to myself last time going home? And I even think I said it to John, I said . . . I don't know if I should say this to you . . . it's . . . you know . . . but anyway, "Gee, I wish I had had a father like Dr. D. or Dr. A."

Pure transference, with deep nostalgic yearning.

DR. A.: Mmhmm.

MR. P.: She wished that she had any father.

MRS. P.: Well, no, I didn't say . . . I didn't feel that way last week, John. This is what I said.

DR. A.: You don't want her to have us?

Therapist brings husband back in. Is he jealous?

MRS. P.: (*Laughs.*)

MR. P.: No, I . . .

MRS. P.: (*Laughs.*) He's jealous. I did say *any* father, I guess so, John, but I didn't feel that way last week.

DR. A.: Well, I appreciate that, but we've got a little, uh, wrinkle here, a little complication. What would happen if you (*pause*) bumped into Dr. D.'s male part and wore the skin off his penis?

MRS. P.: What would happen, are you asking?

DR. A.: Yes, you were worried about wounding him, that you'd wear him out.

MRS. P.: Well, not in that respect, but . . .

DR. A.: You agreed that you bumped him just as much as you bump John.

Therapist crystallizes the issue of collision with both Dr. D. and husband.

MRS. P.: (*Laughs.*) I think we both do that to Dr. D. Give him a hard time sometimes.

DR. A.: Hm.

MRS. P.: And we sort of, you know, we feel we have to see him, and we just don't feel like saying any-thing. . . .

DR. A.: Can you stand up to the bumping, you and John?

MRS. P.: (*Laughs.*) Sometimes.

MR. P.: (*Laughs.*)

DR. A.: Well, let's interrupt now, but I hope if you take another look, you can believe your eyes, that you've got an opening there, instead of a wall or a penis. And maybe something will happen.

The summing up.

MRS. P.: I hope so.

DR. A.: Because you keep bumping him out of there. All right. Good luck.

MRS. P.: Thank you very much, Dr. A.

(Several weeks later, the couple completed the act, which ushered in a new phase of therapy.)

7

Child-Oriented Intervention

It should be apparent from what has already been said that the child cannot be considered apart from the family. Each stage of his growth is related to the family environment; from the very first, his adaptation to it must be viewed as a biosocial process. Only with this process in mind can the therapist approach the questions of diagnosis and treatment as they involve the child.

Although hereditary factors influence such qualities as physical type, affectivity, motor reactivity, and intellectual potential, the processes of socialization pattern all behavior. The channels of expression of physiological need are organized by the social interaction of the child and the parent and by the typical interpersonal relationships within the family. The individuality of the child is incomplete; he develops only a relative autonomy.

The stages of development of the child are, in effect, advancing levels of biosocial integration with, and differentiation from, his family environment. At each stage of maturation, his drive, defense, perception of self and others, conflict, and anxiety are conceived of as interrelated elements in a unit of adaptation.

1. The immediate postbirth stage reflects mainly a vegetative adaptation. The organism feeds, sleeps, cries when hungry. The integration of the functions of the nervous system is incomplete; perceptual responses are crude and relatively unorganized and do not yet leave permanent psychic residues.

2. The second stage is one of the primary symbiotic union with the mother. Though physically separated at birth, the infant is to-

tally dependent for survival and development on the symbiotic union with the mother. He requires nourishment, tender warmth, touch contact and stimulation, and protection from danger. At this stage the child's behavior alternates between utter helplessness and defenselessness and a striving for omnipotent control. The urge for omnipotent mastery is conceived of not as a function of the child as an individual, but rather as a function of the child's symbiotic union with the mother. The child commands, the mother obeys; the mother commands, the child obeys. The child is not yet able to distinguish the mother's self from his own self. The mother functions not only as the source of love and security but also as the perceptive and executive agent of the child, communicating through her behavior her own affective interpretations of the prevailing realities and also her devices for dealing with them. At this stage the child is already capable of a tender, warm response to the mother. Premature, excessive, shocking, or sudden withdrawal of the mother induces in the child feelings of panic, helplessness, and fear of loss of life and may produce outbreaks of aggression.

3. The third stage is one of gradual separation of the infant's self from the mother's self. As the child matures there is progressively less panic and less aggression on separation. The child begins to assert his separate self with increasing firmness. As he becomes ambulatory, he develops the power of speech and greater physical mastery over his environment. As the original symbiotic unity with the mother lessens, omnipotent behavior gives way to an increasing measure of real control and to progressive testing of reality. Along with these trends social discipline of the child assumes increasing importance. The child comes to terms with his parents and family. The mother's care and control of the child are influenced by the quality of her relations with the father and family. As a child submits to parental discipline, he begins to internalize social standards, at first depending on the parent as an external source of control, but gradually incorporating these standards into his own personality.

4. The fourth stage reflects the child's differentiation of the two parents according to sex and the redirection of the child's love needs in accordance with the parents' masculine and feminine qualities and the relationship between them. In a parallel process, corresponding identifications emerge with each parent. There is

deeper internalization of functions of conscience, now influenced by the distinction between male and female parent and the emerging sexual identity of the child. The further stages of submission to parental discipline are differentiated accordingly.

5. The fifth stage is one of expansion of the emotional and social spheres of the child's interaction with his environment beyond the confines of his immediate family, of the testing of social reality, and of learning in the context of wider contact with peers and parent substitutes. This is a period of broadened social growth, education, and preparation for adolescence.

6. The sixth stage is one of pubescent growth, bringing in its wake the struggles of adolescent adaptation. Differentiated sex drives emerge; the lines of identification are reorganized; group allegiances and roles are realigned in anticipation of and preparation for the tasks of adult life.

The role of the family in the induction of child disorder rests on the emotional hurts inflicted on the child, the timing of these assaults, and their duration. The eventual outcome is determined by the maturational condition of the child as organism, the vulnerability of the child's personality, and the healing powers that can be mobilized by child and family together.

The more disturbed the family, the more are the relations of child and family bound to the theme of sacrifice, an emotional sacrifice imposed upon the individual as the price of membership. The child suffers this sacrifice as the victim of a form of prejudicial scapegoating that is characteristic of the given family. In malignantly disturbed families the prejudice is, in effect, that *the child must not be;* in less disturbed families, that *the child must not be different.* The scapegoating of the child may revolve around a range of prejudices that attaches to those qualities of the child that represent a threat to the parents. The prejudice may take the form of an antagonism to anything new, to any expression of change or growth; it may be opposition to the assertion of difference, or to the expression of spontaneous feeling. The prejudice may revolve around issues of conflict between the younger and older generations. It may attach to the war of the sexes. It may become connected with brain vs. brawn, smart vs. stupid, fat vs. thin, light vs. dark skin, or to a variety of habits concerning food, clothing, and cleanliness.

The emotional injury inflicted on the child may involve (1) a fundamental threat to the child's survival, in terms of bodily injury, neglect, or starvation—physical or emotional or both; (2) a pathogenic symbiosis of child and parent with a fixation of the child's growth; or (3) susceptibility to either a major or a minor mental illness.

The emotional sacrifice that the family exacts of the child as the price of membership may be relatively total, or it may be partial and selective. In total sacrifice, *the child must not be*. He is denied the right to live, breathe, eat, or move. The sacrifice imposed is extreme. The family maintains itself in a static equilibrium at the expense of the emotional life of the child. The growth potential of the child is impaired, warped, or destroyed. It is this pattern of emotional injury that predisposes to psychotic development.

In the case of partial sacrifice, the relations of the child and the family are bound to the theme, *the child must not be different*. In order to assure security and approval, he must conform by surrendering a segment of his individual being. The family maintains its equilibrium by imposing on the child this forced partial surrender. In this configuration of child and family, as long as conflict is contained and defenses are compensated, the disturbance results mainly in psychoneurotic development.

In a deviant pattern of partial sacrifice, where defense operations decompensate and there is a relative failure to contain conflict, the outcome becomes either exile or forced complicity in disordered family relationships. The result of this trend may be (1) alienation of the family members, each going his own way; (2) a pattern of sociopathic rebellion, indulgence in alcohol or drugs, and so forth; (3) a perversion of family relationships to the goal of power, degradation, and destruction; or (4) psychosomatic disorder. Such disorders sometimes serve the purpose of offsetting a complete breakdown of defenses and forestalling the outbreak of overt psychosis. By identifying patterns of prejudicial scapegoating and the characteristic forced sacrifice, it becomes possible to define those features of the family environment which act as "sensitizers," "pressurizers," "precipitators," and "reinforcers" of disturbance in a child. At each stage of child development, the healing of conflict and anxiety may be either healthy or pathological. It is when healthy healing fails that deviant patterns in the child become fixed and persistent. As a child moves to the next stage, new deviations may be superimposed and added to the clinical picture. Thus, multiple types of pathogenic response and mixed symptoms may emerge that are referable to different stages of development.

The child may react to threats in the family environment in one of the following ways.

1. The child may attack his family and attempt thereby to coerce gratification of need. Into this category fall the aggressive conduct disorders and the sociopathic forms of behavior disorders.
2. The child may withdraw from contact with his family. Into this category fall the recessive personality developments and trends toward excessive preoccupation with self and body.
3. The child may react with excessive anxiety, internalization of conflict, and the production of one or another structured form of psychopathology:
   (a) excessive anxiety with internalization and encapsulation of specific conflicts, as in the production of psychoneurotic reactions;
   (b) excessive anxiety, defective emotional control, decompensation of defenses, or paralysis or disorganization of adaptive functions that may induce sociopathic or psychosomatic tendencies;
   (c) excessive anxiety, disorganization of adaptive behavior, arrest of development, or regression and reintegration at a primitive psychic level, as in psychotic forms of reaction.

Intervention in the emotional disorders of children by means of family therapy is based on a rationale quite distinct from that which underlies the traditional procedures of child psychotherapy. The disorders of family are here seen as being central to the pattern of the child's disturbance, not as a peripheral, pathogenic influence, but of the essence. In traditional child therapy, the influence on the family is viewed as accessory to the therapy of the child. In the family approach, the movement of therapeutic influence is mainly from the outside inward, from the family to the child. In conventional child therapy, the movement is mainly from the inside outward—from the child to the parents and family. In the family approach, the basic premise is that a shift in the pattern of marital

and parental complementarity and a change in parent-child interaction lift a load of anxiety from the child and reduce the child's
need to internalize elements of parental and family pathology. It
frees the child to work through residues of conflict in the ongoing
processes of family interaction. In traditional therapy, the emphasis
is on direct alleviation of the child's intrapsychic conflict. The
family is treated separately, and the therapist takes the place of
the family in transference. The influence on the parents is adjunctive to the direct therapy of the child as an individual. In family
therapy, the therapy of the child as an individual is adjunctive to
the treatment of the family. It is accessory; it follows family therapy
as and when needed.

The object is to reach and loosen up the pathogenic defenses
of the child by first modifying the conflicts and pathogenic defenses of the parents and family. The path is then opened for the
child to cope more directly with the conflicts with and between
his parents. The child's internalized conflicts are brought to the
surface so that he can struggle with them at the interpersonal level
in the family interview. The child deals directly with the parents;
the parents deal directly with the child.

The child's transference responses are divided between the
parents and the therapist. Reality testing is more immediate. In
family therapy one has the opportunity to intervene in those interactional processes through which the parents parcel out in a special
way among the group of children selected elements of their identities, character traits, conflicts, guilts, and fears. One views the
constellation of disturbances among the children as a product of
the dynamics of family process, each child reflecting in his disturbance a specific aspect of parental and family pathology. In this
context, the child's disturbance is only a single element in a
patterned cluster of disturbances in the group, a cluster that defines
the pathology of the particular family. The relief of the child's
disturbance requires, therefore, a parallel intervention in the cluster
of interrelated disturbances, viewed as a defined psychopathological
family entity.

It is amazing how often in the course of family therapy the
children respond with a striking improvement in their adaptation
as the burden of displaced conflict is retransposed to its prime
source, conflict in the parental and marital pair.

In the clinical setting, it is common for parents to push the child out in front as "the patient." However inaccurate this labeling may be, the diagnosis and treatment of family groups often start with such a situation. A case in point involves the A. family, which also demonstrates how a single family environment can encompass two distinctly different patterns of child disturbance.

At the moment of acute crisis, the A. family consisted of mother, father, and nine-year-old fraternal twins—Jim, *the child who must not be,* and Robert, *the child who must not be different.* Jim had written a suicide note, and in the first interview, Mrs. A. offered a ready explanation: Jim had threatened to kill himself because of his acute fear of his father. His father had been beating him severely in order to control his provocative behavior. His mother, peering into the father's face, had seen the face of a wild man, crazy with rage and seemingly out of control. She became very alarmed. She felt sure that the boy had threatened to take his own life out of sheer fear of his father's violence. The mother went on to describe Jim as a difficult boy, overactive, intrusive, defiant, and stubborn beyond description. She also said he had nightmares and wet the bed.

In brief, the background was as follows. The parents were intelligent, close, and mutually devoted. After four years of marriage, the wife decided that they would have one baby—and one baby only. In the final phase of pregnancy, when she entered labor, the obstetrician told her that he thought he heard two heart sounds, not one. Since she was already under sedation, the doctor's warning that there might be twins did not register clearly on her clouded consciousness.

She delivered nonidentical twin boys. The first and larger of the two, Robert, was in fine condition. The second twin, Jim, was underweight and was placed in an incubator. The mother returned home from the hospital within one week with the first-born twin, but Jim was not brought home for a month; the mother seemed to "forget" the second baby. From then on, she behaved as if she were trying to deny that she had two babies instead of one. In alternating phases, she seemed unaware of Jim's existence, or was provoked by him, or acted seductively toward him. As long as they were infants, she felt able to handle the two boys as if they were one.

When the two boys began to walk and talk and run about, however, she began to experience acute distress. As she described it: "One twin ran to the left and the other to the right. I tore my hair." She became acutely panicky and feared that she might lose her mind. In this state she put pressure on her husband to intervene and to discipline the twins so that, in effect, she could keep them together, as one.

The father did her bidding; with his usual compliance to her dictates, he disciplined the boys. There was no particular trouble with Robert, the larger of the twins, who was tractable and submissive. But there was a critical problem with Jim, who was defiant, provocative, and stubborn. The father beat Jim repeatedly and violently, but the beatings did not make Jim a good boy. He continued to be overactive, omnipotently defiant, and aggressive, and he provoked the very beatings that he so deeply feared.

There is another side to the picture: when Jim was a good boy, his mother supported him in the special privilege of "beating up" his father. Here again, the father was compliant. On cue from the mother, he lay down and Jim jumped on his stomach with his knees. This game seemed to amuse the mother.

Under ordinary circumstances, the father of these twin boys— a big hulking man—expressed little feeling, was constrained, and showed little initiative and little spontaneity. In fact, he immobilized his big body. He held one hand down with the other, crossed his legs, bowed his head, froze his whole muscular system as if not daring to move. He expressed his submerged rage only when he was given the signal by his wife.

At first glance, this family seemed to be a close, harmonious unit. The mother was obviously the governing figure. She talked much; she talked *for* her husband and continually analyzed his and her motives and actions. Her husband deferred to her. He liked being "one of the boys" rather than the man of the house. In this small group, the only member who refused to conform was Jim. In a superficial sense, mother, father, and Robert were respectful, obedient persons, whereas Jim was the incorrigible, destructive rebel. Mother and father had a tacit agreement that there would be no open or serious quarrels between them. (This attitude can only be understood in terms of a background of common fear: the threat of a violent eruption in their respective families of origin.) In effect, however, this agreement meant that the father did what the mother wanted.

Mr. A. was five years old when his father deserted the family, leaving the children in the care of their mother and grandmother. He grew up with the image of his father as a violent man. When he was barely five years old, his mother—severely frightened by his father's violent temper—called on Mr. A. to step in to protect her from his father's violent assault. For many years he accepted his mother's view that she was the good parent and his father the bad one. He became a well-behaved, obedient youngster, inhibiting his own assertiveness and masculinity in order to keep his mother's approval. He stayed as far away as he possibly could from the image that his mother painted of his father as a killer. He therefore grew up in a very constrained way, submerging his anger and other spontaneous feelings. He became a bound, immobilized, frozen, overcontrolled person.

On the other side of the family, Mrs. A. had the illusion that her parents had enjoyed a good relationship for the first twenty-five years of their married life. In the last ten years, however, an intense hatred had exploded between her mother and father; it was a severe shock to Mrs. A. As a result, Mrs. A.'s attitude toward her parents changed radically. Throughout her whole growing-up period she had never been sure of her mother's affection; when this open antagonism erupted between her mother and father, she took sides with her mother. She consciously affirmed her mother's stand that her father was a male beast, a brute. By supporting her mother's indictment of her father's badness, she hoped to buy her mother's acceptance. Later, she withdrew from her mother and tried to be strong and independent.

In a sense, then, the parents of these twin boys were drawn close together by the common experience of a family ghost—that is to say, by the ghostlike apparition of the outbreak of murderous violence between parental figures, with a special emphasis on the image of the male as a brute animal and a potential killer. This was the picture drawn by the respective grandmothers and is the background for the silent conspiracy between the parents—no hostility, no danger of violence—which meant, however, that Mr. A. must not disagree with Mrs. A. but must accommodate by submission to her dictates.

Mrs. A. decided that they would have only one child, who would have satisfied her idealized concept of a family unit. This idea was fixed in Mrs. A.'s mind as a consequence of her own childhood experience of rejection by her mother, who favored her older sister. The birth of twins was a profound shock, therefore, one that menaced Mrs. A.'s design for family living. Jim, the second twin, came to symbolize the dangerous intruder. When the mother could no longer preserve the illusion of an only child, she experienced acute panic and fear of insanity. Her underlying death anxiety emerged sharply.

In this setting Jim was the hostile invader. He came to symbolize the family ghost—the brute male figure, frighteningly created by the maternal figures in the parents' respective families of origin. Hence the need to erase Jim's existence.

Jim reacted sharply to his mother's concealed urge to rub him out of the family. He responded to the threat in a number of ways: (1) by developing an omnipotent power fantasy by which he could control the whole family and thus neutralize the mother's power to destroy him; (2) by keeping his mother and father apart, to prevent the mother from using the father as a stooge for her own hostility; (3) by obeying his mother's implicit commands to remove himself from the scene by fading out of the picture, literally and figuratively—that is to say, by removing himself from the situation in a symbolic sense, and in an actual sense, by threatening suicide; and (4) by an attempt to deny the threat of destruction at the hands of his mother by clinging to her, by conforming to her seductive attitude toward him, and by fortifying her defensive need to project the source of danger away from herself onto the father. It is Jim's reaction that has finally brought the family to awareness that their entire pattern of existence is being threatened. His inability to disappear—his healthy opposition to the implied command to wipe himself out—and his counteraggression precipitate the family crisis and ultimately bring the long-needed relief.

Robert, on the other hand, is seen by his parents as the perpetuator of the family. Robert finds safety and security in going along with the parents' conception of him. He would like to be more assertive but fears to risk his parents' disapproval. Robert adheres to his father—he imitates him and identifies with him, he speaks up in his defense. Robert is ingratiating, castrated, mildly feminine.

His relationship with his mother is obscured, but there are hints of his feeling that Jim got more of her than he did. In his desire to intrude on his parents' sexual privacy, his covert desire for his mother appears. Robert would like to express both aggressive and sexual drives but is afraid to do so without parental approval. He is the child who must not be different. His conformity to the family sickness is regarded as health, and only closer acquaintance with the unhealthy distortions of the family relationships reveals the underlying disturbance. Robert's disturbance provides an example of the challenge to relate the goals of treatment and prevention in the field of family psychotherapy.

The R. family, with one son nine years old, presents an example of a different kind of challenge for family intervention. The parents came for therapy, acutely worried because their only child had been diagnosed elsewhere as psychotic. The complaints about him were numerous: he was a poor eater, a nail-biter, he had tantrums, nightmares, and night terrors. Family therapy led to a different diagnostic interpretation.

The mother was suffering from a borderline psychosis. The boy was only apparently mentally ill, manifesting a kind of pseudo psychosis. His symptoms, while obviously severe, proved to be essentially psychoneurotic, although they looked for all the world like psychosis. These symptoms were the product, by contagion and projection, of living with a near-psychotic mother. In our view, in this special instance, the father's tender and devoted relationship with the boy provided the needed antidote; it offered just enough immunity for the boy to offset the danger of actual psychosis.

Thus it was not the boy, but rather his mother, who was fundamentally psychotic. The mother projected to the boy her pervasive fears of catastrophe and physical mutilation. She was full of panic; she had an overwhelming fear of fires; she had a fear of intruders who might kidnap, assault, and choke the boy. She was plagued with fantasies of violence and killing. Against these perceived perils she pulled down the shades, double-locked the windows, and chained the doors. She punished the boy by refusing to speak to him for days on end. The boy felt that he was at war with his mother. With his father he formed a close protective alliance.

The father listened to him and did not punish him. The father was a warm person who had himself suffered real catastrophe by losing all of his relatives to the Nazis. He was a lonely man who had faced stark death. He no longer feared it but only hoped that he would be spared the agony of death in the bleak, cold days of winter. He wished only that he might die warm, not freezing cold.

When he met his wife in this country he indulged in a form of rescue fantasy. He would marry her and save her from the hate and persecution of her family. He would take her away from her parents and, with his tender devotion, would cure her of her fears and superstitions. This dream never came true.

By this time there is little contact between husband and wife. The father feels rejected and unappreciated by the mother. He has suffered a painful disillusionment in his rescue fantasy. He withdrew from his wife and turned his affection to his only son.

In the following interview the splits and the alignments within this family are sharply focused, as are the necessity of liberating this boy from the burden of the mother's scapegoating of him and the need to retranspose the problem to the mother and to the relationship between the parents.

Verbatim Record

DR. A.: There we are. Mom, since you were very troubled about what happened the last time and felt that certain things maybe shouldn't have been talked about in front of Richard, I've had you very much in mind. If you feel they should not, tell me right away. Do you?

MOTHER: Well, I don't know, Doctor, what if he got frightened somewhere . . . in school, outside! What would happen?

DR. A.: Mm.

MOTHER: Since that time, you know, that week, he started, I mean, he was afraid before, but not as much, you know, since we were here. Now, even if I have the lights on, he's afraid to go from one room to the other.

Interpretive Comment

Therapist's consideration for mother's fear of exposure.

Mother's effort to evade problem, by displacing it to school.

Boy's night fright.

DR. A.: Mm.

MOTHER: And he's taking revenge on both of us. Not only on myself. He keeps on . . .

Boy's revenge on both parents.

DR. A.: Tell me how.

MOTHER: Like at night. He's afraid to go to sleep. First we had him in our bed, he slept with us.

DR. A.: Mm.

MOTHER: We tried to fall asleep, and he said, no, we can't fall asleep until he falls asleep before us. And he was fighting it. We wanted to go to sleep, and he wouldn't let us. And he didn't go to sleep himself. He'd stay up all hours through the night.

Boy fights sleep; does not allow parents to sleep.

DR. A.: Were you taking revenge on your parents, like Mommy said?

SON: What for?

DR. A.: You don't feel that way. You mean you were just frightened?

SON: Mmhmm.

DR. A.: You weren't trying to get back at Mommy at all?

SON: For what? There's no reason why I should.

Boy defends himself against mother's accusation.
Therapist supports him in facing mother.

DR. A.: Well, ask Mommy, because she felt you were getting back at both Mommy and Daddy. Ask her.

SON: Why did you say so, Mommy? 'Cause that isn't true. Then just tell me one thing that you think I'm taking revenge on you for.

MOTHER: Why is it you can't sleep at night? What are you afraid of?

SON: You know.

MOTHER: What, what do I know? What are you afraid of? Nothing has ever happened to you up till now, no crooks ever came into the house, and I don't expect ever will come in. Nothing has ever happened in the building. . . . Why should you say you're afraid the minute it gets dark? Even in the apartment, especially to go to the bathroom.

Boy's fear of the dark.

SON: I'd go . . . I can go to the bathroom by myself.

FATHER: He can go. He says he's not afraid. But if it's dark, we have to put on one light, till he reaches the bathroom door.

Father supports boy.

DR. A.: Speak up a little bit, Pop.

SON: That's late at night.

FATHER: In the bathroom he's not afraid by himself. Nobody stays with him, never. But soon as he goes from his bed to the bathroom, he has to go through . . . our bedroom.

DR. A.: Mm.

FATHER: Then he even puts on the light and then the other light, as soon as he's finished in the bathroom.

DR. A.: Well, Richard, would you like me to explain to . . .

MOTHER: Richard, turn your chair around.

Boy turns his back on mother, provokes more anger.

DR. A.: . . . you why Mommy felt that you were taking revenge?

SON: Because I don't understand it.

DR. A.: Well, let me try to help you understand it, then. When Mommy felt that way a little bit, and she's not sure she's right, but she just felt that way, because you insist on getting into bed with Daddy, in the big bed, and Mommy has to get out of the bed and she has to sleep in your bed. Isn't that the way you do it?

SON: Mmhmm. I told . . .

DR. A.: Mommy felt you were pushing her out of her own bed.

> Boy pushes mother out of bed; takes her place with father.

SON: Well, she didn't have to. It's all right with me, that she can sleep . . .

DR. A.: You mean it'd be all right for you to sleep all three of you together in the one bed?

SON: Mmhmm. But usually if all three of us sleep, me and my father have to go out because my mother's feet are cold. But otherwise, the minute my father makes her feet warm, the whole bed's burning, just like there was a fire in the bed.

> Note the phrase "me and my father."
>
> Mother has cold feet. Father makes mother's feet warm, also son's—"like a fire in the bed."

DR. A.: Is that right! Gee whiz, I didn't know that!

SON: That's why . . .

DR. A.: What do you do?

SON: So me and my father have to come around.

DR. A.: Explain that to me. You mean that everybody in the bed starts burning up when Pop begins to warm up Mommy's cold feet?

> Father burns them up.

SON: And mine.

DR. A.: Oh, he must have rubbed his . . . I don't know how you do that, Pop! When you rub the feet, you, you burn them up.

FATHER: They're putting dead feet on me, and mine are always warm.

> Mother has "dead feet"; father has hot feet.

DR. A.: You warm them with your feet? Playing footsie? Or with your hands?

FATHER: No, just putting their feet on mine. When they do, they get warm. They say then three people become

> It is "too hot" for three in the bed.

too hot in the bed. I wind up taking him out and going away with him.

DR. A.: Well, who complains first that it's too hot? Do you?

SON: Me 'n' my father.   Again, "me and my father."

DR. A.: Mommy doesn't complain?

SON: She's all asleep.

DR. A.: Is that right, Mom?

MOTHER: I don't know.

DR. A.: The two boys in the family complain and Mother doesn't complain?   Son and father join in complaint.

MOTHER: I'm in everybody's way, I guess.   Mother feels unwanted by both father and son.

FATHER: I don't complain.

DR. A.: Do you feel that way? . . .

SON: . . . and mash it around two ways . . .

MOTHER: In a way.

DR. A. (*to mother*): You feel in the way? That's why Mommy feels bad. Somehow . . .

SON: So even if Mommy says if we would go out . . .

DR. A.: Is she in the way? . . .

SON: . . . better to have . . .

DR. A.: Is she in the way?

SON: What?

DR. A.: Is she in the way?

SON: No. It's just, it's just like Daddy says; it's a plenty big enough bed and it's enough for three people.   Boy again denies accusation.

DR. A.: Yes.

SON: You have a little room, but still, it's too hot. Because all our feet are piled up on Daddy's.

DR. A.: So Daddy's the one who complains. Too many feet.

SON: No. We all get so gathered together that we get . . . My father has
to warm up everything, till everyone's
so hot that the whole bed starts burning up.

"The whole bed starts
burning."

DR. A.: Hm. Well . . .

SON: And if Mommy complains we
go out of the bed and let her be happy
and stay in her own bed. That's what
we do always if Mommy complains,
or I complain, or Daddy complains,
me and Daddy go into my bed. We
let Mommy stay in her bed.

Father and son separate from
mother.

DR. A.: But that leaves Mommy very
lonely.

Mother deserted and alone.

SON: So she didn't . . .

DR. A.: And her feet get cold again.

SON: After we, after the bed gets
burned up, it stays like that almost,
almost twenty-four hours.

FATHER: They use me as an . . . electric heater.

Father is an "electric heater."

DR. A.: Electric heater?

FATHER: Heater.

SON: Because we never get steam.

DR. A.: What a man! What a man!
Hm! But Mommy feels bad, Richard.

FATHER: Because really they're saying
to you, Doctor, that it's seldom I get
cold feet. Very seldom.

DR. A.: Mm.

FATHER: Even if they are cold, I
don't feel they're cold. I'm used to it.

DR. A.: But you complain it gets too
hot for you. *You* complain.

FATHER: I don't really complain. But
if it really gets too hot, I can't stand
a hot room.

DR. A.: Mm.

FATHER: And I don't like to be covered, it doesn't matter how cold it is.

Father can't stand being covered (dead).

DR. A.: When Mommy . . .

SON: And I love to be covered.

FATHER: He loves to be covered. My wife, she loves to be covered, but no matter how cold it is . . .

Mother and son want cover; for father it means to be buried and dead, like his relatives killed by the Nazis.

SON: Once it was burning . . .

FATHER: . . . what I have . . .

DR. A.: You're burning up.

FATHER: I'm not burning up.

SON: When he was burning in the summer, at night, I still always cover myself up, up to here so I can breathe.

Son wanted to be covered, but not choked.

DR. A.: Mm.

SON: Then around twelve o'clock at night, *a hurricane comes from my feet.* The blankets go kicking up in the air and fall on the floor, and I stretch out and instead of lying straight I start to spin around and I end up this way.

Son stirs up a "hurricane" with his feet.

DR. A.: You must be a pretty powerful fellow to throw up a hurricane in bed. Do you blow your winds a hundred miles an hour?

Son, a "powerful fellow," blows a powerful wind.

SON: No, my feet, they go kicking all over the place. That's, that's why, uh, the blankets always end up on the floor.

DR. A.: Mm.

SON: He wanted to cover me up, at night, because I uncovered myself and he knows that I want to be covered, the blanket had to go down, because the blanket was on the floor, like always.

DR. A.: Mm. But you know, I'm worried, you know why?

SON: Why?

DR. A.: Because I know Mommy feels very bad.

SON: So she . . .

DR. A.: Look at Mommy's face, she's sad . . . She's sad.

SON: Well, if she wants anything, she just should tell us. 'Cause me and Daddy always go into our bed if she wants.

DR. A.: You want to ask her what she wants?

SON: What's wrong?

MOTHER: No, I'd like to know, Doctor, what do you think, what's the situation, what's it going to be? I mean the way he's been acting lately . . . Is there any way of straightening things out?

DR. A.: We're trying to do that, right now.

MOTHER: I mean . . .

DR. A.: I don't know yet.

MOTHER: . . . It's been on my mind so much, I don't know, I do everything I possibly can.

DR. A.: I know, I know you're trying your best. I'm trying my best, but part of the thing is that you feel so bad.

MOTHER: Pardon me, do you have any cases . . .

DR. A.: Yes.

MOTHER: . . . Doctor? May I ask?

DR. A.: Yes.

MOTHER: You did? I thought mine was the only one, because . . .

Therapist stimulates son's awareness of mother's bad feeling.

Mother is sad.

Therapist stirs closer interchange between son and mother.

Mother is perplexed.

Mother sees her problem as unique.

DR. A.: Really?

FATHER: The only one thing . . .

MOTHER: . . . I mean in a case like that, I never heard of anything like it. I mean I have friends . . .

SON: And so I'm trying to help too, because we already got . . .

> Here, son seeks recognition, but mother, in her preoccupation with self, seems oblivious of his presence.

MOTHER: . . . they have children, sometimes they tell me, you know, the way they act, and other things. But, uh, nothing like this.

DR. A.: Somehow you felt you were different from everybody else on this earth, nobody like you.

> No one else on earth is like Mother.

MOTHER: But I know everybody has a problem. There isn't one person in the world that hasn't got any.

DR. A.: To me it's not so mysterious.

MOTHER: Well, uh, we . . .

DR. A.: To you it is.

MOTHER: It is, yes.

DR. A.: But, you know, I'm trying to see what Richard and Poppa feel when you look so sad and so depressed, so unhappy. Richard asked you what you want.

> Mother's vagueness makes it difficult to focus problem.

MOTHER: Well, I'd like he should be a man, you know, he's not a child any more, he's nine years old, and he should act like a nine-year-old child. He's got to go to bed, he's got to go . . . I want him in bed at eight-thirty; nine o'clock he should be asleep. When it comes night, you know, I start up at eight—get undressed, go to sleep, talk to the ceiling, nobody's there. Then we wait a half hour.

> After some display of vacillation, mother dictates her orders about bedtime.
> Here again, she seems unaware of her son as a real person. Instead, she responds exclusively to her perception of him as a personal persecutor. Her compulsion to make him sleep is, in effect, to make him "dead," to rid herself of her persecutor.

DR. A.: Have you been after him a long time to get to bed on time?

MOTHER: Not a long time, Doctor.

DR. A.: All these years?

MOTHER: Since he got into the first grade . . .

DR. A.: Hm.

MOTHER: . . . I began, you know, to have trouble with sleep.

DR. A.: Do you have trouble going to sleep?

MOTHER: Me?

DR. A.: You have trouble going to sleep?

MOTHER: If I had a chance, just give me the opportunity, I wouldn't hesitate, just give me a chance and when the time comes, after all, I'm only human.

> Mother blames son for keeping her awake.

DR. A.: The moment you hit the pillow you're ready to sleep? If he lets you, is that it?

MOTHER: Sure. . . .

SON: So who's stopping her? My father can make me go . . .

> Son defends himself against blame.

DR. A.: She says . . .

SON: . . . to sleep. Why, Mommy? If Mommy's so tired then she can go to sleep, because my father always goes to sleep late. So instead of reading the paper he can do it, if Mommy wants to go to sleep so bad. And usually she always does.

> He tries to appease mother's complaints.

DR. A.: Why does anybody have to make you go to sleep?

SON: 'Cause I like to stay awake and watch television, or read, mostly read,

> Son stays awake out of fear. He reads to keep wakeful.

and 'cause I just finished this book in three days.

DR. A.: Well, Mom, will you believe me if I tell you what you should do?

MOTHER: Yes.

DR. A.: Let him stay up all night if he wants to. Let him read all night, let him watch TV all night.

Therapist offers solution.
Father agrees.

FATHER: That's what I want to do.

DR. A.: He'll get very sleepy.

FATHER: She won't do . . . keep him up the whole night, so . . . tomorrow . . .

MOTHER: Well, what about . . .

DR. A.: Well, Pop, she'll listen to me, but she won't listen to you.

MOTHER: Well, what about going . . .

FATHER: I, I'm not sure, Doctor . . .

MOTHER: . . . to school the next day?

Mother is unsure, perplexed. She lacks faith in doctor.

DR. A.: Hm?

FATHER: . . . she'll listen.

Here and later in the record, notice the repetitive and interruptive pattern resulting from the obsessional characteristics of this family.

SON: I always fall asleep. . . .

MOTHER: You know if he doesn't . . .

DR. A.: Well, that's no problem. . . .

MOTHER: . . . get enough sleep.

DR. A.: I'll tell you why. That's no problem.

MOTHER: . . . his eyes are always blue around. Just like he's been getting black eyes.

Is this mother's death fantasy for the boy?

DR. A.: Mom, that's no problem.

MOTHER: What shall I . . .

DR. A.: If . . .

MOTHER: . . . do then? Anything you say, I'm willing to cooperate.

SON: Doctor?

DR. A.: In one minute. I want to answer your mommy and then you can talk, all right? Well, if I can somehow get you and Father to agree about what to do . . .

MOTHER: Yes.

DR. A.: . . . the two of you, there'll be no problem about school. . . .

MOTHER: Well, we're willing to do whatever you say.

DR. A.: I'll tell you why there's no problem about school.

MOTHER: Yes.

DR. A.: If he stays up very late one night, he'll get very tired. And he might even miss one morning of school—even if he misses a whole day—but he can't stay away from school because there's a law. Every child must go to school.

FATHER: Not . . .

DR. A.: It is required. He must go to school by law; you know that, don't you?

FATHER: Compulsory.

DR. A.: So the most that can happen is he misses one morning, because he's too tired.

MOTHER: Yes.

DR. A.: Children straighten out their own sleep habits, even though they have these fears. But we'll deal with those fears, those robbers and crooks, in a moment. He'll deal with those fears. But the first question is, you and Father never agree.

Mother makes a gesture of respect and deference to doctor.

Therapist shifts attention to parental conflict.

Sensing the mother's imperviousness, and fixed imagery of the boy, therapist assumes authoritative position and offers direct advice.

Therapist returns again to parental conflict.

MOTHER: What do you mean?

FATHER: May I interrupt a moment, Doctor? Happened one night, he was asleep, he felt that I'm not there. I went down to read the paper, read in the light, a book or something, have a cigarette. Richard . . .

DR. A.: I didn't hear you.

FATHER: I said, Doc . . .

MOTHER: Talk a little louder, Pop.

FATHER: And Richard came to me . . .

DR. A.: Yes.

FATHER: . . . in the living room. And I said it's okay. Put on the television, you want the television, stay here as long as you want, the whole night, even, stay . . . So, it started off, why are you going to chicken? So what goes on so late here? I said, "Richard, I hope you're not mad, you have to go to bed." I want, uh, I want to do the same way that you mentioned before, Doctor.

Father finds ally in therapist.

DR. A.: She wouldn't let you?

FATHER: No.

SON: Maybe like I'll remember.

DR. A.: Of course, that's part of the . . .

FATHER: My bed . . .

DR. A.: . . . that's part of the trouble.

SON: He wouldn't . . .

DR. A.: You and Pop always fight about this. Let me tell you, Mom, you don't know about these things, so let me tell you. There were experiments made, studies at the Medical Center, of these problems.

Therapist uses medical authority to strengthen influence with mother.

MOTHER: Yes.

DR. A.: Not only with sleep habits, but also with diet. Children from six months to a year, they were not given the regular diet. For about two months a great big tray of all kinds of food was brought to these babies, they were given the whole tray to take whatever they liked. And these were kids with disturbed feeding habits, wrong eating habits. Some of them wouldn't eat at all. Well, they were allowed to take no food, too much food, only one food, or six different foods, whatever they wanted.

MOTHER: I see.

DR. A.: And it was all put down on paper.

FATHER: What they did.

DR. A.: And at the end of two months, it was discovered that every child had a balanced diet. In other words, the child's body does what is good for the body. The same with sleep, same experiments with children's sleep habits. So, if you let his body alone, it will take care of the sleep habit. Are you a good eater? You look like a good eater. Are you?

Therapist wants mother to let boy alone.

Mother is obese, looks as if she overeats.

FATHER: He had . . .

DR. A.: You like food?

MOTHER: Up to a few years ago, Doctor, I was up to here with his food, as you say.

Mother is obsessed with image of her boy rejecting her food and dying of starvation.

FATHER: And everybody's got trouble with the children.

MOTHER: He used to yell at me. He was so thin, like a toothpick.

Mother projects own fear of going hungry and dying.

FATHER: He didn't want to eat. Taking many vitamins. He will eat.

MOTHER: I used to sit and talk to him and read to him and tell him everything under the sun, until I was able to push a spoon into his mouth. He used to yell at me. . . .

Mother engaged in forced feeding.

FATHER: (*Unclear, but talking in the background during whole of above speech.*) Of course, what's wrong?

MOTHER: . . . the kid was like . . .

DR. A.: Don't both of you talk at once. Mom talks to me, Pop talks to me, there's a telephone connection here and here, but we've got crossed wires.

"Crossed wires"—neither parent listens to the other.

SON: And I want to talk to you.

DR. A.: You both talk at once.

FATHER: We got two-party lines.

DR. A.: Now imagine the . . . That's a good crack, you said it so softly. Two-party lines, three-party lines. Here's one line, here's another line, here's another.

FATHER: Okay, I'm going to cut it out.

DR. A.: So you got crossed wires.

MOTHER: I mean the way he looks now, if I wasn't up to here, I mean he'd still be like this.

DR. A.: I don't believe it, Mom.

MOTHER: No matter what you gave him, he wouldn't take anything. I had all kinds of vitamins the doctor gave him. . . .

DR. A.: Mm.

MOTHER: And still, do you know, he wouldn't eat a thing.

DR. A.: But if you did what they did in the hospital, bring in a big tray and mind your own business, he'd have a balanced diet in a month.

MOTHER: Well, then I didn't know anything.

DR. A.: Well, I'm teaching you.

MOTHER: Well, now, yes, it's good to know. No, you know, I put food on the table, it stays there, it can stay for an hour or two, if he wants to eat it all right, if he doesn't want it, I take it away. That's it.

DR. A.: All right, so you learned something. So why don't you do the same with his sleep? If he doesn't sleep at night, he'll sleep in the morning. What's the difference?

MOTHER: Well, when I know he's got to go to school in the morning . . .

DR. A.: The worst that can happen is he doesn't stay awake in school.

Mother coercive with boy's eating and sleeping habits, also with going to school.

MOTHER: What I'm worried about, I want him to go to school.

DR. A.: The worst that can happen is that he stays away one morning.

This is a good example of mother's rigid ruminative thinking, her difficulty in perceiving anything new and different.

MOTHER: I want him to have a little education.

DR. A.: That's the worst that can happen. He's a very smart boy. And he loves to read books.

FATHER: And I'll tell you something else.

DR. A.: He's going to get an education. Because he likes it.

FATHER: He just didn't lie to her. I know he was supposed to go to school today. I didn't want to take chances.

Let him go early to bed. He wants to go early to bed.

SON: At eight-thirty. I'm looking at the bed . . .

Boy's voice is plaintive; he pleads for recognition.

FATHER: At eight-thirty, he wants to go, to go early to bed . . .

SON: . . . clock in the room . . .

FATHER: . . . but I thought, not to have trouble, if he should wake me up a few times during the night, I'm going to take a chance, I said, "Richard, I'm going to put together the puzzle." He stayed up to a quarter, a quarter to eleven. He fell asleep . . . five minutes later he was asleep. He didn't wake up the whole night, he slept till eight-thirty this morning. Is it true? You know the same thing. It's true . . .

Father pleads with mother to be tolerant.

DR. A.: What's the matter with the connection between you and Mom? The telephone connection? If you talk at once, the two of you talk at the same time, how can you hear? What's the matter?

Once again, "crossed wires."

MOTHER: I didn't say anything then, while he was talking.

DR. A.: A moment ago you were both talking at once.

FATHER: I did not.

DR. A.: Serious?

MOTHER: Sunday night it was his birthday. I made him a little party. . . .

SON: Wednesday was my birthday.

Notice here boy's bridling, angry response to mother's "error" as to the day of his birth.

MOTHER: Well, there was . . .

DR. A.: Congratulations. How old are you?

SON: Nine.

DR. A.: Very good.

MOTHER: Whether it was the excitement or what it was, but he couldn't go to sleep. He wanted us to lie down with him, he slept, he tried to fall asleep, he was fighting it. Two o'clock, he's not asleep yet. We said to him, "Richard, we're tired, let us lie down just for a little while, go to sleep now." So he got my husband so upset, he took the strap . . .

SON: You told him.

Boy accuses mother of inciting father to beat him.

MOTHER: . . . that he gave it to him.

DR. A.: Did you hear what Richie said? You ordered Papa to take the strap to him.

MOTHER: He was standing in the . . .

DR. A.: Is that right?

MOTHER: . . . other bed . . .

DR. A.: Wait a minute, is that right? You ordered Papa to take the strap to him?

Therapist actively penetrates mother's denial and projection of hostility. She provoked father to punish boy.

MOTHER: Yes.

DR. A.: So he's, he's angry at you.

MOTHER: We spoke to him, "Richard, lie down, lie down, now."

DR. A.: Is that right, you're angry at Mother?

MOTHER: My husband didn't feel good. . . .

SON: I feel . . . I was scared, and I wouldn't be scared with Daddy, and that's all, if Daddy had laid down the first time I said so, everything would be good and we could sleep the rest of the night. This way.

DR. A.: Except Pop . . .

SON: I got in a fight, I got hit. There was a fight, and still the plan didn't work out, till I worked out to keep the lights on till I fall asleep.

A big family fight.

DR. A.: So you get very angry at Mommy. She gets angry at you, you get angry at her, and Pop, he just loves her. He's a great boy scout, is Pop. I tell you, Pop's a wonderful guy, but there's one complication, Richard.

Therapist here casts an ironic reflection on father's compliance with mother's punitiveness.

SON: What?

DR. A.: He burns you up with his feet.

SON: He's all right, I . . .

DR. A.: Well, I mean, that's serious.

SON: Well, I'm always cold, so . . .

DR. A.: If the bed's on fire and you have a hurricane in bed, that's pretty serious.

The bed is "on fire." Boy kicks up a hurricane, kicks mother out of bed (anger at her). A question: Does his anger conceal a repressed erotic stimulation caused by closeness of mother's body?

SON: Yes, but when he burns me up when my feet were cold. So then at night when I start making a hurricane with my feet, they cool off.

DR. A.: I see. You cool off by making a hurricane with your feet.

Cools off anger by kicking.

SON: Yes or . . .

DR. A.: You go like this?

SON: Just the blankets.

DR. A.: You kick.

SON: I don't know, but one time, I got up just before in the middle of it when it started and I saw I had banged my head, because I was lying the wrong way, and my feet were kicking all over, and . . .

DR. A.: You were banging your head against whom?

Head-banging (angry frustration).

SON: The wall.

DR. A.: Well, that's not a very smart thing to do. You're a smart boy; smart boys don't bang their head against the wall.

SON: But I was sleeping, at the time, and when I woke up I . . .

DR. A.: Yes, but Mommy feels bad because . . .

SON: And another time . . .

DR. A.: . . . you raise a hurricane, and you kick her out of bed.

Therapist repeats: Boy's urge is to kick mother out of bed (father is his ally).

SON: No, when I do the hurricane and stuff, I always kick *this* way. My mother always sleeps on the other side.

Boy tries to deny therapist's interpretation.

DR. A.: Oh, Pop's on this side? So you kick Pop? Does he kick you, Pop?

SON: And I kick the blanket, the blanket goes all over.

FATHER: Don't pay any attention to what he does to me.

DR. A.: Now wait, draw me a picture. This is the big bed, and when you're all three together, in the bed, you sleep in the middle? Or on the side?

SON: Like, this is where my father sleeps, Mommy?

MOTHER: Sit down.

SON: This is where my father sleeps. Here's where I sleep and here's where my mother sleeps.

Boy gesticulates to indicate the respective positions in bed.

DR. A.: All right, then . . .

SON: Except in a row.

DR. A.: I see. Then you sleep between Mommy and Daddy? Pop is on your left side?

SON: My father's on this side, and my mother's on this. And I'm always kick-

His obsessive explanation obscures rather than clarifies

ing the blanket this way. Because when I sleep, the wall's over here where my mother is, and the empty space is over here. So that's where I kick the blanket, in the empty space. So it falls on this side. I'm so used to it that when I'm not in my bed, I kick this way too, and it always lands on my father.

DR. A.: So, when you raise a hurricane with your feet, it's always toward Pop. His side?

SON: Well, he doesn't mind it because when I kick I always kick the blanket, nothing else. But the blanket makes a lot of trouble. Because when Mommy, if Mommy wakes up if she wants to get covered, she has to go down and pick it up from the floor. And my father, my father almost gets thrown off the bed because the blanket, like he likes to lie on top of the blanket, because he doesn't want to be covered, so until I get the blanket on the floor, by kicking, he almost falls on the floor with the blanket.

DR. A.: Oh, you kick both of them out. Pop and the blanket?

SON: Yes, that's what happened to-day.

DR. A.: I see.

SON: That's why he had to go out of bed for a few minutes.

DR. A.: Difficult, Mom.

SON: But me and my father always get along.

DR. A.: And you and your mother never get along.

SON: She's always sleeping, and I . . . you're right, we hardly ever do get along.

what happens. He protests his innocence of any motive to attack mother.

Boy repeats denial.

Boy arranges for mother to be stripped of blanket.

Note again: "Me and my father always get along." Not so for boy and mother.

DR. A.: What's the trouble between you and Mom?

SON: I don't know. I think I know one reason. Because me and my father, we always make agreements. Like one day we went to the movies, I said, "Dad, can I have some popcorn?" And he didn't like the smell of it. And I didn't like the smell of the cigarettes. Any cigarette.

He is able to make deals with father, not with mother.

DR. A.: Mmhmm. Mmhmm.

SON: So, uh, I said to my father, let's make an agreement. And we made an agreement that for each time he smokes a cigarette, I get a bag of popcorn. He smokes another cigarette, I get some candy. So . . .

DR. A.: You got that problem right now, because Pop is burning up right now. You didn't hear him, but he said it's burning up, too hot here. Burning up.

Therapist confronts father with meaning of body gesture. He is now "burning up."

FATHER: Red hot.

"Red hot."

DR. A.: So you'd better get . . .

SON: That's one . . .

DR. A.: You'd better get some popcorn or candy. Here's some candy.

SON: That's cough drops.

DR. A.: Well, it's candy, it's the only candy I've got here. You don't like it?

SON: I'll take one.

DR. A.: You want one, Pop?

SON: Thank you.

FATHER: No, thank you.

MOTHER: He said, you know, that we stick together. I mean, we did one night or two. Now I'm sleeping in his room and he sleeps in my husband's.

Family splits in bed. Boy and father sleep together; mother alone.

FATHER: He very seldom slept with us together, the way it is when he's . . .

SON: Only . . .

FATHER: . . . he was afraid when he came in the middle of the night and I wouldn't throw him out, he would stay.

DR. A.: Pop, you're burning up right now, aren't you?

Therapist repeats: father "burning up."

FATHER: Yes, it's hot.

Father is agitated and angry, but unable to express it.

DR. A.: How hot are your feet?

FATHER: I don't know.

DR. A.: You're hot all over?

FATHER: All over.

DR. A.: You want to kick the blanket off?

Therapist speaks figuratively.

FATHER: No blanket here.

DR. A.: Well, you've got a jacket, sweater . . .

FATHER: I can't, because . . .

DR. A.: Take your jacket and sweater off. . . .

MOTHER: Take off your jacket.

FATHER: No, thank you.

SON: Can I say something?

DR. A.: Wait a minute. In a moment, Richard. Why don't you want to take your jacket off?

MOTHER: Take your jacket off.

DR. A.: Sweater, too. It is hot. . . .

FATHER: It's just because it seems impolite without the jacket, that's all.

Father fears exposure.

MOTHER: That's all right.

DR. A.: I'll take mine off, too. We'll both take it off, okay?

Therapist sets example.

FATHER: Still feels uncomfortable.

Father is still uneasy.

DR. A.: How about the sweater?

FATHER: No, sweater . . .

MOTHER: Put it on the back of the chair.

DR. A.: Now take the sweater off too.

FATHER: It's still hot.

DR. A.: You're still burning up, Pop?

FATHER: No, now it's a little better.

SON: Why don't you take off your sweater?

FATHER: I took off one blanket, a little better.

Father takes cue from therapist and speaks figuratively of removing one blanket.

DR. A.: One blanket.

FATHER: Yes.

DR. A.: Take off another?

SON: We have three blankets.

FATHER: No, this one . . .

DR. A.: I think you're bashful. That's it, Father is bashful.

FATHER: Bashful?

DR. A.: Because a girl's here.

FATHER: No.

DR. A.: You don't want to undress in front of a girl.

FATHER: Just a kind of custom, that's all.

DR. A.: That's the way your Momma trained you?

FATHER: It's been that way all my life. At home I can take off my sweater and even my shirt. But in here, in a public place, I could never be seen by people without a jacket.

SON: (*Whispering to father.*)

FATHER: No secrets here, please. Leave me alone.

SON: Please?

DR. A.: What's the secret?

MOTHER: You don't want it, take it out.

Mother reacts here to boy's urge to spit out the cough drop.

SON: . . . so much.

MOTHER: Take it out of your mouth and put it in the ash tray.

DR. A.: You're burning up, too. You just want to get rid of the cough drop, nothing else? You want to kick off any clothes?

SON: No.

DR. A.: Hm? Well, now, Pop, how about changing chairs with Mommy? What did you want to say, Richard?

Therapist challenges mother and father to get together.

SON: Well, the only times that I sleep mostly with my father and mother are Saturday and Sunday. When my mother lets out my two birds, they fly around and we lie in bed. That's the only days we want to sleep together. Otherwise at night I sleep a few minutes; then Mommy usually goes in my bed.

On weekend mother, father, and son are in bed together.

A question: Does therapist's initiative in seating parents together stimulate disclosure of a different sleeping ritual? Is the weekend the time for sex?

DR. A.: I don't catch that. Sunday . . .

FATHER: He goes to bed straight.

DR. A.: You say Sunday, you and Mommy sleep together? You let the birds fly around and you sleep with Mommy Sunday? You like to . . .

SON: Saturday, not only my mommy, my father and my mommy.

DR. A.: Oh, the three of you. All three of you. But Sunday you don't get too hot? You don't burn up Sunday?

SON: Nope. I'm always burning. That's why Saturday and Sunday my father and mother are covered up and I'm not. Me and my father switch around. On the weekends, in the week, my father uncovers and me and my mother are covered.

DR. A.: Well, is it true, you have more peace in the family on Saturday and Sunday?

Peace in the family on Saturday and Sunday.

MOTHER: To me it's the same thing.

SON: Not to me.

DR. A.: How come you turn your back on Mommy? You didn't turn your back on Daddy. The reason I asked Mommy to move over is that I want to see why you and Mommy don't get along.

Therapist again confronts boy with hostile rejection of mother.

FATHER: I understand.

DR. A.: Look at her. Don't you want to look at her? Why don't you and Mommy get along?

Therapist challenges boy to face mother.

SON: Because first of all, we're always never getting along, like I said before, that me and my father always make agreements.

DR. A.: Well now, Mom . . .

SON: If I say that I want this, and my father wants something else, and we both have to do one thing, we always get along. . . .

DR. A.: You always make a deal with Daddy. You can't make a deal with Mommy?

SON: I don't know. When we try, the only deals we make is bets.

DR. A.: Well, let's see right now. Let's see you make a deal with Mommy. Turn to Mommy, make a deal with her.

SON: About what?

DR. A.: I don't care, about anything.

SON: Oh great, I got a good one.

DR. A.: What?

SON: For both, my mother and father.

DR. A.: Well, let's hear.

SON: Well, Mommy, instead of giving me only ten cents allowance, if I don't go to sleep inside, you can give me the same twenty-five cents, and Daddy can give me the fifteen cents. But also, we'll have to make an agreement on how many comics I can buy a week.

> Boy proposes deal with mother.

DR. A.: How about that, Mom? He wants to make a deal with you.

MOTHER: We'll make the deal, but the comics are out. Because he doesn't buy regular comics that a child should read, he buys the monsters . . . everything else . . . and he gets nightmares.

> Mother balks. Objects to comics. She makes a deal that is no deal.
> Comics cause nightmares, says mother.

DR. A.: Well, he doesn't get nightmares from the comics.

MOTHER: He does, Doctor.

> Here, mother opposes therapist with her omniscient way of thinking.

SON: No.

DR. A.: Who knows better, you or I?

MOTHER: Before, I'm telling you, before we came here, he started reading the comics, dinosaurs and the others, and he wakes up at night and thinks he's flying.

FATHER: Dinosaurs . . .

DR. A.: Well, they're only in the books.

MOTHER: . . . but he, he wakes up, you know, I'm flying, I think there's someone in the piano, somebody shooting.

> Mother has nightmarish frights. She projects these experiences to son.

FATHER: Oh, come . . .

MOTHER: . . . somebody's doing this, somebody's doing that.

SON: I do not. I never said I was flying . . .

DR. A.: Well, now . . .

SON: . . . I only think about it before I go to sleep. I think I'm Superman. And I enjoy myself, just like reading the comics, you enjoy yourself.

Boy has fantasy of being Superman.

DR. A.: Let him be Superman, Mom, why not? Why don't you make a deal with him? He wants to make a deal with you. Very important.

Therapist tries to neutralize mother's way of binding boy's powers.

SON: Doctor, what's your name?

DR. A.: You can call me Nathan. I call you Richard.

FATHER: Dr. Ackerman.

SON: Dr. Ackerman, when I read comics, they're just to enjoy myself. Like if I read one about the Justice Lever members—that's all the Superman people who are on earth—then I make believe that I . . . then I start reading it . . . after I finish in around five minutes, the whole book . . .

DR. A.: Tell me, do you feel the comics with the monsters and the supermen and the dinosaurs, they give you nightmares?

SON: No, they, when I read them, they, they give me dreams; I'm happy when they give me dreams.

DR. A.: They give you happy dreams?

SON: Because when I read it, then I think that I'm Superman. I enjoy myself, and I enjoy myself by making a comic in my mind. You know what I mean?

DR. A.: Sure, I know exactly what you mean. Now, Mom, let me ask you . . . Would you make a deal with him? Let him be your Superman? Hm? (*To son*) Turn around to Mommy. She's willing to make a deal, quick.

Is mother willing for son to be her Superman?

SON: How many comics you want me to buy with my allowance? We're going to get forty cents allowance. Twenty-five from you and fifteen cents from Dad. . . .

DR. A.: Forty cents a week? All right, that's your money. And you can do with it what you like.

SON: But my father . . . I bought a monster comic . . .

MOTHER: Put your feet down. Please sit up straight.

No—mother binds his feet.

SON: . . . and Mommy didn't let me buy it, so I bought another one with a Justice Lever member. And I put it on the couch, and now it's disappeared. That's why I'm trying to make it out that if I buy three comics and I'm supposed to get two, then she can take away the third comic I bought. Now take away one . . .

DR. A.: Well, no, I tell you. I don't want Mommy to take away any of your comic books. I tell you, I want you to listen carefully because I'm going to tell Mommy something about you. Mom, if you make a deal with Richard, and you give him a quarter, Pop gives him fifteen cents, he has forty cents a week allowance. Let him buy whatever comics he wants. And if you let him be Superman, he will have less nightmares. I guarantee you. You want him to have less nightmares?

MOTHER: Okay. Yes, when I first came here . . . Anything you say, I'm willing to do as long as it will help. That's all.

Mother again makes gesture of compliance with therapist.

DR. A.: How come you're willing to make a deal with me? But you won't make a deal with your own son, Richard?

Therapist still insistent on "a deal" with son.

MOTHER: I let him have the comics, but my husband refuses, Doctor. Why doesn't he say that?

Mother reverts to placing blame on father.

DR. A.: Oh, he's the bad guy?

FATHER: Yes.

DR. A.: You won't let him have the comics?

MOTHER: Ask him how many comics he has. He couldn't buy them for ten dollars.

SON: Forty-five dollars.

DR. A.: . . . You better shut your mouth now.

MOTHER: I'm in between. Whatever I do, it's still bad.

FATHER: He told it by himself.

MOTHER: (*Unclear.*)

FATHER: He keeps some comics, mysteries, and he got bad dreams. And such things he asks me all the time. I try to explain to him everything is fiction. It's nothing true.

SON: That's in stories, that, but not in comics. . . .

FATHER: I said stop reading comics. . . .

SON: Like once I saw Superman, you know . . .

FATHER: What should I say?

SON: . . . when he comes to that place . . .

FATHER: I even tried to explain . . .

SON: . . . with those darn headed monsters.

FATHER: . . . that is fiction . . .

SON: When I see movies, I can never remember.

FATHER: . . . that's make believe . . .

SON: . . . So the night I came back from "Sinbad," I went to sleep, and I thought I saw a whole bunch of them on the piano. Wow, did I get scared!

DR. A.: Well, all you'd have to do is be Superman.

Therapist uses "superman" as a magic, protective ally.

FATHER: I'm asking you.

SON: That time I couldn't read yet.

FATHER: He's mad at me.

DR. A.: Well, now you can read, so you don't have to be scared. Now, you can be Superman.

SON: I'm scared about the back room because I think there's crooks. That's the only thing I was scared about. Otherwise . . .

Boy elaborates his fantasy fears. They are a product of a contagion of fears shared with mother.

DR. A.: There are no crooks. Only in your head, up here.

SON: Sure, I know

DR. A.: You got crooks in the head.

Therapist uses colloquialism to emphasize the unreality of these fears.

SON: I tried one way to get it. I said that if I'm Superman, if you throw knives, bullets, or anything except kryptonite, which doesn't exist on earth, it's just an action in the comics, well, I make believe I'm Superman, of course, so Superman, nothing can harm him. So, why do I have to be afraid? I tried it once, and it helped a little, but my father wanted to help it always. He says, Think, there's no

Here son distinguishes clearly between fantasy and reality.

crooks. So, I kept thinking, and five minutes later I was in his bed.

DR. A.: Well, you've got crooks in the head. Are you listening to me, Richard? You've got crooks in the head. You understand that? You've got a screw loose. You're a little wacky. Those fears of crooks, you understand now?

SON: Otherwise everything would go good, without no crooks. I could always dream funny things, or . . . about Superman.

DR. A.: That's what you're going to have now. You're going to have funny and happy dreams.

SON: I hope. Because my father wouldn't let me read comics, so I wasn't Superman. I was afraid and, first of all I was afraid, second of all, I had a good dream, like I taught my bird to say something to the other bird. Go jump in the lake, one bird said to another.

DR. A.: (*Laughs.*)

SON: I laughed that night. . . .

DR. A.: That's what you're telling your mommy.

SON: No.

DR. A.: Go jump in the lake.

Therapist again emphasizes boy's disguised attack on mother.

SON: That's what I . . .

DR. A.: You shove her out of your bed.

SON: That's what I had in my dream. And the other bird says, ah, awkkk, awkkk, the same to you. And I laughed when I woke up.

DR. A.: Yes, but I want to know why you make your mommy feel so bad?

SON: Don't ask me!

DR. A.: You make her feel very bad.

Both boy and father make mother feel bad.

SON: Don't ask me. She tells me what she wants and I'll try and do it.

DR. A.: She felt you didn't want her and Daddy didn't want her.

Mother feels abandoned.

SON: Dr. Ackerman . . .

DR. A.: Well, Mom, you don't have to get out of the family.

SON: Doctor . . .

DR. A.: What had you thought, you had to leave?

MOTHER: It looks that way.

DR. A.: You feel very bad now? You . . . you have a handkerchief?

Mother shows sadness, dissolves in tears. Note her gesture of righteous self-sacrifice.

MOTHER: As I told you, Doctor, before, I sacrificed my life. Whatever I do for the kid . . . if he wants comics, and my husband says, "Don't give it to him," I'll take the quarter, I'll go and buy him comics. Maybe I overdo it. At times I say to myself, I overdo things. My husband says: "Don't buy him a toy." I figured, you know, the other kids have it. He comes into the house, "Mommy, this one has a toy. I have no brothers and sisters, I want a toy." I'll go and buy him a toy. Whatever I do, whatever I do, you know, it's no good.

Whatever mother does is bad.

DR. A.: Pop, you're making Mom very unhappy. You tell her whatever she does is not right, with Richard.

FATHER: I don't know what to say. About the comics, he told me himself,

"I don't want to, I wouldn't need comics any more. I got bad dreams." Did you tell me this way?

SON: Uh, you told me to try for three weeks, so I said I won't read comics for a week, see what happens. But the same thing happened. I didn't read for a week, and in the week I had that very bad one that I stayed up from two o'clock on.

DR. A.: I don't think it's such a good idea for you to kick Mommy out of the bed.

SON: Who said I kicked her out?

DR. A.: Well, Pop burns up the bed, he gets so very hot, he can't stand it.

SON: And he, we all get hot. So me and my father go out. We let Mommy stay in any bed she wants.

DR. A.: Why don't you sleep with Mommy? Why don't you put your father out of your bed for a change?

Therapist uses a provocative challenge as a means of confrontation.

SON: It's . . .

FATHER: I told . . .

SON: I like to stay with him because if my feet ever get cold again, my mother can't warm them 'cause she's always cold. But my father . . .

Mother is cold; father is warm.

DR. A.: She can warm your feet with her hands. If your feet get cold.

SON: If our feet are cold, we're all over cold.

MOTHER: Excuse me, there's another thing, Doctor. We live in a building, next door, there's two little boys—he always played with them. He's a year older. And they claim, while he plays with the older one, he picks on the younger one, the younger one gets beat up. So several times they called

Mother is evasive, tends to displace conflict to external events. Son is "bad boy."

me in the house and said whenever
Richard is with Steven, Robert gets
beat up, so why can't you try and keep
your son away from our children.

DR. A.: Mm.

MOTHER: I tried to talk to him. . . .

DR. A.: Well . . .

MOTHER: So he brings out that he's in
the way, he's doing it because . . .

DR. A.: Just a minute.

MOTHER: . . . he's jealous, he hasn't
got anybody. He has no brother or
sister. Maybe, he's bringing it out that
way. I tried to talk to him. . . .

Mother feels alone, imagines
boy also feels alone.

DR. A.: Tell me, Richard, what did
you just say to Pop? Hm?

SON: I said, I said that it isn't true.
They pick on us. Robert's always like
a big shot. He, he wants to boss me
and all my friends.

DR. A.: I see.

SON: When we're older, then he
thinks that the younger people boss
the older.

DR. A.: Why did you go tell Daddy
that, why didn't you tell that to
Mommy?

SON: I don't know. And also, if he
didn't do nothing, this one guy, he,
like yesterday we, my friends got beat
up because he took our ball and
threw it across the street, and when we
took his ball and threw it across the
street, they said he can throw your
ball across the street . . . they said he
can throw your ball across the
street . . .

DR. A.: Wait a minute, Richard . . .

SON: . . . but if you throw ours, we'll
hit you.

DR. A.: Wait a minute, Richard. I don't think it's very good for your sleep—because you have nightmares sometimes, bad dreams, frightening dreams—I don't think it's so good for you just to sleep with Pop. The bed gets too hot. And you . . .

SON: Yes, with three people.

DR. A.: . . . you blow up a hurricane, with your feet.

SON: And then everything cools off.

Therapist tries to pierce boy's obsessive cloud.

DR. A.: Well, now, if you get scared, you can get in bed with Mommy and Daddy, but then you go back to your own bed. You'll sleep better. You'll have more room . . .

SON: Well . . .

Therapist suggests boy can turn to mother for warmth.

DR. A.: . . . you can kick more. You try it out, all right?

SON: Okay.

DR. A.: All right.

SON: But let me tell you one more thing?

DR. A.: Yes.

SON: Also, uh, to tell you the truth, I found a better way. I asked my father, when I sleep in your bed, you can go out millions of times and I'm not afraid.

DR. A.: Well, that's good. All right, try that, if you like.

SON: Because I like his bed. I tried it already three days and so far everything's good.

DR. A.: All right, you try that this next week.

(In the next interview, son said we had "licked the night thing.")

8

Rescuing the Scapegoat

The adolescents of our day are hoisting distress signals. In ways both direct and indirect, teen-agers let us know that they are in trouble, not only in the United States but throughout the world. There are conspicuous signs of disorientation, confusion, panic, destructiveness, and moral deterioration. The disordered behavior of the adolescent needs to be understood not only as an expression of a particular stage of growth, but, beyond, as a symptom of parallel disorders of the family and society.

Historically viewed, the philosophy of treating the emotional disorders of adolescence has undergone many extraordinary shifts. In each successive era, the style of the psychotherapy of adolescents shifts in accordance with society's view of the oncoming generation, its threat of rebellion, its nuisance value, its threat to the stability of the family, and also its potential loyalty and commitment to the future destiny of the family and community.

The adolescent's instability, his tenderness, his fluid ego, and the fragility of his personality have impelled psychoanalysts to give up the idea of therapy during this transitional phase; the rapidity of change and growth has made the adolescent seem a poor risk, inaccessible to psychoanalytic treatment. Psychoanalysts say, in effect, we must wait until the adolescent grows up and becomes a stable citizen; then we can treat him. Nevertheless, modified forms of dynamic individual therapy have brought good results. Group therapy, too, has had notable success with adolescent patients. What of family therapy? Intervention at this level can be extraordinarily effective if it is undertaken in an appropriate situational context.

Family therapy can help substantially with some types of adolescent disorder, as long as it is not viewed as total therapy. Disturbances of identity formation, conflict with parents, shifts in standards of conscience, problems of acting out—all respond well. Family therapy is useful in conflicts involving image of self and image of family. It can liberate the adolescent to change and grow in his own way. When, as is often the case, scapegoating is used to maintain a precarious family balance, treatment of the family group may provide the only access to the adolescent.

In the family study that follows, it was necessary to remove the load of anxiety from the scapegoat, the youngest son, and to shift the focus of conflict back to the relations between the parents, so as to illuminate the nature of the basic disturbance of the whole family.

The family had four children—two sons, Morris and Fred, at college and thus living away from home, Henry, aged fourteen, and Jane, aged twelve. It was the father who came for help, because Henry had been involved with two other boys in a plan for a holdup. This incident brought him to the school authorities. He had previously engaged in petty pilfering. His actions verged on open delinquency and alarmed his parents, especially his father.

Henry had planned the holdup of a store, but at the last minute he himself warned the school authorities of the plan. There had been several previous incidents of Henry's stealing money from his father and brothers and from the Boy Scout treasury; in these episodes the father had covered up for his son. At an earlier stage, Henry had been quite conforming; now he is sullen and withdrawn. His recent misbehavior came as a terrible shock to both parents.

Henry is the third of the four children. The other three, including a younger sister, fit well into the family pattern. The brothers, aged seventeen and nineteen, are doing well in college. The younger sister, aged twelve, is a brilliant student. Both parents view Henry as different from the rest of the family, as the black sheep. The father is a hard-working salesman of Austrian background, who takes great pride in his upright and honest character, and who has made every sacrifice to provide his children with educational opportunities. The mother is also an intellectually ambitious person, who joined her husband in impressing on the children the importance of intellectual and moral achievement, the values of hard work, and the need for renunciation of immediate pleasure for a future reward. The couple had a severe economic struggle. The mother worked as a manicurist to supplement the father's earnings. Everyone fitted into the family plan except Henry, who openly flouted the family's image of solidarity and sacrifice. He seemed selfish, egoistic, lazy, inept in his school work, impulsive, uncooperative, and interested only in immediate pleasure. He often fled from the family into solitary athletic pursuits, or to a male neighbor who was fond of fishing, guns, and the out-of-doors. Henry's daydreams were filled with fantasies of leaving home. He was outstandingly the black sheep who menaced the identity, stability, and value strivings of this family group.

When the family was seen together as a group, there was ample evidence that the scapegoating process had proceeded to the point where Henry was effectively ostracized. It was five against one: father and mother, two brothers, and one sister against Henry. Henry's only effective support came from outside the family, from his friendship with the older man who liked guns, fishing, and the out-of-doors, and from his cronies, whose acceptance Henry bought with special treats.

At the outset, the father delegated himself as spokesman, but both parents treated the interview almost as if it were a hearing in a court.

Henry acted like a criminal and an outcast. He was isolated and stiff; he slumped in his chair and showed a blank stare, a face without feeling or expression. When he spoke, he sounded flat and dejected. He denied the implication of his past acts and assured the therapist and his family that he had learned his lesson. It became clear that the only way in which this boy could integrate himself into the family group was by suppressing all feeling and all protest and by consenting to play the role of a lifeless, submissive automaton within the family. His aggressive and rebellious strivings and his need for independence, as well as his craving for warmth and emotional contact, could only be expressed furtively, outside the family group. The exchange of emotion in this family had become fragmentary, stereotyped, and restricted; effective communication had broken down. Henry was monosyllabic and gave to the early interviews a peculiar atmosphere of hopelessness and futility. Henry's tight, sullen withholding, his imperviousness, and his obstinate clinging to his difference were an acute threat to his family. His attitude challenged its entire value orientation, its very survival. A closer look at the marital relationship showed that this couple's unity was partial and superficial. They had achieved an uneasy compromise with one another through a tacit agreement to avoid close emotional contact, which would surely activate dormant resentment at the failure of each partner to fill the needs of the other for a parental surrogate. Mr. N. has channeled his emotional needs largely toward the children and has chosen for himself the role of a solicitous, martyred parent, partly to live down his guilt-ridden memory of his own irresponsible gambler father. He is an angry servant to his children, since he never can obtain from them sufficient satisfaction of his own strong cravings for a generous parent, and he experiences their growing away from him as a threat. Mrs. N. has been assigned the role of "commander" in this family and has been given authority to wield, but she has on a deep level experienced her husband as shutting her out from any real emotional closeness with him or with the children; she feels thwarted in her own longing for emotional warmth and support from her environment. Both parents are thus repeating in their marriage aspects of their early family experiences, in which there was extreme deprivation, a need to suppress resentment in order to preserve security, and a precocious assumption of adult responsibility at an early age.

Against this background, we can understand that for these parents the threat of violence, as epitomized by Henry, has many ramifications. On one level, both parents fear the resurgence of their own suppressed resentments and frustrated longings, in relation both to their primary families and to the marriage partner. Insofar as Henry expresses the forbidden, underlying rebellious feelings of both parents, they need to deny him and punish him. In directing their hostility toward him, they can maintain their solidarity. The father especially has never dealt adequately with his murderously hostile fantasies toward his delinquent father, and there is in him a deep fear of Henry's potential violence, which may be similarly directed against him. Furthermore, behind the parents' need to assert rigid control over Henry and to forestall any expression of aggression, there is also a fear of losing the re-assuring support and protection of Henry as a parental surrogate. Henry's renunciation of his parents is the symbol of their abandonment by their own parents. They mobilize themselves to forestall a repetition. For Henry's siblings, who have been able to fit themselves into the rigid framework of family role relations, Henry also represents a threat. They scrupulously avoid joining with Henry, which would involve them in a rebellion against parental control and expose them to the parents' retaliatory wrath.

For the first interview, the family (Mr. and Mrs. N. and son Henry, aged fourteen) arrived half an hour late. Dr. A. and Miss K., their usual therapist, went out of the interview room to meet them. Mr. N. gave elaborate apologies for being late. He became absorbed immediately in relating to the psychiatrist and the social worker, leaving his wife and son in the background. Mr. N. spoke of his great pain and preoccupation with his hemorrhoid condition; he was planning to go to the hospital in the afternoon. He was very tense. Son Henry had a blank expression and was carrying his mother's book, *The Enemy Camp*. The parents were nervous; the boy seemed cool. The father took over in hanging up coats, fussing like a mother; things became disorganized and there was some dropping of possessions. Henry turned to Dr. A. with a blank, bewildered expression on his face and asked what was going on, why they were here. Dr. A. asked Henry about the book he was carrying, and his mother immediately claimed it as her own (*The Enemy Camp*).

The family entered the room, Mr. N. first, and Henry was seated between his parents. Mr. N. spoke about his pain. Dr. A. said he wanted to understand their troubles and asked who would begin.

Verbatim Record	**Interpretive Comment**
MOTHER: It's embarrassing.	Therapist invites expression; there is a pause of embarrassment and shame, indicating fear of exposure. Parents are anxious, inhibited, and wait for therapist to take initiative.

DR. A.: You're uneasy before these people [professional staff].

MOTHER: A little. Can you start a line of questioning?

DR. A.: Henry is puzzled and wants to know what it's all about.

HENRY: Who are all these people?

DR. A.: Professional people, here to help. Your parents are worried about you, about what happened. Are you worried?

HENRY: I don't know.

DR. A.: You look all mixed up; do you feel mixed up? You don't know whether you should or shouldn't be worried.

MOTHER: Henry, tell how you feel.

HENRY: I don't know what you mean.

DR. A.: Why don't you move your chairs so you can see one another?

MOTHER: I know what my husband looks like.

DR. A.: Perhaps you'd want to see your son, since you're asking him to express himself.

MOTHER: He's the one we're concerned with. I'd like to help him to present his case. I've never been

(A group of staff people are auditing this interview.)

Therapist stirs parents with their son's blank, bewildered look.

Therapist challenges the "identified patient," Henry, who is confused, elusive, difficult to reach.

Mother pushes Henry out in front. She is willing to expose him rather than herself.

Henry's face is blank, uncomprehending. Therapist observes that all members are looking at him, not at one another. He challenges them to rearrange chairs in semicircle, so that they may see and respond to one another.

Mother then points attention to Henry's "case." Within sixty seconds, the parents'

present when he presented his case.

DR. A.: You call it a case?

FATHER: I'll explain, Doctor. I'm the one who first approached the Clinic. So I was the one always to be with Henry. It's easier for me to explain. Henry, are you embarrassed by all these people? State the way you feel about it.

HENRY: Not too good.

DR. A.: I tried to talk with you, Henry. You're mixed up. You wait for some idea from others. Mama pushes you. Papa gets concerned because he feels he knows more than Mama. Is that true?

FATHER: In this problem, yes.

MOTHER: (*Wryly.*) In every problem, Doctor.

DR. A. (*to Mr. N.*): Should she keep her mouth shut while you talk?

FATHER: Well, she might have something to add, and then I would prefer that she interrupt. But if you feel she should keep quiet, Doctor, that's okay.

DR. A.: I thought you preferred her keeping quiet.

MOTHER: You have the wrong impression, Doctor. We have nothing to hide from one another. It doesn't matter which one of us talks; he can talk.

FATHER: I went to a hearing at Sheepshead Bay and presented my case. They said they'd get me the earliest appointment and then I spoke

scapegoating of Henry is revealed.

Father takes over from mother, assumes role as spokesman. He now pushes Henry out in front. He exposes Henry in lieu of himself. At the same time, he claims first concern for Henry.

Therapist turns to Henry, interpreting parents' maneuvers.

Mother makes a sarcastic thrust at father for his attitude.

Therapist exploits remark to challenge father.

Father turns defensive and projects responsibility to the therapist.

Now both parents reveal their proneness to engage in hypocritical denial.

Father takes possession of Henry's case as therapist "tickles the defenses" of parents.

there with Mrs. M. She asked me to take the kid to see a doctor. So all the facts were presented.

DR. A.: Your wife called it a case and you call it a hearing.

FATHER: (*Getting angry.*) I just went up there to state my case, and here. To me, it is a problem, and you might call it by any name you call it. I have a problem.

Father is provoked, turns anger on therapist. It is to be noted, too, that father speaks of "stating my case."

DR. A.: You think I'm quarreling with you.

Therapist, sensing father's defensive self-absorption, counteracts tendency to ignore son's feelings.

FATHER: No, maybe I didn't express myself properly. But I think that it is a case.

DR. A.: Do you have any idea how Henry feels now?

FATHER: Let him express himself. Henry, does it make any difference to you whether it is called a case? Or anything else? Does it bother you to speak so openly in front of all these people?

Father goes through a ritual gesture of concern with son's feeling.

HENRY: I have no objection.

DR. A. (*to Henry*): This is all about you, you understand that. Do you feel like a case?

HENRY: Is this a hearing?

The question now: Who is on trial, father, son, or both?

DR. A.: I don't think it is, and that's why I'm discussing it.

And who exactly is the prosecuting attorney?

HENRY: I think it is a hearing. There are two groups of people discussing their problems.

Henry, now for first time, asserts conviction; this is a hearing.

DR. A.: We call it an interview. My idea of a hearing is people appearing at court, with someone being charged

In order to catalyze the expression of deeper currents of conflict, therapist chal-

with an offense, being tried. Do you feel that these people [professional staff] are the jury?

HENRY: Yeah, they're the jury anyhow, if it's a case.

DR. A.: That makes me the prosecuting attorney?

HENRY: Yes.

DR. A.: Do I look like a prosecuting attorney?

MOTHER: This is a consultation, not a hearing.

DR. A.: So you're on my side?

MOTHER: Definitely, or I wouldn't be here.

DR. A.: And Pop is on the boy's side?

FATHER: No, this is not a hearing. We're here to help him. Henry, we're here to help you. We're here to listen to your problems, and our problems. Maybe we're the guilty ones. We're not here to prosecute a case.

DR. A.: Henry, what is your problem?

HENRY: What do you mean, where should I start? . . . About two years ago, I stole some money off my father, went to Coney Island.

DR. A.: How did you take it? How much?

HENRY: Took it from his pants pockets. About thirty dollars. Next year there was more difficulty. In our Boy Scout troop, we embezzled thirty dollars and went to Coney Island. . . . Took it from the troop treasury. Then we planned a stick-up with a bunch of

lenges family. Is he really a prosecuting attorney?

Mother joins therapist to deny that this is a criminal hearing with therapist acting as prosecutor.

Therapist provokes more feeling.

Is the group now split— mother siding with therapist, father protecting son? Here father seems self-righteously to assume son's guilt.

Therapist now stirs son to speak for himself.

He confesses stealing, and the planning of a holdup with knives.

fellows. But I didn't go with them, didn't do it.

DR. A.: With guns?

HENRY: No, knives.

DR. A.: Why didn't you go? Afraid?

HENRY: No, it was too risky.

Henry, in a frozen, dead way, denies his fright.

DR. A.: Were you scared?

HENRY: No, but I was afraid of getting caught. I went to the school and told them. The guys didn't carry it out, because the school office was warned.

Instead of carrying out the crime, son exposed the crime to school authorities.

DR. A.: Did you like these guys, were they your buddies?

HENRY: One of them I had known a while. I warned him and stopped him too.

Henry wanted to be stopped, wanted protection.

DR. A.: So you were scared for him too.

HENRY: Yeah.

DR. A.: How did your buddy feel about it?

HENRY: He wasn't happy. Was a little sore. But that was nothing compared to if we had been caught.

DR. A.: We can't hear you, Henry. (*Henry gets up and throws out his chewing gum. Dr. A. asks if he has more, and father says he's carrying the gum.*)

DR. A. (*to father*): You want to make Henry happy.

FATHER: All parents want to make children happy. (*Cliché.*)

Father and son each claim desire to please the other.

HENRY: I want to make him happy too.

DR. A.: But you haven't made your parents happy, Henry. You've made

Therapist challenges them.

them unhappy and worried them very much. Yet you say you want to make your father happy.

HENRY: That was past, and this is the present.

Son claims a change of heart. He is going to be a good boy now. No more stealing.

DR. A.: You're not going to worry him any more?

HENRY: No.

(*Father begins to weep uncontrollably. Henry sits impassive. Mother wipes eyes, but shows little expression; hands father Kleenex. Dr. A. tries to talk with him, and father becomes more upset, stands up with his face against the wall, sobbing.*)

This opens the floodgates. Father seizes center of stage with a burst of weeping.

DR. A.: Now, Papa, you are worrying Henry.

Therapist turns the tables on father. He points out instantly that father's sobbing now worries son.

FATHER: Excuse me. (*Sits down.*)

DR. A.: You feel you should apologize for crying?

FATHER: Yes, it's just an emotion. (*He breaks down again.*)

Father makes defensive gesture of suppressing emotion, but again breaks down.

MOTHER: My husband always takes it more emotionally than I. I agree with Henry, it's in the past. What troubles me now is his reason for doing this. He never did anything like this before. The redeeming factor is that he told the school office, and then we found out what was going on. Up to then, we didn't know. We're not rich, but if Henry came to us we'd always try to give him anything. His father especially would do everything in his power to give it to him. We want to get at the underlying motivating fac-

Mother compensates with intellectual formulation of problem.

tor, the stealing itself isn't that important.

DR. A.: I want to go back to what just happened. When Pop cried, Henry looked at him and there was the first feeling I've seen on his face.

Therapist counters father's exhibitionism, calling attention to son's show of feeling. Now, for first time, Henry gives up his blank, frozen face and reacts to father's crying.

MOTHER: He's always cared more for his father.

DR. A.: Henry, did you ever see Pop cry before?

Therapist objects to father's martyred need to steal the show from his troubled son. He therefore offers a special support for son's show of feeling. He teases out more of Henry's conflicting emotions in relation to father.

HENRY: Yes, when he came to the dean's office at school.

DR. A.: So this is the second time he cried over you?

HENRY: Yes.

DR. A.: How did you feel?

HENRY: Not too good.

Father's sobbing causes son to feel guilty.

DR. A.: That's the first time I saw a troubled feeling on your face.

Therapist feels an urgent need to proceed further in melting son's frozen face to activate a deeper release of his blocked emotions. Once again, Henry promises to be a good boy. By implication, he reproaches father for excessive worry. He tries to deny the seriousness of his actions.

HENRY: He takes the past too seriously, it's in the past.

DR. A.: Your father doesn't think he takes it too seriously, right?

HENRY: I do take it seriously.

MOTHER: Of course.

DR. A.: So they don't agree with you, Henry, they don't think it's just a joke. You don't want to take it seriously, Henry?

HENRY: It's in the past.

DR. A.: It's all wiped out?

Here therapist supports the validity of father's worry.

HENRY: Well, it sticks in your mind, you can't wipe it out completely, but you can't go back to it.

DR. A.: It's on your record.

HENRY: Yes.

DR. A.: Are you sure you won't do these things again?

HENRY: I'm sure.

Son promises: never again.

DR. A.: Is Father sure?

FATHER: I hope so. Yes, I'm sure, he's learned his lesson.

DR. A.: He's been scared?

FATHER: It was the biggest scare when he told the school. Almost stepped over the border. They all would have gone to jail. It put enough fear into him not to do it again.

Father here shows need to deter son through fear of punishment.

DR. A. (to Henry): Did you think about going to jail?

HENRY: No.

DR. A.: So you don't think that's what's going to make you a good boy?

Therapist reality-tests this emotion in son. Did he really fear jail? At first, he denies fear, then turns about to admit it.

HENRY: No. I won't do it again.

DR. A.: Pop says you could have gone to jail.

This whole sequence illustrates the capacity in family

therapy of loosening up pathogenic defenses in a child by piercing pathogenic defenses of parents and family.

HENRY: Yes.

DR. A.: Did you think of that, Henry?

HENRY: Yes.

DR. A.: Did it frighten you?

HENRY: Yes.

DR. A.: (*After pause.*) You know, Henry, I don't think your parents understand you even now. You're a big mystery to your parents.

At this point, therapist shifts gear from the presenting symptom to a deeper problem, the emotional barrier between Henry and his parents.

MOTHER: I do understand him. Well, to a certain extent he is a mystery. He's entirely different from the other children. We'd like to help him.

At first, mother denies barrier, then admits that somehow Henry is different and she does not understand him.

DR. A.: Is it true, Henry, are you different?

HENRY: Yes. I like hunting and fishing. Father doesn't like it, can't go with me. I like cowboy pictures, like to listen to the late show.

Henry now is more open. He responds to the therapist's support by expressing his uniqueness, his difference from father. Through this difference, his urge to fish, hunt, and shoot, he loses his father. He leaves the living space of the family to find a father substitute outside.

DR. A.: You like hunting. Do you have a gun?

HENRY: Father won't let me.

DR. A.: What kind of gun do you want?

HENRY: A .22.

DR. A.: Did you speak to Pop?

HENRY: Yes. Maybe for one thing he thinks I can't go hunting, can't shoot it around the place, it's a weapon. (*Mother interrupts to explain parents' concern about a real weapon in the home.*)

DR. A.: How did you feel when Pop wouldn't let you have a gun?

Father refuses to allow son a gun.

HENRY: I felt bad. All my friends have guns.

DR. A.: For hunting, or other purposes?

Therapist here tosses in a teasing question. Does Henry need a gun against his father? Again, a gun for whom?

HENRY: They have guns on hand.

DR. A.: They're ever-ready. For what?

HENRY: They have target practice.

DR. A.: Have you been with them?

HENRY: I used to practice with a man who lives around my way. Mr. G. My parents know him. He has four guns. I haven't been going with him any more.

Mr. G. is the father substitute.

DR. A.: Why not?

HENRY: Winter's coming.

This is an all-too-patent rationalization.

DR. A.: I can barely hear you.

Here Henry chokes off the flow of his feeling. He talks under his breath, sucks his words back in. His friendship with Mr. G. (rejection of own father) arouses guilt and anxiety. He fears punishment.

MOTHER (*to Henry*): Talk a little louder.

DR. A.: I have a feeling you want me to hear you, but nobody else, not even your folks. Do you want to talk to me alone?

HENRY: I was saying something. I didn't go over to his house since June, or the middle of the summer.

The issue is: What may he do with a gun?

DR. A.: Why not? Why did you stop seeing him?

HENRY: I don't know, I just stopped one day.

MOTHER: The season for target shooting is over.

DR. A.: Henry must have given up hope of owning a gun.

Therapist interprets Henry's resignation to surrender of his weapon.

MOTHER: His father took him to the police station to inquire. He'd have to be sixteen to get a license, can't use a gun unless he's with an authorized adult. Mr. G. was the only one we knew to take him. He wanted to go to a conservation camp this summer, and we found out about it for him.

HENRY: We used to go shooting in a summer camp in Queens. There was a shooting club, but something happened to it. There are others, but they're too far. I just stopped.

DR. A.: You're fourteen now. Two years is a long time to wait to play with a gun.

Therapist alludes here in a veiled way to the symbolic equation with masturbation. Henry fears the dangers of "playing" with a "gun." It could be lethal.

HENRY: I don't play with it, I shoot it. It's not something to play with, it's a weapon.

DR. A.: Yes, it might kill someone. Your father is worried about that?

HENRY: No.

FATHER: Yes, I am. But I wanted him to have it if he wanted it so badly. But then we found out at the police station that he couldn't have it. He wanted me to buy it in my name. I could go to jail for that.

Father again takes possession of son, also responsibility for son's destructiveness.

DR. A.: If anybody goes to jail, you want him to go, not you.

Therapist challenges father to admit ambivalent feeling toward son. Does father really mean it? Would he take the punishment for son's aggression?

FATHER: (*Angry.*) No. (*Tries to explain.*)

HENRY: He's afraid I'd get caught. The law says you can't go on the streets with a gun, but I wouldn't go on the street, I would keep it safe in the house. I'd keep the barrel open, so even if a cop stopped me in the car, he couldn't do anything.

DR. A.: You want your father to have more faith in you, to believe that you wouldn't do anything with the gun to send him to jail.

HENRY: Yes. There can be an accident in everything.

DR. A.: So you have to be careful, can't play around with a gun. How does it stand? Are you supposed to get it when you're sixteen?

HENRY: I'm going to buy one for myself, so if anything happens my father can't blame me.

Henry wants to be relieved of guilt that he might injure his father (or self).

DR. A.: Are you saving up?

HENRY: I hope to save up in the near future.

DR. A.: So you want a gun that's all your own. (*To father*) How do you feel about it?

Therapist now challenges father. Would he allow his son a gun, permit him to be a man in his own right? The son craves to be his own man and not to carry a guilty responsibility for his father's fear of male destructiveness.

FATHER: If that's what he wants, I'll get it for him.

DR. A.: How do you feel about guns?

FATHER: I don't like them, and I don't even like going hunting. Accidents happen. But if he likes hunting, there's nothing I can do about it, if it's going to make him happy.

Father fears possessing a "gun" and again makes a hypocritical gesture of yielding to son.

DR. A. (*to mother*): How do you feel about it?

MOTHER: I feel the same about guns, but it is an outdoor sport, and Henry likes outdoor sports.

DR. A.: Your husband is afraid he might use it otherwise than for a sport.

MOTHER: No, it is a sport that Henry likes. He likes a lot of outdoor sports. My husband doesn't. He hates the outdoors. Hates fishing. Afraid of worms. He won't catch fish, though he'll eat them. (*This is a joke, and everyone laughs.*)

Here, mother sides with son against father. She ridicules father for his fear of worms.

FATHER: (*Smiling, Mr. N. speaks of a "silly incident." He had to go fishing as part of job relationships. He couldn't stand baiting his hook. Was repelled by skates. Caught fish, threw pole and fish back in water, and passed out [laughter]. He can't stand seeing a fish caught with a worm, and won't eat it if he sees it caught, etc.*)

DR. A.: So you fainted dead away. It's easy to knock you out.

Therapist confronts father with his fear of aggression, and his underlying feminine identification. Father is a castrated male.

FATHER: In all my life I never saw such an ugly thing as a worm.

MOTHER: That's why Henry feels so frustrated. There's no one to do the things he likes.

Mother again sides with son.

DR. A. (*to mother*): How about you, can you play with Henry?

Does she have a suppressed desire to play with him?

MOTHER: What do you mean, in what respect? In most respects, I can.

Mother plays dumb, like Henry, as if she doesn't grasp therapist's allusion.

DR. A.: What did you think I meant?

MOTHER: I didn't know what you meant.

DR. A.: What do you play?

Therapist challenges mother. She substitutes "culture" for love and sex. This is her typical intellectual defense. She denies her underlying yearning for an empathic intimacy with son.

MOTHER: Scrabble. We tried to satisfy his desire for good music by taking him to the opera. We've tried to take him places. Outside of hunting, fishing, skiing. Henry wants to ski. We tell him it's too expensive. He wants to rush things.

FATHER: I've taken him bowling in a group for men. Didn't tell his age. Last few weeks he's gone alone and bowled with the men. He only has to express a desire, and if it's humanly possible, we'll do it.

Father again usurps the first position with son.

DR. A. (*to Henry*): How are you at bowling?

HENRY: Pretty good.

DR. A.: Henry is a better bowler than Pop?

FATHER: That's true.

Father admits son "shoots" better than he.

DR. A.: So Henry is a boy who likes outdoor games and likes to do things with his body, not with his mind.

Son prefers brawn to brain, with one exception: chess. But chess is a symbolic killing.

HENRY: I like chess too.

MOTHER: Henry could play chess all day long, never do his homework.

HENRY: Yeah.

DR. A.: I'm like that too, could play all day. (*To father*) Do you play chess too?

FATHER: Yes.

DR. A.: Who wins?

FATHER: I used to win, but now Henry begins to.

Now, son is stronger in chess than father.

DR. A.: So chess is something you do with this. (*Taps head.*)

MOTHER: There are other games with the mind. Scrabble. And other games we play at home. Henry is part of the family.

Mother competitively asserts her position with son.

DR. A.: But you've said he's so different, hardly belongs to this family.

Therapist challenges her earlier assertion that son is so different, he hardly belongs.

MOTHER: He belongs, all right.

DR. A.: I don't think Henry feels he belongs. He feels different.

MOTHER: He is different.

DR. A.: How about it, Henry? Let's hear how he doesn't belong to this family.

HENRY: I like agriculture. My brother's in the country. I asked him to give me the name of game preserves, so I could write and see what it's like. He never answered me, I never found out.

Henry again speaks for self. He likes out-of-door activities that have to do with his body, not his brain.

DR. A.: Can you raise your voice? Do you ever yell, Henry?

Therapist points again to the way in which Henry chokes up his feeling.

HENRY: Yes, outdoors.

DR. A.: Can you yell now?

HENRY: I yell in the afternoon.

DR. A.: Why not in the morning?

HENRY: I have a hoarse voice. Have a frog.

A frog in the throat—a symbolic expression of what is caught in Henry's throat, the threat of father's punishment which paralyzes his feelings.

DR. A.: A sore throat?

HENRY: No.

DR. A.: What kind of a frog is it?

HENRY: You know, the kind with dots and dashes.

DR. A.: It comes and goes?

HENRY: Can't you feel it? It's okay now.

DR. A.: Can you cough up the frog?

Therapist encourages Henry. Can he free his own mouth? Can he cough up what is stuck in his throat?

HENRY: It's okay.

DR. A.: So you got no sympathy from your big brother, he brushed you off.

HENRY: When he comes to town, he goes straight to his girl friend's house, he doesn't even come home first. I asked him to go fishing, and he either took his girl friend along or went alone with her when she didn't want guys along.

Henry felt abandoned not only by his father, but also by his older brother.

DR. A.: You got the brush-off. Were you sore?

HENRY: Yes.

DR. A.: What do you do when you're angry?

HENRY: I didn't do anything. I went alone or with the man next door.

The only alternative is for Henry to separate himself from family and adopt substitute father outside.

DR. A.: That makes you a lone wolf.

HENRY: Yes, with fishing.

DR. A.: How about your other brother?

HENRY: He doesn't like the outdoors.

MOTHER: He gets sick in boats and was always the type of child to get nauseated in cars.

FATHER: (*Describes a time when brother tried to go fishing, came home so sick he just lay on the floor.*)

Older brother is just like father in this respect.

DR. A.: Fishing is murder for your family, for all except Henry.

Therapist speaks symbolically.

FATHER: Henry must have been born on a rocking boat.

HENRY: My father came from Austria, there's no sea there. I was born near the sea and I like it.

Now comes a comparison of father's and son's background, along with a history of the parents' marriage. Henry listens quietly.

(*Dr. A. asks about Austria, and father describes how he went swimming and boat riding, but that was fresh water. Dr. A. says Henry likes it salty, and father says then we'll give it to him salty. Focus turns to parents' background, during which discussion Henry is quiet. Father came to the United States in 1936, married in 1939. Mother also born in Austria, came to the United States at age of one and a half, but remembers the old country because she visited it twenty-six years ago, just before she married father. Her own father had just died; she wanted to see her sisters again. The following year mother's sisters came to this country because of the Nazis. This was last vacation the mother ever took. She got her divorce when she returned. She explains that her first marriage lasted eleven years; they weren't compatible. Her first husband was eighteen years older, not the same type as herself. It wasn't enough that he made a good living and that her parents liked him. She waited for the opportunity for divorce, and then when he proposed it, she took him up on it immediately. She met father soon after her return to this country. She was still living with her first husband; it was the week they decided to get a divorce. Father, at that time, had ringworm and was confined to Ellis Island, so she visited him every week, and was the only one there to comfort him. They went out for coffee and got acquainted during this period.)*

DR. A. (*to mother*): How did you feel when you first laid eyes on Father?

MOTHER: Thought he was terrible, so different.

Note the emphasis on difference.

FATHER: (*Smiling.*) Don't talk so much, there are witnesses here.

MOTHER: Then I got to see he was a very nice person, we had a lot in common. When my divorce came through, he asked me to marry him and I accepted.

DR. A.: Why terrible?

MOTHER: He was different.

Being "different" was an issue at the very birth of this family.

FATHER: I had been in this country for a short time, wanted to return to Austria. Found New York crowded and dirty. Walking through Brooklyn, they dropped garbage on the street. Then I no longer wanted to go back.

MOTHER: I changed his mind.

DR. A.: Henry is having fun now.

Henry is here peeking in on his parents' intimacy. Therapist interprets his curiosity.

HENRY: I'm listening back and forth.

DR. A.: Have you heard this story before?

HENRY: Sort of.

DR. A.: Does it interest you?

HENRY: They're married. Doesn't interest me. It's none of my business.

> Again, Henry makes a defensive denial of interest in his parents' "affair."

DR. A. (*to Henry*): Would you like to sit next to me and have the married couple sit together?

FATHER: It makes no difference to me.

DR. A.: I don't believe you. You'd rather keep Henry between you. Why?

> Therapist removes Henry as a barrier between the two parents.

FATHER: Honestly, the kids always chose to be near me, took my hand.

> Father claims position as the more tender of the parents. He was "mother," seductive to the children, while mother became the "boss."

DR. A.: That's the history of your family, the kiddies always come to you.

MOTHER: I was the disciplinarian.

DR. A.: The roughneck.

FATHER: The "general." I never interfered. I came home at night and played with the kids. My mother . . . I mean wife . . . was the disciplinarian. I was close to all of them.

> Father contemptuously calls mother the "general." Note also the slip of the tongue.

DR. A.: Henry wants to keep his nose out of your romance.

> Therapist interprets Henry's anxiety about peeking.

HENRY: They got married. I wasn't around, didn't have anything to say about it.

DR. A.: What would you say if you had been there?

FATHER: Say it, Henry.

MOTHER: He'd object to me. He feels I'm too old. It seems to bother him.

Mother competes. She is now seductive with Henry.

DR. A.: What was family situation when Henry was born?

MOTHER: I had Henry's older brother nine months and one day after we married.

DR. A.: You were in a hurry?

MOTHER: I wanted children, but I didn't think I'd conceive so quickly. Financially we could have waited.

DR. A.: Pop, were you surprised?

FATHER: I wanted a child, a little girl.

Father was closely identified with own mother. Wanted a baby girl.

MOTHER: He wanted one to name for his mother.

DR. A.: But you had one girl already. (*Pointing to mother.*)

MOTHER: She was too big.

Mother "too big," meaning too aggressive.

DR. A.: So you had two boys, and Henry. How did you feel to find Henry was a boy?

MOTHER: He looked like a girl, was a beauty. But I still wanted a girl.

Henry was meant to be a girl.

DR. A.: Now that you have a girl, what will you do with the "old lady"?

An example of a light touch of humor, echoed by father.

FATHER: I'll pension her.

DR. A.: How was the birth?

MOTHER: It was easy, took twenty minutes. I wasn't disappointed it was a boy, since I had one daughter of my own.

FATHER: We never mention this.

Father's attitude: It is taboo to mention mother's first marriage and stepdaughter.

DR. A.: Should we keep quiet about this in front of Henry?

FATHER: (*Hesitation.*) Yes. I wasn't disappointed, but I didn't believe I'd ever have a girl and when they told me I had a girl, I didn't believe them.

DR. A.: Could we talk again next week?

HENRY: Yeah.

DR. A. (*to Henry*): How do you feel?

HENRY: No different.

MOTHER: I was embarrassed at first, not now.

FATHER: I'm not embarrassed. I want to help Henry and will do anything that's necessary. (*Explains he might not be able to come next week because he may enter hospital for operation. Dr. A. comments that he suffers below and on top too. Mr. N. says he suffers most below. Social worker walks out with them, and once again father monopolizes her attention with explanations of his illness and dealings with hospital. Henry stays withdrawn and in background.*)

Father once again steals the show from Henry, referring to his poor, suffering body, his hemorrhoids and need of surgery.

Staff Summary Reports

Over the next eighteen months, this family was seen as a group about once a week, the two older sons being present occasionally during college vacations. Sometimes, of course, one or another family member could not attend because of illness (especially the father, because of his concern with his ailing body). In addition, the father and mother were seen without the children. Progress was made in closing the split created by their long-standing reversal of roles—the mother as the disciplinary general and the father as the softer, gentler figure. The mother was depressed as the result of being regarded by the whole family as strong, independent, and in no need of emotional support from her husband and children. She felt the father clung to the children to maintain his role. Eight months after the first session, the parents took a trip to Washington without the children. Significantly, they describe this as a "first honeymoon."

Henry gradually overcame his distrust of adults sufficiently to ask for individual therapy, as did his sister, Jane. The two younger children symbolized two opposite aspects of parental identity. Henry symbolized the longing for physical activities and pure bodily pleasure; Jane, the devotion to education, work, and duty. In a period of eight months the family had moved toward a recognition of this split. All the children are now doing well at school, including Henry. Henry also got an excellent character recommendation from one of his teachers.

Henry is no longer the misfit in a family concentrated on work and educational advancement. His father recognizes now how he identified Henry with his own father, a gambler and ne'er-do-well who left his family to starve. But even with his own pattern of martyred self-denial, Father was not unsympathetic toward his gambler father. He had, in fact, unwittingly cultivated in Henry the characteristics that had so disturbed him in his own father. He had made Henry into a gold digger by giving him presents and bribes and acting out the indulgence that he himself would have liked as a child.

From the daydreams of the entire family, it became apparent how deeply rooted was their resentment of their self-denial. Henry's fantasies of living in a lush, warm country with nothing required but to pick food from the luxuriant trees were typical of the entire group. He was not really the outsider, different and alien, as they had thought. Rather he was their spokesman in an important but neglected area of life. As such, he had been singled out and made the scapegoat. Only when the emotional balance of the family was restored could the family members move forward to a healthier way of living.

9

The Return to Reality

In its relation to family life, schizophrenia presents to the psychotherapist a unique challenge. The family approach offers, through the phenomenology of the illness itself, a special access to the dynamics of family life and a different context for examining the interconnections of mind, body, and society.

In the evolution of a theory of schizophrenia and the family, there is a curious paradox: on the one hand, the traditional bias for organicity continues; on the other hand, there is a progressively mounting interest in the role of social process, and more particularly in the significance of family interaction.

In exploring the potentials of family treatment of schizophrenia, we may begin with an obvious problem. It has been repeatedly conjectured that the neurotic person succeeds in establishing a love bond and an identity connection with at least one of his parents, whereas the schizophrenic fails to do so. It is somewhere within this conceptual scheme that Freud was moved to characterize schizophrenia as a narcissistic neurosis, one in which the capacity for transference is lacking. As subsequent studies have revealed, however, the issue is not nearly so clear-cut. Contemporary investigations suggest that the question of the capacity for an affective response in the schizophrenic cannot be dealt with in terms of *yes or no,* but rather in terms of *how much* and *in what qualitatively different way* the patient responds. In tracing the development of the schizophrenic, we must ask a series of questions. Did this person succeed originally in establishing an effective bond with parent and family? If so, was it attenuated in the later course of development? Was it distorted or destroyed?

In family treatment of schizophrenia, we are setting out to treat a set of relationships that in principle ought to be there, but that in fact may not now exist. We are launched, perhaps for the first time, on an effort to create anew what should have been there long ago.

In terms of the family approach, it is essential to make explicit the preferred theoretical orientation concerning the schizophrenic phenomenon and associated family disorders. Two alternatives are possible: (1) schizophrenia may be seen as a separate and distinct disorder of the individual organism; the family environment, seen as a peripheral factor, influences the course of illness, but mainly affects the secondary manifestations; or (2) the family environment may be viewed, not as external but rather as belonging to the very core of the illness process. According to the second view, ongoing relations of patient and family are of the very essence; they are relevant at every stage to the vulnerability of the premorbid personality, to the onset of overt psychosis, to its course and outcome. Family interaction thus affects primary as well as secondary manifestations. Given this theoretical scheme, heredity may lay down a degree of susceptibility, but it is the social and emotional influence of family life that translates a dormant weakness into an overt psychotic illness. The illness is then a symptom of the family warp, which can only be comprehensively understood across three or four generations. It seems to me that this latter perspective is the more promising.

Assuming the existence of multiple types of schizophrenia, there may well also be multiple types of associated family structure. A given type of family may contribute to a greater or lesser extent, in greater or lesser depth, or with more or less malignancy to the development of the schizophrenic disorder. Also, the relation of illness and family process may not lie with the totality of family functioning, but rather with selected components of family inter-action. Significant elements of difference may be discovered, for example, between those families who want to "take care of their own" and those who tend to exclude the schizophrenic member. In some families, there is a tendency to hang together while main-taining an attitude of devotion to the schizophrenic member. In other families, it appears clear that at a certain critical point in time the living connection of the patient and the family is irrevocably ruptured. The relatives seem to close ranks; they cease thereafter to make emotional room for the patient within the group; the family maintains a kind of unity by shutting the patient out. When a schizophrenic has abandoned the family, and the family and the community have abandoned him, it is most difficult to restore the connection.

Bearing in mind the present-day striving to keep schizophrenics in the "normal" community, rather than to allow them to go to seed in hospital wards for chronic cases, the need to identify the psychosocial characteristics of these family types becomes an urgent matter. We must discover ways of classifying them. Which of these types preserve a measure of unity and want to "take care of their own"? Which disintegrate and are no longer able to do so? Is there a difference in the relationship patterns, emotional climate, identity, and value orientation that affects the course and outcome of the illness? Such considerations are relevant to a first effort to prevent hospitalization, and to the later task of rehabilitation, following the patient's discharge from a hospital.

The family approach to the treatment of schizophrenia requires consideration on three levels: (1) the schizophrenic disorder; (2) the analogue of this pathology in the family group; and (3) the psychotherapy of the family group, focused on the unique features of the relation between the patient and the family.

Taking the unknowns fully into account, we may outline a tentative, schematic interpretation of the nature of the psychopathological process. For present purposes, we assume that the predisposition to schizophrenia emerges out of a matrix of deviant symbiotic union. From it comes a psychosomatic dysfunction that becomes manifested as a deviant pattern of biosocial development. Once initiated, the process becomes associated with a subtle biochemical alteration, not yet clearly identified. The premorbid condition may be analogized to a kind of marasmus, a special type of affective neoteny.

For the schizophrenic-to-be, the biological striving for an appropriate, full, and satisfying union with the mother is somewhere aborted and left incomplete. The infant can neither achieve union nor individuate in a biologically required way. The pathogenic quality of union gives rise to a pathogenic type of separation. The twin processes of union and separation become distorted by the perception of threat, reciprocally experienced between child and mother. In basic biosocial terms, the infant needs the mother as a lifesaver, but instead feels her as a potential life-destroyer. The mother appears to assume a receptive, protective, maternal position, but then wheels about treacherously, as if threatening a destructive invasion of the infant's psychic being and body. The infant is caught partly inside, partly outside the mother and is trapped and rooted to the spot. He can move neither toward nor away. The perception of threat freezes the infant's affect and movement; he is paralyzed in a condition of stasis, a fixed condition of biosocial immaturity. This condition becomes manifested in a critical disturbance of homeodynamic balance in his relations with his inner and outer environment—a failure of balanced interchange of warmth, food, energy, emotion, and information. The end result is a critical arrest, a stultification of movement, growth, and social learning.

The schizophrenic dies slowly at the mouth. He ceases to ask and to give. The intake stimulation of all his sense organs is reduced. He does not breathe or move on his own. His vital potential is choked off. He is in terror of accepting nourishment. He pretends to take it in, ruminates, toys with it in his mouth, but he is too suspicious and frightened to swallow and digest it. He spits it out instead. He apprehends treachery, though he does not clearly perceive its source. It is somewhere vaguely in the atmosphere, in the living space of his family relations. In a confused way, he feels the destructive threat as emanating both from his mother and from himself. Because of the hazy boundaries of self and mother, and the dread of devouring, incorporative impulses, he cuts off contact. In place of a genuine joining with the mother, he substitutes a magical coercive manipulation of her services, which he receives, if at all, only impersonally. He clings tenaciously to a fantasy of possessing magical, omnipotent powers of destruction. Whenever the "significant other" gets too close, he thrusts out a menacing threat to warn the other off. He shows an extraordinary dread of emotion, as if all emotion and bodily experience portend catastrophe. Although frightened by the dangers of closeness, he nevertheless craves bodily contact. He yearns to mold his body to that of the "significant other," as if thereby to experience a reassuring sense of being joined and thus deny his conviction of abandonment and aloneness. But a renewed sense of panic drives him away again.

The schizophrenic dies a lingering death. He is the ghost of a person. He is somatically in one piece but psychically fragmented. His inner experience clashes with the interpretation of experience offered by those about him. What he experiences subjectively is ignored, negated, or contradicted by others. Therefore, he suffers a critical lack of affirmation from his human environment. He is plagued by doubt. He cannot integrate emotion or build tolerance for anxiety. Thus his proneness to panic leads to disorganization and fragmentation of thought, and they in turn, in a vicious circle, intensify the tendency to panic and further impair the capacity for healing and growth. The result is a progressive failure to regulate emotion, to establish interpersonal joining and identification, and to achieve a sense of the wholeness of the self.

Relevant to the schizophrenic mechanisms are those ingredients of the family which prohibit or distort the capacity for affective union. In healthy families, true joining is a necessary condition of life and growth. In the families of schizophrenics, a true and full joining seems not to occur, except perhaps after a special type of dying, the dying of schizophrenic experience. In other words, in these families, a form of psychic dying seems to be a preconditioning of joining, but the quality of joining is different; it is an "as if" kind of joining; it is pseudo, partial, and compensatory.

In the relations of the schizophrenic-to-be with the mother figure, the apparent joining is a caricature, not a true joining. On the one hand, the mother loudly protests her selfless devotion to the offspring; on the other hand, she periodically forgets his very presence. In one way, she smothers and invades; in another, she erases his existence. Despite intense denial and compensatory overprotection, the relation is as if only one of the two can be sure of survival. The one stays alive only at the expense of the other. A deep-rooted mutual perception of forced sacrifice pervades the bond. It is all or none. If the offspring comes to life and is expressive, the mother seems emotionally to lie down and die. If the mother is strong and vocal, the child seems to fade out. To protect her own survival, the mother launches a disguised, prejudicial assault on the offspring; unable to muster an adequate defense, his psychic unity and growth are sacrificed. Eventually, when he becomes overtly psychotic, he turns the tables on the mother; he punishes her with an omnipotently destructive counterassault. In neurotic families, a different condition prevails; there is more give and take. The unconscious prohibition placed on the offspring in the two types of families is distinct, as we have said before. In neurotic families, the child *must not be different;* in psychotic families, the child *must not be.*

The mother projects the fantasy of catastrophic danger hanging over the head of the offspring. She assigns the source of this destructive force to some demonic agent outside. Being oversolicitous, she designs imagined threats to the patient's health. With this attitude as a rationalization, she invades the patient's psychic being and body. Often there is a prominence of forced feeding, wiping of the behind, rectal insertions, handling of the sexual parts, and other body manipulations. Hidden beneath the self-delegated, conscious role of lifesaver lies the need to govern every aspect of the patient's being, to prevent any effective initiative or free movement. The offspring is allowed no life of its own; she wipes it out. His effort to separate himself is felt as a threat to her own survival. Were she to permit movement in the offspring, it would be as if she must then die. Inherent in this behavior is the unspoken feeling, "If I drown, I take you with me." To assure her own survival, the mother chokes off the life breath of the offspring. He in turn plays her game. He echoes obediently the mother's image of self as an omnipotent lifesaver. He, too, must deny the covert assault, the invasion of his being. In such mother-child interaction, there is a critical failure of homeodynamic balance.

In order to restore this balance, some force must intervene from the outside to serve as an antidote. Conceivably, the needed reparative influence might be introduced by the father. But there is a peculiar schism between mother and father. The child is caught and trapped in the parental conflict. He worries profoundly lest the one destroy the other. As one patient put it, "If I'm in the middle, I'm squashed." So far as the vulnerable offspring is concerned, the father might provide the required antidote, but he generally fails in this role. He himself is detached. He hangs back. He waits for the mother to make the first move. If she does, it is often a camouflaged attack, but the father's primary concern is to protect himself. At all costs, he must preserve a smooth routine with the mother. While appearing to defend the offspring, he is really barricading his own position; he also forgets that the offspring exists. Thus he fails to inject the necessary antidote to the destructive symbiosis of mother and child, and is unable, therefore, to compensate for the loss of homeostatic balance in the mother-child pair. If and when the child protests and yet fails on his own part to mobilize a healing of the family disorder, he is then rendered susceptible to breakdown.

Except for intermittent episodes of violent eruption, a quality of affective deadness pervades the family of the schizophrenic. The interpersonal climate lacks vital quality. It is robotlike, routinized, and empty. Family interaction is ritualized, mechanized, and lacking in mobility. Everything stays the same; nothing ever changes. The joining and sharing are spurious; they are stereotyped and disembodied. The family atmosphere contains a disguised, shared prejudice against new life. Life is movement, emotion, bodily experience; it is action. The family of a schizophrenic permits a minimum of such vital movement; it is too dangerous. The only possible shift is toward a magical world of fantasy.

With this denial of life, what remains is an empty shell of presumed human relations. There is a pervasive trend of make-believe —make believe there is a genuine emotional bond, make believe there are loyalty and caring—but the family relationships are shadowy and ghostlike. Contact is static and hollow. The members mouth the right ideas but without feeling. They look at one another and yet they do not see. This not seeing is of the essence. The other person is an apparition. Thus family relations are dehumanized. The capacity to adapt to new experience, to learn and grow, is critically reduced.

Confronted with such a family, the psychotherapist must as a first step appraise the patient's affectivity, must check his emotional temperature, so to say. To what extent does the patient freeze or deaden his affectivity? Does he shrink away from or reach out for contact? With appropriate support, is he able to thaw out, to warm up? Does his psychic wound gape wide open, or does it appear merely as a break in the skin, which hides beneath it the deeper malignancy?

Turning to the family, the therapist must determine how far the emotional climate is pervaded by the shared dread of the impact of close touch, perceived as a foreboding of violence and catastrophe. Who in the family acts as persecutor? Who is being attacked and made the scapegoat? Who is driving whom crazy? Who acts as protector? Who personifies healing? What is the quality of healing? How fixed is the denial of these dangers? How far do the parents exhibit a ritual worry over the patient's welfare, as against a willingness to feel him as alive and warm? How far do they cloak their fright with gestures of righteous devotion and hypocritical self-sacrifice? Do the parents lean toward a "wrong" joining with the patient, one that moves backward or sideways rather than forward?

Family therapy of this condition is challenged to counteract such specific pathogenic trends as the following: (1) the family's perception of threat in the patient's urge to come alive, to grow, to get well; (2) the family's acting as if the patient possessed a malevolent destructive power; the fear of his explosive violence is profound (the consequence of projection); (3) the parents' sense of threat to their sanity when the patient asserts his magical power; (4) the parents' shared denial of the prevailing emotional realities; and (5) the parents' resistance to the patient's vital striving; their tendency to press him backward or sideways, or to foster a pathological rather than a healthy healing of his psychic wound.

The goals of family-focused therapy, therefore, are to neutralize the fear of destruction, to lessen the need for denial, to substitute progressive reality testing for magical thinking, to make way for the discovery that the impact of close touch raises rather than lowers the viability of the family as a whole and that only a true emotional joining assures the privilege of life and growth for all members of the group. The therapist must win the allegiance of the family, especially the parents, for a shared search for new and more human kinds of emotional intercourse. For the schizophrenic member, the therapist must truly be a lifesaver, a rescuer of the "living dead." He must reawaken the patient's trust, rekindle his interest in life, encourage him once more to eat, breathe, move, and grow. This the therapist can do only as he is able to ease the patient's fear of the malevolent destructive powers that he feels exist in and about him.

Because of the extreme complexity of the schizophrenic situation, it is instructive to look at a single case history in some detail, to illuminate these theoretical formulations and also to provide an adequate background for the therapeutic interview material that follows. This later interview reads like a "whodunit" story. Who in the family committed the crime of crippling the patient's mind?

The patient was a sixteen-year-old girl brought by her parents for a psychiatric consultation because her mental condition seemed to be deteriorating. The parents were alarmed. For three years, the patient had been undergoing psychotherapy in another clinic, with the assumption that she was suffering from a psychoneurosis. Neither this nor any other diagnosis was shared with the parents; they were befogged as to the true nature of the patient's illness and falteringly tried to deny its seriousness. They preferred to view the patient as a child with a "vivid imagination."

The patient was withdrawn, had no associations with her peers, and refused to attend school. At home, she alternated between periods of barricading herself in her room and engaging in belligerent quarrels with her parents and, more particularly, with her grandmother. She made recurrent threats of suicide and exhibited an odd array of schizophrenic mannerisms—a bizarre cough, twirling her hair, averting her gaze, and making twisting, writhing gestures with her hands and body. At times, she used awkward, pretentious phrases that verged on neologisms.

Overt signs of illness had appeared at the age of eleven, against a background of lifelong shyness and withdrawal. The patient was born while her father was overseas in military service; he met her for the first time when she was three. On his return home from the war, he was in poor condition physically and mentally. He suffered from a long, debilitating infection, was malnourished, depressed, and irritable. At home, he was accused by his wife and mother-in-law of being overdemanding and of monopolizing his wife's attention, while, at the same time, being critical and irritably rejecting toward the child. When, in later years, the mother and grandmother joined in blaming him for causing the child's mental breakdown, he took sides with the women against himself. He assumed the total burden of guilt and hung his head in shame; he fully believed that he had inflicted severe damage on the child.

But this was not the true story. The women had made a scapegoat of the father. Clinical study revealed that the child had already suffered serious emotional trauma before the father's return from the war. In these first three years while the father was away, the grandmother had governed the family. The mother and the grandmother were tightly bound in a dependent, ambivalent relationship. The grandmother was sharply critical of the mother's care of the baby. Although resenting the grandmother's carping attack, the mother was unable to fight back. The grandmother accused the mother of neglecting the child, of total ineptness in failing to control the baby's crying. The grandmother charged that the noise disturbed the grandfather's sleep. The grandmother nagged the mother to take the child out in the fresh air and sunshine, on the score that the air of the home was close and foul. In a rationalized, obsessional way, the grandmother pushed the baby out of the home. Though resentful, the mother complied with this coercive pressure. She was split between the need to care for the baby and the need to appease the grandmother. Nonetheless, the tight alliance between the two women continued. They joined in isolating and making a scapegoat of the father. They set father against daughter, daughter against father. They fortified in the child a barrier of suspicion and fright against the one male member of the family.

Examination of the patient revealed active hallucinatory experiences. She maintained regular communication with a planet in space called Queendom; she did so by sending and receiving something akin to radar waves. More of this material is discussed later.

The presenting situation was critical. A prompt decision had to be reached on whether hospital care was necessary, because of the danger of violence or suicide. Following close study, by means of filmed family interviews, a tentative decision was made to assume a calculated risk in keeping the patient within her own home and undertaking psychotherapy of the whole family.

The living unit consisted of the two parents, the maternal grandmother, and the patient, an only child. The grandmother, in her mid-sixties, had been widowed six months earlier. The father was forty-seven years old, the mother forty-five. The parents had been married for twenty years. The father earned a salary of about $12,000 a year; the grandmother contributed $60 a week. Both parents were college graduates, native-born, and Jewish (although the father was avidly atheistic).

The parents were drawn to one another out of their mutual dependent need and their shared ideals of family closeness, loyalty, security, and intellectual striving. In their respective families of origin, they had certain insecurities in common. The father came from a broken family. The paternal grandfather died in the father's early childhood; the paternal grandmother, domineering and long-suffering, was oversolicitous and intrusive. The father's main defenses were repression of aggression, obsessive obedience, and emotional detachment. The mother identified closely with her own domineering mother, whereas she viewed her father as temperamental, ineffectual, and yet someone to be feared.

The father is a tall, handsome, distinguished-looking man. He is a rigid, obsessive, perfectionistic person, with profound feelings of inferiority. He gives the impression of a frightened, guilty, self-doubting boy, rather than a man. He is inclined to be ingratiating and apologetic. He is almost womanish in demeanor. He talks in quick spurts or does not talk at all. He is fearful of his emotions and dresses up his thoughts in pretentious intellectual phrases. He withdraws into scholastic pursuits. Nevertheless, he projects a certain childlike appeal and reaches out frantically for approval and support.

The mother is an attractive woman, but has a bland, vapid, expressionless face. It is difficult to find in her any trace of animation. In a shallow sense, she is an obsessively good person, self-righteous, judgmental, and full of clichés about right and wrong. She shows little spontaneity. She is given to periodic hysterical outbursts and also suffers from migraine. Now and then she bursts into high-pitched, eerie laughter.

The grandmother is a rigid type, a severely dogmatic and aggressive person. She is never wrong and has an immediate answer for every problem. Beneath her hypocritical, self-righteous protests, she is contemptuous of everyone. If she does not get her way, she sulks and makes intimidating threats. She has intruded herself as the mother's mouthpiece, harassing the father and driving him into an isolated position. Both the grandmother and the mother have the urge to talk for the father and also for the daughter. A fragment of symbiosis characterizes the relationship of the mother and the grandmother. Trying in a futile way to appease the woman's fear of masculine aggression, the father has shrunk from the expression of his male powers.

The patient is an appealing teen-ager who looks pathetically disorganized and lost. She alternates between panic and explosive, defiant aggression. Her native intelligence, imagination, and perceptiveness show clearly through the curtain of her disturbance. At times, her verbal expressions are exquisitely sensitive, almost poetic. Mainly, she is in despair; now and then, she lashes out in desperation and again withdraws.

On the surface, these parents gave lip service to their close partnership, but had not achieved a satisfying marital union; it was, instead, a parent-child relationship. The father feared the invasive powers of a woman; the mother was suspicious and fearful of male aggression. An undercurrent of competitiveness and hostility had aborted the establishment of a firm emotional bond. The parents seemed tacitly to collaborate in minimizing the importance of the sexual aspect of their union. The arrival of the child seemed to shatter the tenuous balance of family relationships. She was an intruder and had to be expelled. When she tried frantically to prove that she existed, that she should be given a place, the result was further disruption of the family group. Her only alternatives were withdrawal into a psychotic world or suicide. It is against this background that the grandmother insisted that the patient must go to a boarding school. This move would presumably force her to make friends among her peers.

Casually viewed, this family might appear to be well integrated, except for the one severely disturbed girl, but this appearance is deceiving. On deeper examination, it is apparent that this is a profoundly disorganized and split group. In emotional terms, it is a paralyzed family, ridden with guilt and anxiety. The members are severely alienated; they live in constant dread of the uncontrolled eruption of violence and destruction. In their inner life, there is severe prejudice and scapegoating. The one nale member of the family is viewed either as a monster or as a helpless boy; the one daughter is treated as a dangerous, disruptive intruder. Both are sentenced by the older women to punishment and exile. On the part of the daughter and the father, there is a barely discernible yearning to get together in a protective alliance against the older women, but this effort hardly gets off the ground. All three adults unite in making a scapegoat of the sick child. They perceive her as a disruptive, dangerous force and act as if she must be either controlled or eliminated in order for the family to survive.

The family has been in a state of constant turmoil; the members are bewildered and acutely frightened of recurrent crises. The group is emotionally fragmented. The one man in the family, blamed and made a scapegoat, has moved into a position of emotional exile. Hurt, humiliated, and frightened, he has withdrawn. He hates the grandmother, but has felt powerless to struggle against the hostile alliance of the women. He behaves as though brainwashed by them.

The patient has also felt excluded. Although in a sly, covert way she showed an interest in her father, she mainly avoided him, as he avoided her. Mutually, they shunned direct gaze; they feared to touch one another. The father sensed an erotic element in his daughter's interest, shrank from it as taboo, and feared violence.

A deep rift has grown up between the patient and both parents. When the patient now and then made an abortive thrust to reach out to them, she was rebuffed. She argued with her mother, but her rage was directed mainly against her grandmother. She resisted parental authority, isolated herself in her room, and threatened violence if they invaded her privacy.

Between the father and the grandmother, there is a smoldering conflict. When he originally failed to oust the grandmother from the family, he gave up. But his grudging resentment has persisted. Behind his back, the grandmother has engaged in an underhanded campaign to tear down his character. At present the relationship between the father and the grandmother is civil, but they hardly communicate. It is a cold war.

The mother, a bland, self-righteous person, slips out from between the father and the grandmother, as if unconsciously waiting for them to destroy one another. In daily relations with the patient, the adult members of the group are confused, disorganized, and defeated, yet they try to control her by means of threats and bribes.

At the conscious level, the mother and father aspire to join in the ideal of a warm, close, loyal family unit. This aim is complete fiction, however. In actuality, there is constant fear of the outbreak of open warfare. But the fiction persists, since the adult members

see themselves as harmonious, peace-loving people. There is, therefore, a sharp, glaring contradiction between the ideal of family
closeness and the actual condition, which is one of profound alienation in family relationships. The emotional climate in the home is
static, half-dead; the mood is that of resigned apathy. The members
of the group feel trapped. The functions of the family are carried
out in a routine, constricted way; the family members have little
contact with the wider community.

Nominally, the father is the head of the family. There is some
pretense of mutuality in decision making, but in fact this responsibility devolves on the mother, and behind her lurks the governing
power of the grandmother. In a showdown, the mother and father
largely abdicate authority and submit grudgingly to the grandmother's control. In the longitudinal view, it is as if the father,
the only male in the family, had been felt as an intrusive threat and
had been punished and driven into exile. Afterward, the only
daughter suffered the same fate. As a family, they are an economic
unit, but they do not hold together either emotionally or socially.
The sexual adjustment of the parents is at a low ebb; child care is
disorganized. The family, as a family, seems to move backward,
rather than forward; the relationships are severely constricted and
lacking in vitality. The emotional atmosphere is pervaded by an
attitude of fear and avoidance of life; the growth potential of the
family group is almost nil.

At the outset, the effort to treat patient and family together
proved extremely difficult. The family was confused and fragmented. The grandmother campaigned forcefully for her plan to
place the patient in boarding school. The patient herself requested
individual therapy, in complete isolation from her family. For the
first four months, the planned procedure of family interviews was
obstructed by the split condition of the group. Feeling thwarted, the
grandmother aggressively sabotaged the whole proceeding. She
competed with the therapist's influence. She opposed his goal of
treating all of them together. This conflict moved rapidly to climax.

In this first phase the patient and her family were seen together
and also separately. Generally, the patient was interviewed first;
then her family. In the beginning, the grandmother came with the
parents, but soon she balked altogether. The early interviews with
the parents were monotonous. They showed their bewilderment,

fright, and guilt, as well as their deep resentment of the child's behavior. Because of their persistent panic, they continued to deny
the severity of the patient's illness. They wrote off her hallucinatory experiences as a case of "vivid imagination." The father
minimized her illness by claiming that, like himself, his daughter
was interested in science fiction. The therapist challenged this view;
he categorically asserted the position that the patient was mentally
ill.

When they were finally forced to admit the girl's psychosis, the
parents came into open conflict with one another. The father displayed a more genuine concern for the child's welfare, whereas
the mother accused him again and again of rejecting the child.
According to both mother and grandmother, the father rigidly
maintained high standards and expectations, especially along intellectual lines. The father was berated for failing to relate to the
child, except in terms of scholastic interests. He submitted to this
mortification. He became depressed. But as the therapist gave him
increased support by firmly disagreeing that the father was the sole
cause of the patient's illness, he felt greatly relieved, his depression
lifted, and he thanked the therapist volubly.

In the ensuing sessions, the father took a stronger stand against
the grandmother's noisy criticisms of the patient. It is noteworthy
here, however, that the father, now more openly opposed to the
grandmother's aggressiveness, was not directly assertive with his
wife. It was evident that he was trying to divide the mother and
grandmother, to free his wife from the grandmother's domination,
and to get her for himself once again. In essence, he was reviving
his original unsuccessful attempt to join with his wife and eliminate
the grandmother from the home.

At about this time, the conflict between the grandmother and the
therapist came to a boil. Talking to her was like conversing with
a stone wall. The therapist forthrightly expressed his anger to her.
The grandmother then withdrew completely from the family sessions. The parents were now driven into a corner and forced to
choose between the grandmother and the daughter. It was either
one or the other. The therapist pointed out how the grandmother
monopolized relations with the mother and competed with the
patient. In effect, the grandmother was denying the mother to the
sick child. In the choice between the grandmother and the daughter,

the father sided with the therapist. He became outspoken in his desire to separate his family from the grandmother. By contrast, the mother showed conflict and indecision. But increasingly she began to ventilate her anger against the grandmother. Finally, the therapist reached agreement with both parents to "place Grandmother in boarding school," so to speak, rather than the patient. The grandmother was moved to the home of a relative, and thereafter family therapy moved forward.

Up to this point, for the most part, the patient had been seen alone. In the office, she paced up and down agitatedly. She had made several suicide attempts by swallowing small metallic objects, and she explained that her recurrent cough was an attempt to expel them. It was observed, however, that she coughed regularly whenever she darted a glance at her father or at the male therapist. At moments of high tension, when she was in acute conflict over the danger of closeness with her father or with the male therapist, she declared that if she only had the guts, she would jump out of the window.

Bit by bit, she revealed the nature of her psychotic experience. She spoke of hearing voices from another planet, Queendom. The inhabitants of this planet lured her to join them. The governing lady in Queendom, "Zena," provided her with a special communication screen called a "Zena-scope." By this means, messages were exchanged back and forth between the beings in Queendom and the patient on earth. By concentrating on this Zena-scope screen, she embarked on a mental voyage and became absorbed in hallucinatory exchanges with Zena.

In Queendom, the beings are of another species. They are not human; they are like machines. On this planet, no males are allowed; they are all feminine, "not female, but feminine." These creatures are gorgeous beings. They have the most exotic coloring of skin and hair. They have hormones, not for sex, but to make them attractive. On this planet, there is no reproduction by sexual union, but only by fission. The beings in Queendom live in solar time, not earthly time. There is no night or day. The inhabitants live perhaps 150 years. They are capable of sleeping for long periods; they hibernate. They are completely self-sufficient and experience no fatigue. They have the power of clairvoyance. Everything on this planet is factory-made by chemical means. Nutrition is neither personal nor human. The source of food is not Mother Earth, but rather the factory where all foodstuffs are chemically produced. On this planet, in outer space, there is no hate, no war, no killing, but also no love. The inhabitants devote themselves to the cultivation of the arts—music, literature, and painting. It is a culture of mind over body. Finally, in this universe, there is magical control. There is none of the hate and danger of the earthly way of life. Yet, some beings in this planet are afflicted with a mysterious disease, which progressively rots the body, whereas the spirit remains immortal.

On several occasions, the patient appeared for her session wearing a rubber mask depicting a horribly deformed, diseased person. She stared into a medical book in which there was a photograph of a patient afflicted with ugly, festering, mutilating sores. By implication, this was her fantasy image of her own deteriorating illness. She explained her urge to be rid of her body. The physical part of her being was an intolerable burden. Continually, it had to be fed, nursed, and cared for; she wanted only to preserve and enhance her spirit. She sought to eliminate her body and to glorify her mind. She was in profound conflict over her bodily needs, especially her sexual urges. She confided a disturbing encounter with a young man, a waiter at a summer hotel. In a strange way she had suddenly found herself alone with him; he took her on his lap and kissed her. She described this young man as a "wolf." He was not even Caucasian; he was "like a Formosan monster." When he kissed her, it was as if she felt abruptly transformed from a little girl to a woman. It was a shocking experience. She became panicky and escaped as quickly as she could.

In a peculiar, paradoxical way, despite her fears of sex and men, she showed flurries of intense interest in both her father and the male therapist. In one family session, she dramatized the conflict of allegiance between her psychotic community in Queendom and her real earthly family. She remarked with high animation how perhaps she had made a mistake. She had allowed Zena and the beings in Queendom to talk her into their way of life, where no males were allowed. Maybe she was too obedient. She should have resisted more strongly. She felt tempted to conspire to take a male or two up to Queendom, "just to show them what the male species is like." The male or two were, of course, the father and the male therapist.

Since no males were permitted in Queendom, she would have to smuggle them in. But then, "They could only stay a few minutes." She would "keep a sharp eye on them." They would have to behave, or "right down to earth they would go."

In the second phase of treatment, family interviews were begun, but the patient was also seen individually. At first, she sat as far as possible from her parents. She was hesitant, unsure, and frightened. Frequently, as her sense of threat mounted, especially in relation to her apprehension of open hostility, she made a gesture of leaving the room. Each time she did so, the therapist persuaded her to stay. In her mind, he had become her "defender."

After several weeks, the patient began to touch and even gently to kiss the therapist on the cheek in her parents' presence. The therapist verbalized his wonder that she exhibited this kind of affection toward him, but not toward her parents. The father remarked that when he tried to approach her, he was generally met with a belligerent, hostile attitude. When he tried to enter her room, she shut the door in his face and threatened him with a stick. The mother regularly intruded with comments that reinforced the patient's fear of her father. She alluded repeatedly to the father's rigid, exacting standards and his rejection of his daughter. It gradually became clear, however, that the main source of hostility toward the patient was the mother rather than the father. When the father was critical, he seemed to be acting on cue from the mother. It was the mother who tended to reinforce the barrier between the daughter and the father.

One incident, in particular, stands out sharply as an example of this trend. The patient brought home from school a failing mark in one of her subjects. Her mother warned her against revealing it to her father. In a family interview, however, the therapist, with the patient's permission, brought this failing mark to the father's attention, whereupon he reacted not with disappointment and criticism, but rather with an expression of genuine concern for the way in which the patient felt about this failure.

As these sessions proceeded, one could observe a shift in the alignment of family relationships. The patient's hostility toward her father gradually diminished; she became perceptively sharper in her attacks on her mother. She alternated these attacks, however, with some recognition, half-apologetic, that perhaps her mother could not really be blamed, because she was so dominated by the grandmother. By stages, the patient expressed her anger toward her grandmother with increasing directness and force. On those occasions when the grandmother visited the family, the patient would say to her, "What do you want here?" "Go home." "We don't want you again." But she did more than this—she appealed to the mother to wean herself from the grandmother.

When the therapist called attention to the father's basic sympathy with the patient's resentment of the grandmother, the father expressed the feeling that after all, "My daughter is fighting my own battle." He referred here, once again, to his original futile struggle to separate the mother and the grandmother.

After about a year of therapy, a further shift was observed. The patient reached out more actively toward her father. She mussed his hair and kissed his hand. The therapist called attention to the exaggerated and overintense way in which the patient expressed her urge to be close to her father. He asked her if she was devouring her father rather than kissing him. At the same time, he referred to the father's fear of these aggressive approaches, his fear of any open dealing with sex, and his consequent shrinking away from contact. The father voiced his fright by telling his daughter to find a boy of her own. The therapist dealt with this fear by interpreting that a daughter might also touch her father, that this was a different touch and need not be the same as the sexual touch of a wife. Inevitably, this interpretation led to extended discussion of father's lifelong fear of women, his relations with his own overpossessive mother, and his submissiveness to the mother and mother-in-law.

Returning to the incident with the "Formosan" waiter, it is noteworthy that the patient talked freely of this with the therapist, but told her parents nothing. In her family, she felt that sex was not allowed; it was absolutely taboo. In her earlier years, when she directed any question about sex to her parents, she was given the brush-off. The parents seemed embarrassed and evaded the issue. She could not get a straight answer from her parents about sex. Instead, she was told to return to her studies or practice on her piano. For example, she once asked her father how it felt to go on a date. Her father bypassed the question with a wisecrack; he quipped that a date is a piece of fruit and gets squashed. The patient ceased to ask about sex.

Another aspect of this same problem was reflected in the patient's feeling about being an only child. Whenever she inquired about sisters and brothers, her parents evaded the whole question. Being an only child meant to her not only a lonely life, without companionship, but a proof that her parents disapproved of sexual activity. In fact, they rarely indulged. Whenever the therapist alluded to the patient's urgent curiosity regarding sex, she showed agitation and abruptly tried to cut off the conversation. On one occasion, she came to the session armed with a hammer. She towered over the therapist with the hammer, threatening to strike him if he persisted in talking of this taboo subject. The therapist had the conviction that she brought the hammer to intimidate him, but would not really use the weapon. She was easily persuaded to put the hammer down as soon as the conversation moved to her fright. The therapist quietly countered her denial of sex with the remark that he is very much interested in sex. He cannot help it. God made him that way. Gradually, she relaxed and became less belligerent. She diluted her tension in this area by intellectualizing the whole subject. For example, on one occasion, she delivered an oration on the role of genes in the human species.

Later, she came with a dream. In her dream, there was a considerable variety of nude pictures on the office wall and a wild orgy was in progress. As the patient entered, the male therapist threw empty beer cans at her. While talking of this dream, the patient produced a deck of cards decorated with nude women. She pleaded with the therapist not to mention these cards to her parents; they would be horrified. Still later, she shared with the therapist a story she was writing in which a student nurse fell in love with a young intern. She spoke of planning a holiday—a real celebration. She would one day bring a bottle of champagne and she and the therapist would "have a ball."

Consistently, however, her admission of sexual interest was coupled with the threat of aggression. In one such instance, the patient took the therapist's hand and dug her fingers into his palm. The therapist said to her that he wasn't sure whether her desire was to touch him or to scratch him. He pointed out that although she wanted to come closer to him, she was frightened of impulses emanating from herself and from him. The patient admitted that although she was terrified, she also felt increasingly safer with him, because he was in no way critical of her. The therapist indicated that they might talk freely of these urges, but need not act upon them. Each time she enacted one of these scenes with the therapist, she referred back to her difficulties with her father. She expressed her conviction that her father was as frightened of sex as she was. She reacted vituperatively "against this man." The therapist countered the patient's denial of wanting to have anything to do with her father by calling her attention to their common interests and their resemblance to one another. She imitated his use of big words, his interest in biology, and his use of medical terms. Gradually, her denials weakened and she admitted her desire to reach out to her father.

In the family sessions, typical patterns of family interaction prevailed. They were re-enacted over and over and thus were entirely predictable. As the family members took their places in the interviewing room, the daughter sat at one end, the father at the opposite end. Between them sat the mother and the grandmother. Later, when the grandmother removed herself, it was the mother who kept the daughter and the father apart. Sometimes the daughter selected the seat next to the therapist; she felt safer in this position, since he was her "defender." As the sequence of interaction clearly revealed, however, the mother and the grandmother not only intruded their physical beings between the daughter and the father, but also their thoughts and words. Whenever it seemed that the daughter and the father might dissolve the wall between them through more direct interchange of feeling, the mother or the grandmother or both intervened to block it. Each time they reinforced the barrier by reminding the daughter of her fear of men and the father of his rejection of his daughter. For example, when the father showed interest in joining his daughter in "Queendom" by way of a "special passport," the mother promptly reinforced the taboo against men. She instantly suggested that it might upset the daughter, that "Queendom" would no longer be as she preferred it, with "no men allowed."

The therapist assumed an active role in counteracting the alliance of the two older women in barring every semblance of personal communication between the daughter and the father. He undertook to put to the test of reality the daughter's and the father's shared sense of catastrophic danger in any closeness between them. In this situation, the daughter displayed a characteristic ambivalence. She alternated between two extremes—a sudden spurt of reaching out to her father, followed by an anxious retreat, often reinforced by the gesture of walking out of the room. The father, in turn, showed a reciprocal quality of ambivalent conflict. He, too, revealed a flicker of interest, followed by anxious withdrawal. In his fright, he was all too willing for the therapist to take the lead for him in making contact with the daughter.

The therapist intervened on this barrier in a special way. At an opportune moment, he suggested a rearrangement of places, so that the daughter and the father sat next to one another. He invited them to look squarely into one another's faces and express their feelings. He particularly challenged the father to come out of hiding, to show himself as a man and express directly his warmth for his daughter.

Time and again, one or the other of the women intruded to cut the contact. At first, the mother sat back and allowed the grandmother to intervene. Later, when the grandmother was no longer there, the mother took over the role of keeping the daughter and the father apart. When the therapist interpreted the invasive quality of the grandmother's interferences, the mother came to the grandmother's defense (and her own), offering righteous justifications of these actions. The therapist countered these interferences with increasing vigor. He told the women that, whereas the daughter and the father might be willing for the mother and the grandmother to talk for them, he was unwilling. The daughter and the father stole furtive glances at one another, testing the dangers of contact. As they did so, the mother and the grandmother persistently interfered. Finally, the therapist requested that they keep quiet, so that the daughter and the father might proceed to get acquainted. Despite the shyness and chary fright of both the daughter and the father, some progress was made.

At a later stage, the daughter stirred the mother to admit that the grandmother was a "virago," which the daughter translated to mean "an old battle-ax." She then projected a gentle appeal to the mother to wean herself from the grandmother and to take this first opportunity to become a full-time mother in her own right. By degrees, the mother and father joined in a better way in their mutual concern for their daughter. The father supported the mother in emphasizing her difference from the grandmother and her good intentions toward the daughter.

With the shift came the opportunity for the therapist to support the daughter in reality-testing her fantasy equation of sex and violence. He encouraged her to ask her parents more directly whether sex was allowed in this family. To this blunt question, both the mother and the father reacted evasively, "I hope so." Later, the father was more firm and answered "definitely, yes." At this point, the daughter projected a deep emotional appeal to her father to admit that he was human, real flesh and blood. She challenged his remoteness, his tendency to act like an impersonal robot with her. Her craving for a show of warm, personal interest from him comes through strongly in the following verbatim record of the family's fourth interview with Dr. A.

Verbatim Record	Interpretive Comment
Father (Henry), Mother (Leah), and daughter (Flora) enter room and say, "Good morning" to Dr. A.	
DR. A.: Henry, how about sitting over here now?	
MR. C.: Over here now? I thought you wanted me to sit next to Flora.	Father shows his fixity and resistance to change, a stickiness about the family "routine."
FLORA: I know that's what . . .	
MR. C.: (*Interrupting Flora.*) Why, why have we changed the routine, Dr. A.?	
DR. A.: Well, we might, we might shift it around. It's not a routine, actually. Good morning, Flora, Leah. Suppose we shift. Flora over there, and you over here, Henry, for a moment. (*Places Flora between Leah and Henry.*)	

FLORA: Acting out . . . uh, re-enacting the scene of the crime.

Flora perceives empathically the therapist's expectation.

MRS. C.: (*Incredulous laugh.*) Re-enacting the scene of the crime!

DR. A.: Who's the criminal around here?

Therapist tosses out a blunt challenge.

(*Mrs. C. laughs nervously, and Mr. C. sighs.*)

DR. A.: You see, it's like it hit Mother's funnybone, but I don't think that's funny.

Therapist reacts to mother's eerie, cruel laughter.

MRS. C. (*to Flora*): I thought you meant that as a joke.

FLORA: No, that certainly was not a joke.

Flora and therapist on the same side—this is serious.

MRS. C.: If I thought there were a criminal around here, believe me, I wouldn't laugh. (*Laughs nervously.*) I'd be very serious.

DR. A.: I think that there is somehow . . . Henry, see if you agree with me . . . some undercurrent of feeling in everybody in this family that somewhere a crime has been done. Hm?

Thus begins a "whodunit" story.

FLORA: Are we . . .

DR. A.: Has a crime been done?

FLORA: I wanted to know. Are we, are we up on display now?

Refers to staff observing behind one-way mirror and the filming of the interview.

DR. A.: Yes. That bothers you?

FLORA: Somewhat.

DR. A.: You've been on display every time we've gotten together here.

FLORA: (*Murmurs inaudibly.*)

DR. A.: It makes you nervous?

FLORA: Somewhat.

Flora feels exposed, naked. She fears the realness of the "crime" repeated before the camera.

DR. A.: Would you be less nervous if we were alone, without the camera?

FLORA: Without the camera?

DR. A.: Mmhmm.

FLORA: I think so, yes.

DR. A.: Mmhmm. (*Understandingly*.) Well, I'll bear that in mind. I understand that. But can we get back to this feeling, a sort of submerged feeling, shared by the three of you, that somehow a crime has been done in this family?

MR. C.: May I answer the question, or did you want Flora to answer it?

DR. A.: It's a free country, Henry.

MR. C.: Well . . .

FLORA: (*Interrupts by muttering*.) A free country . . .

DR. A.: Hm, what?

FLORA: It's a free country, but the prices indicate differently.

Therapist turns to the mystery of the family crime.

Flora injects a touch of her special brand of humor, reflecting an extraordinary quality of psychotic insight. The price of her belongingness in this family was critically inflated; her whole life was at stake.

DR. A.: Mm. You don't have much faith in that idea that you can be free in this life.

FLORA: Yes.

DR. A.: You haven't felt alive and free in your own family at all.

This is the crucial issue.

FLORA: No.

DR. A.: Mm.

MR. C.: All right, let me tell you how I feel about it.

DR. A.: Sure.

MR. C.: One good result, one of the good results that we've had so far, is that I've lost all my feelings of guilt. I don't feel guilty any more. So as far as I'm concerned, I feel no crime has

Father now takes a changed view.

been committed. So that, you might say, is on the plus side.

DR. A.: You feel you've been liberated.

Now, father is quick to deny that he did the killing. Earlier, he assumed total guilt for the crime.

MR. C.: I've been liberated.

DR. A.: So the treatment of this family has done an awful lot for you, hasn't it?

MR. C.: In that respect it certainly has.

DR. A.: Mm.

MR. C.: I don't feel guilty any more.

DR. A. (*to Mrs. C.*): How about you?

MRS. C.: (*Deep sigh.*) I'm confused, I'm very confused. I don't know how much these things are environmental. I don't know, I don't know whether the personality that a person forms is involved in this thing. I don't know whether the parents have played a part in it. I'm confused, and the more I read about it, and the more I live with it, the more confused I become.

Mother throws up a projective smokescreen to obscure the issue. She makes a gesture of innocence. She prefers through innuendo to toss the blame back to daughter. Yet some part of her confusion is genuine. The killing is somewhere vaguely in the family atmosphere.

DR. A.: Mm.

MRS. C.: I can't, I don't feel that . . .

DR. A.: (*Interrupts.*) In other words, you are saying, if there's been a crime, whoever did it, it must involve Flora. Is that the crime you had in mind?

MRS. C.: I don't say, I'm not saying it's a crime. I'm saying if we had anything to do with it, then naturally I would feel, I would feel guilt. I don't like to feel that I've caused so much unhappiness in any way. That's why I would feel guilt. That's why I would feel it's a crime. If unhappiness has been caused, and there certainly has been, then the guilt is somewhere and I don't know where.

Such remarks as these are typical of the mother's perplexity. She lowers her cloud of confusion over the whole family.

DR. A.: Mm.

MRS. C.: I'd say this. I say that the way (*sighs*) . . . the philosophy of this particular type of psychotherapy is all cockeyed. This is my own feeling.

Mother turns more honest, shows real anger.

DR. A.: Hear, hear!

MR. C.: Right, and I'll tell you why.

DR. A.: Glad to have you say. What's cockeyed?

MR. C.: Here's what's cockeyed. The family bond is one factor, important as it may be, in a person's psychological growth. But I still say that it may turn out to be, a hundred years from now, a very minor factor. Because I'm becoming more and more convinced that other factors are more important, or as important as the family environment. Now . . .

Father supports mother's angry protest against therapist.

DR. A.: (*Interrupts.*) You're backing up Mama now.

Therapist makes clear father's alignment with mother against himself. Now that grandmother is out of the home, he makes the therapist the object of his attack.

MR. C.: Well, she . . .

DR. A.: Mama says she's confused, she is not sure.

MR. C.: I'm not confused about this.

DR. A.: Oh, you, you're rather convinced about it. Other factors are more important.

MR. C.: Well, I . . .

DR. A.: Well, let's hear, let's hear.

MR. C.: There are other factors, the genetic factors, which we all know about.

FLORA: (*Angrily.*) Oh, genetic factors indeed!

Flora instantly challenges father's righteous hypocrisy.

DR. A.: What's the matter, Flora? That makes you sore?

MR. C.: Well . . .

DR. A.: Wait a minute, Henry. You'll have a chance in a minute. Flora?

She continues to be on therapist's side.

FLORA: Because I feel, I feel this way. I feel that it's, that it's environment. A man is the sum total of his environment. Not only, not necessarily the genealogical tree or things like that. I mean . . . uh . . . there's no . . . I don't think there's been any traces of . . . uh . . . schizophrenia or . . . or, or criminals in our family. I don't feel that way.

Father tries to shut her mouth. Therapist stops him. Flora confusedly denies the family crime and her illness.

DR. A.: So you say, "Heredity—bunk!"

FLORA: Yes.

DR. A.: Tommyrot! You don't agree with Pop?

FLORA: No.

DR. A.: He made you very angry when he did that.

Therapist sharpens Flora's assertion of a difference. He releases her anger.

FLORA: Yes, he did. Because the family . . . When the family sits down to talk things out, then where does the genealogical, the genealogy, or whatever it is, come into it? It's as minor as the color of your eyes or the color of your hair.

It is to be recalled that at an earlier stage Flora had lectured the therapist on genetics (like father).

DR. A.: You didn't come here to talk about what's in the germ plasm . . .

He fortifies Flora in puncturing parents' denials and rationalizations.

FLORA: No.

DR. A.: . . . in your family. So you're angry because you feel this is a way your parents seek an out, a nice alibi. . . .

MRS. C.: (*Interrupts.*) I'm not seeking an out that way.

DR. A.: . . . Excuse me one minute, the things other than environment. Pop says this type of psychotherapy is screwed up, it's out of balance, I try to make too much fuss about the family environment. It's heredity, it's physiology . . .

Therapist offers himself as object of attack.

MR. C.: No, I didn't exclude it. Don't quote, don't misquote me.

DR. A.: . . . *and* the family environment.

MR. C.: Right.

DR. A.: But you give that a minor role.

MR. C.: No, I give that, I give that one third, let's say.

This type of obsessional compromise is positively unholy.

DR. A.: One third?

MR. C.: Well, how do you put these things?

DR. A.: Now, wait a minute. Flora emphatically disagrees with you. (*To Flora*) You don't restrict it to one third?

FLORA: No.

DR. A.: . . . the factor of family environment?

FLORA: No, I think one third is too much value to give. I mean family environment is . . . Well, I don't know what to say. I say it's important but I don't know what percentage to give it.

Here, Flora, in her confused way, says the opposite of what she means. She backs down.

DR. A.: Well, Pop says one third. Two thirds have nothing to do with family life, he says.

FLORA: Well, where do the other two thirds come from?

DR. A.: He adds heredity.

FLORA: Heredity? No, no, I don't feel heredity is that important. I mean . . .

DR. A.: Well, how much importance would you give it, your two parents, the way your family grew up?

FLORA: Well, the way they grew up in what way?

DR. A.: One third, two thirds, three thirds, what?

FLORA: Are you talking about their environment or their heredity? Which?

DR. A.: I'm talking about the actual emotional events that have gone on privately in your own family. I'm talking about the environment you've lived in and with—Mother, Dad, Grandma.

FLORA: Grandma is out of the picture. How they, the way they grew up. I think they were raised very precisely. They grew up . . .

DR. A.: (*Interrupts.*) Now, that's off the subject. I'm talking about how you grew up with these people here, Mother Leah, Papa Henry, Grandma.

FLORA: Well, they weren't, they weren't, they're not rich, but they, but they gave me things that a parent should give a child.

Flora shows her ambivalence, turns back to support parents.

DR. A.: They tried to be good parents.

FLORA: Yes, they gave me a nice home. When I was younger, they gave me dolls, toys to play with. And they lived happily for a while.

DR. A.: Yes, but for a split second when you got angry and remonstrated with Pop here, did you for a moment feel that there was a kind of sliding out of their responsibilities as parents?

Therapist offers support to the patient in reasserting her difference.

FLORA: Because he's always expressing scientific data. You know, like everything is in the germ plasm, germ plasm this, germ plasm that, and I don't feel it's that important. I mean, back in the old country they used to think that the parents, that if the child didn't come from a long line of geniuses, he was a moron. I mean . . .

DR. A.: Well, we're still with the mystery, the "whodunit" part of this thing. What's been the crime? What's been the crime?

FLORA: The crime?

Now Flora executes another turn in her ambivalent feelings to parents.

DR. A.: Yes, in this family. Who got wounded?

FLORA: In fact, we're all, I think we're all culprits.

DR. A.: Oh, you're all criminals?

FLORA: Yes.

DR. A.: And . . .

FLORA: Myself included.

DR. A.: Yourself included.

FLORA: Yes.

DR. A.: Mm. Well, now, who's the victim of the crime?

FLORA: Well, we're all culprits and possibly we're all victims.

Still another turn; she obscures the crime, while making herself one of the guilty.

How true!

DR. A.: Well, how do you feel about that? Every one of you is a criminal and every one is a victim of a crime.

MRS. C.: We're all victims of our mistakes, aren't we? If we've made any, I don't say that we, I mean I don't know. That's why I'm confused, but usually if we've made a mistake we are the victim of it, aren't we? So Flora makes a lot of sense to me.

DR. A.: Yes, she's a very intelligent girl. She makes sense to me too. But I still don't know "whodunit."
(*Mrs. C. and Flora laugh.*)

DR. A.: How do we define the crime? What was the crime?

MRS. C.: Well, I don't see why you mention crime constantly. I . . .

DR. A.: I just took my cue from Flora.

FLORA: Yes. (*To father*) You're at fault. (*To mother*) You're at fault. And I'm at fault. (*To father*) You're at fault because every darn move you took you, you, you had that guilt underlying it. (*To mother*) You just couldn't do anything with a free mind. Probably you got that from your mother. And him [father] because he was like me in certain respects; he hadn't come out, so to speak.

DR. A.: I understand. But somehow all of you evade the question of *the* crime. What was *the* crime?

FLORA: The, the crime?

DR. A.: Who was destructive?

FLORA: Well, possibly a little bit in each of us.

DR. A.: Yes, but what was the actual crime? What was the damage done?

MRS. C.: Well, this is all the product of the damage that we've done, isn't it?

DR. A.: It is.

MRS. C.: Well, the fact that . . .

MR. C.: (*Interrupts.*) Well, Dr. A. wants you to define the crime.

MRS. C.: What crime?

MR. C.: The crime.

Therapist acts the role of detective—he again pressures the family to pierce their self-created fog.

Therapist confronts them with their shared evasiveness.

Therapist presses here for Flora to admit her role as victim.

MRS. C.: Well, I think crime is where you lose so much out of life. Where you don't really enjoy life to its fullest. Or where, like Flora, you know (*pauses, sighs deeply*) she can't seem to enjoy life. I think that is a crime.

DR. A.: You mean something of her vitality was killed off? That's the crime?

FLORA: So part of me was killed off?

Now therapist begins to get what he is looking for.

DR. A.: Is that it, part of you killed off?

FLORA: Dr. M. [the other therapist], I mean Dr. A., let me point out one thing, that I don't think life in any situation is exactly a ball. I mean life can become very difficult at times, very trying. So I don't think it's entirely, I don't, I can't put my finger on it. The point is, when life gets very difficult, you want a warm shoulder, a hand to hold, or . . . I know it sounds irrelevant, but it's not, Dr. A.

DR. A.: And when things get rough and a little painful, disappointing and painful in life, do you have a warm hand to hold?

Is mother comforting daughter or daughter comforting mother?

FLORA: Yes, and usually when it's painful, it's my mother, I hold her hand.

DR. A.: Would you be willing to show me how you reach out for Mother's hand?

FLORA: Well . . .

MRS. C.: (*Reaches out and takes Flora's hand.*) What do you think? That she, that we don't . . .

Therapist invites daughter to reach out; instead, mother seizes initiative, cuts off daughter's move, and substitutes her own.

DR. A.: (*Interrupts by shaking head negatively.*)

FLORA: I want to hold his [father's] hand too.

DR. A. (*to Mrs. C.*): You reached out first!

MRS. C.: Well, uh, well, that was because . . .

DR. A.: You "jumped the gun." (*Mrs. C. laughs nervously.*) You didn't wait for her to reach out. You reached out. To please me, as you said at one time, months ago perhaps. Do you remember?

MRS. C.: You know, it's very difficult, because I really don't think that one is quite natural in these surroundings.

Mother is upset at being caught in the act of aborting daughter's movement.

DR. A.: I understand that.

MRS. C.: You watch yourself because you know that every word is being scrutinized very carefully, and you say things probably that you wouldn't think of ordinarily, of saying or doing. I mean when I laughed before, you, you made something of it (*laughing nervously*) you know. And that one time I . . .

MR. C.: Not to mention the fact that you suppressed her once.

MRS. C.: And that one time I stopped Flora from telling an off-color joke, and I said . . .

MR. C.: And you became a dominating female.

Once again father teams up with mother against therapist.

MRS. C.: Yes, and very suddenly I was a very dominating mother.

MR. C.: In other words, you fellows, you fellows are quite a bit like the patients. You have an *idée fixe,* and that's it.

Father here attacks therapist as if he were the grandmother.

DR. A.: I'm a joker. (*Mrs. C. laughs.*) I don't let you win, eh?

MR. C.: What I mean in general is . . .

DR. A.: (*Interrupts.*) I indict you in a one-sided, unfair way. Pop is afraid I'm going to kill him.

Therapist interprets father's fear of attack.

MR. C.: Well, this isn't a court of law really. Is it? Do you feel this is our trial in a court of law? Why do you agree with Flora?

Now, it is two against two.

DR. A.: I just picked up Flora's term.

MR. C.: I know, but why do you?

DR. A.: Because there is some mystery, some confusion here about what really was done, by whom, to whom in the family, who's responsible. I'm more interested in understanding how things came about; *how,* not who's to blame.

Therapist tries to ease everyone's guilt.

MR. C.: (*Clears throat.*) All right, so let's dispense with legal terminology. It's now a question of finding who's to blame, only it's not a legal question.

Parents' defensiveness is here blatantly clear.

DR. A.: You didn't listen to me. I just said I'm interested in understanding better, in a shared way, all four of us, how these things came about, rather than who's to blame. You didn't listen. You went right back to the feeling that I'm blaming you.

Therapist tries to ease defensiveness.

MR. C.: No, no, no. On the contrary. It's your use of the word indictment that made me feel that this, that we're on trial.

Mother and father are now allied against therapist as if he takes the place of the critical, carping grandmother.

DR. A.: Mm.

MR. C.: Would you like to retract that?

DR. A.: No, not at all. You're getting me mixed up here. I'm as bad as you are here. Flora confused, and you

Therapist uses a ploy and a bit of humor to lighten tension.

[father] confused, and you [mother] confused, and also me. (*All laugh.*)

MR. C.: I'm confused.

DR. A.: You're getting me all mixed up here.

MR. C.: So you're confused too. You know, I'll tell you, that's very reassuring to me.

Father falls victim to the ploy; begins again to attack therapist.

DR. A.: At least the sequence of events as I experience them.

MR. C.: Anyway, it's reassuring to know that you're confused too, or at least that you admit it.

DR. A.: You turn to me with a kind of troubled, angry, reproachful look that we fellows, we're as sick as our patients, we see things in a "screwed-up" way too, and I indicted her; you implied I indicted her earlier, for being a dominating, intrusive, and evasive mother.

MR. C.: Which I felt was completely unjustified. And I still do, I still do. I think it was a completely unwarranted conclusion.

DR. A.: Well, how did you feel a moment ago . . . It's a little difficult to talk about events that took place maybe a year ago . . .

Therapist permits himself to be the target of parents' hostility. He is now being made the scapegoat.

MR. C.: (*Interrupting.*) All right, go ahead.

DR. A.: This morning when I asked Flora, I think gently, "Flora, are you willing to show me how you reach out for a warm hand, a reassuring hand?" Eh?

FLORA: Yes.

DR. A.: She said that she did that mainly with Mama. And what did I notice? Well, Mama perked up. . . .

FLORA: Like she was on a string.

Daughter sees mother acting like a puppet.

DR. A.: She didn't wait for you [Flora] to reach out for her hand. Mother reached out first. That's what I would call . . .

MR. C.: (*Interrupts inaudibly.*)

DR. A.: How would you call it? I call it "jumping the gun."

Therapist charges mother with cutting off patient's initiative and free movement.

MR. C.: And I call it trying to be helpful.

DR. A. (*to Flora*): How do you feel about that?

FLORA: Well, I called it a controlled action on her part. I figure, I think she was acting like she were on a string, you know. . . .

DR. A.: Like a puppet.

FLORA: Yes, like a puppet.

MRS. C.: (*Laughs loudly.*)

DR. A.: Doing what she thinks she's supposed to do, what the puppeteer commands on the puppet strings.

MRS. C.: You work the strings.

Therapist is in place of grandmother.

FLORA: Yes, yes. You're the one with the strings and she's on the strings.

DR. A.: In other words you feel she was obeying what I expected of her. I pulled the string and she obeyed.

Mother's automatized obedience hides her true feelings (her disguised aggression).

FLORA: Yes, yes.

DR. A.: But in the meantime I was waiting for you to reach out for Mom, and it didn't happen. Mom reached out for your hand, instead.

MR. C.: Do you draw a conclusion from this?

DR. A.: Well, I'm kind of thinking about it. I haven't drawn any conclusions yet, but I'm wondering what it means.

MR. C.: Well, did it ever occur to you that we're enacting a scene under abnormal circumstances?

Father again comes to mother's side.

DR. A.: (*Affirmatively.*) Mmhmm.

MR. C.: Well, all right. Then how can you draw any conclusions from this?

DR. A.: Maybe we can't, maybe we can't.

Again, therapist receives the attack.

MR. C.: That's more like it; maybe we can't. Because this is not a real-life situation. I resented it then, I resent it now, that you called her dominating. Because she is, if anyone is dominating, I'm perhaps more dominating than she is.

MRS. C.: Any time I open my mouth now, I put my foot into it. . . . (*Laughs.*)

MR. C.: You see what you've, all you've done is to make her careful of really . . .

Father continues to indict therapist.

MRS. C.: . . . expressing myself.

MR. C.: Expressing herself, that's right. Because she feels that every word is being used, is being used in a way against her. And I don't think we're going to get a natural response from Leah any more.

DR. A.: So I did a lot of damage to you, Leah, hm?

MR. C.: Well, you sure . . .

MRS. C.: Well, in this particular case, if Flora didn't move and I didn't move, you'd say, "Well, there it is, cold-bloodedness in the family." Yet Flora knows as well as I do that she's quite emotional and that she is not frigid at all as far as loving is con-

Mother again protests.

cerned. (*Laughs embarrassedly.*) She does quite a bit of it. Am I right, Flora, am I right?

FLORA: You're right.

This is the patient's automatized compliance with mother, out of fright.

MRS. C.: I mean, she loves to kiss and hug and that sort of thing. But when you didn't reach out right now, certainly that didn't give Dr. A. that impression of your real self. Unless I'm always being misinformed about these things, maybe I just didn't understand things, that's all.

DR. A.: No, that isn't quite the way I felt. Knowing you people pretty well by now, knowing each other for some time, and having been in this circumstance before, I've *seen* Flora reach out for your hand before. So I know she can do it, she has done it.

FLORA: So what was your reaction?

DR. A.: This morning I was just waiting for her, to see if she herself would reach out. And there was some kind of hesitancy, something was delayed, and you [mother] reached for her.

Therapist highlights daughter's ambivalent fear.

MRS. C.: What did that imply to you then?

DR. A.: I'm afraid of your husband now. (*All laugh.*)

Another therapeutic ploy.

MRS. C.: (*Laughingly.*) What do you think he's going to do?

DR. A.: He has such a sharp scientific eye on me every split second, I might, I might slip and put my foot in my mouth.

Father is ever ready to spring on the therapist, and wants now to rub him out of the family as he finally succeeded in doing with grandmother.

MR. C.: Well, why not, why not? After all we've done it. Get your feet wet like the rest of us.

DR. A.: Well, I'd say that was coming to me. (*All laugh.*)

MR. C.: Well, may as well get your feet wet.

DR. A.: Well, you heard what I said. I said Mom "jumped the gun." She did it ahead of Flora, she did it fast, she didn't wait for Flora . . .

Therapist points out how mother suppressed daughter.

MRS. C.: (*Trying to interrupt.*) As I said, I don't know why I . . .

DR. A.: . . . she had all of the initiative. Now we agreed a little while ago, I thought we were reaching toward that little piece of agreement, that if there has been any crime in this family, *somehow* it has to do with the way a piece of Flora has gotten dimmed, a piece of her emotional life, of her personality. Some part of her was killed off, some part of her vitality. Is that right? (*To Flora*) Did we talk about that long ago, you remember, your feelings about body and soul and your . . .

Therapist defines the family crime.

MR. C.: Right.

DR. A.: . . . and your desire to elevate only your spirit and get rid of your body, which was flooding you, hm?

FLORA: Yes.

DR. A.: And then you talked about that awful disease . . .

FLORA: Yes.

DR. A.: . . . that the people in Queendom have, you know. Three stages, a terrible disease. Remember that?

FLORA: Yes.

DR. A.: So I mainly think your, your, your mental picture of that disease has something to do with the question of who's been hurt in this family.

Therapist further defines the connection of the family crime with daughter's illness.

MR. C.: We, we've all been hurt.

DR. A.: That's right.

MR. C.: We've all been hurt. There's no question about that. There isn't one of us who isn't suffering.

DR. A.: Now at that time, Flora, I asked you who had this disease. Did you have it, and you said no. I asked you if I had it, and you said no. And yet you were very absorbed in the three stages of that disease. Do you remember the three stages?

FLORA: Well, yes.

DR. A.: Well, what were the three stages?

FLORA: Well, one, one stage, the first stage you, you don't know if you have it and you feel fine, you feel all right. But you don't know that you have it because you feel perfectly fine. And then the second stage, you become, you're aware you have the disease. You, well, you . . .

MR. C.: Speak freely. You, you know you're, it seems to me you're . . .

Father makes a false gesture of encouragement, but is really stopping daughter (a "double bind").

FLORA: Yes, hemming and hawing.

MR. C.: You're inhibited.

FLORA: Yes. (*Then changes her mind.*) I'm not inhibited.

MR. C.: Oh, yes.

FLORA: And then the second disease, and the second disease, you, you feel it, you feel pain, you feel pain. There is, there is internal bleeding and even bleeding from the pores. And, and you go into convulsions, and, and you can't control them. And, and you're, and you become spiritual-minded and

A vivid description of psychotic freezing of the affects.

all that sort of thing, you know, that's there. And you're, you have these wooden thoughts of the fingers and toes, I mean the limbs, they become totally useless, they can't do anything, no feelings, no feelings at all. And then you . . .

MR. C.: (*Interrupting.*) A neurological form of epilepsy?

FLORA: Well, it is a form of it. And you are paralyzed in this stage.

DR. A.: That's really the first stage.

FLORA: No.

DR. A.: The second stage?

FLORA: Yes.

DR. A.: Well, the first stage, as you describe it, is a stage of well-being.

FLORA: Well-being, but that's when the germ is growing.

DR. A.: I see. It is, so to speak, the latent stage of the disease.

FLORA: Yes, the calm before the storm.

DR. A.: Mmhmm. Then comes this deterioration of the body.

FLORA: Yes, the body deteriorates. It's hideous and it starts to deteriorate. The worst part is the feeling it's going and watching it deteriorate. And it turns into, becomes nothing, just a mass of cells and that's it.

DR. A.: And that's all the disease, then. There is no other stage?

FLORA: No, well, the third, there's another stage of the disease. . . .

DR. A.: Go ahead.

FLORA: Well, by this stage of the disease you, you, you can't, you can't even communicate any more because

"These wooden thoughts . . . . . . no feelings at all." Father misses the message completely.

even the muscles of the face have become paralyzed too and . . .

DR. A.: Mmhmm.

FLORA: . . . and by this time you're as good as dead because you can't move, you can't talk. You could probably articulate somewhat but it doesn't make sense, even what you say any more.

DR. A.: Is that the stage where the person goes mad?

FLORA: Yes, dormant, he lies dormant. And at other times, he, uh . . .

Again, daughter reveals her extraordinary psychotic insight.

DR. A.: Loses his mind.

FLORA: He loses his mind, yes.

DR. A.: That's what you told me.

FLORA: Until he finally dies.

DR. A.: And the person ends up, as you described it, as a putrefied, foul, stinking ball.

FLORA: A putrid mess, yes.

DR. A.: A putrid mess.

DR. A.: You feel very bad.

DR. A.: But you said you didn't have this disease.

FLORA: No.

This is denial and projection.

DR. A: Just certain people in that other planet up there, Queendom.

FLORA: Yes.

DR. A.: We don't talk about that planet any more.

FLORA: No.

DR. A.: Well, then, you got awfully uncertain when I asked you, "Are you sick in *some* way?" You said you didn't have *this* sickness.

FLORA: Mmhmm. Dr. A. . . .

DR. A.: I asked you, "Physically sick?" and you said no, you've got a pretty sound body. "Mentally sick?" and you wavered. You didn't know what to do with that question. You weren't sure.

FLORA: Well, I, Dr. M. [the other therapist], I mean Dr. A., I say what the hell, pardon the expression, what the hell good is a sound body, if you don't have the sound mind to go with it? If you can't, if you can't communicate. If you're in this sort of shell, you know, this cocoon, and you can't get out?

Here, daughter once more contradicts herself. She first denies the disease, then admits her affliction.

DR. A.: Well, what stage are you in now, Flora? I haven't seen you in a long time.

FLORA: Well, I don't feel that I've quite gotten out of it yet.

DR. A.: You're better?

FLORA: (*Pauses.*) Well, yes, I think I'm better. I see the world with a more mature point of view.

DR. A.: Flora says she was made to feel like an intruder.

At a later point, the "touching" quality of the therapeutic experience is again highlighted, as is the family's difficulty in allowing Flora's "right to be."

MR. C.: No, that's what you said, about feeling like the intruder. Is that what she said?

FLORA: Yes, that's what I said. That's almost the exact words.

This is important!

MR. C.: That you were made to feel like an intruder?

FLORA: That's right.

DR. A.: In this relation.

MR. C.: Well, look at it another way. Did you ever feel you wanted to intrude?

Father sees Flora as intruder, like grandmother, like therapist.

FLORA: Well . . .

MR. C.: In our marriage? I'll give you an example. We were walking along . . .

FLORA: I remember, that was the time . . .

Again, daughter is put in the wrong, and submits guiltily.

MR. C.: Yes, yes, we were walking along.

FLORA: (*Very distressed.*) That was wrong of me.

MR. C.: Well, right or wrong doesn't matter. Because you acted out the way you felt.

FLORA: It was wrong. (*In tears. Dr. A. pats Flora's hand reassuringly.*)

MR. C.: We were walking along and she grabbed hold of Leah and she said . . .

Neither father nor mother feels daughter's pain, a lack of empathy.

DR. A.: She's very agitated. (*Again pats Flora's hand.*)

Therapist comforts daughter. She feels crucified.

MR. C.: No, don't be agitated. This is, that's why I say, your words . . .

FLORA: (*Tearfully.*) It was terrible.

MR. C.: Stop, Flora. You acted out something.

DR. A.: She feels very bad. Maybe we should ask her. Flora, what did you do that was so terrible?

FLORA: Last Sunday we took a drive out to, well, it doesn't matter where. But anyway the two of them were walking together window shopping, and, and for a while that didn't bother me. But they were, they were a couple of paces in front of me, and that, and that got me a little, uh, morose, so to speak. And I didn't like it. And, uh, I felt like a trail-along, you know, so to speak. And even though there were a lot of goodies in the window, they didn't, they couldn't decide on any-

Daughter feels excluded, a "trail-along."

thing, so I came up, I came up to them. And the first, the first person I wanted to touch and reach was, was, was her [mother]. And that was wrong. And, and I said, and I, uh, I exclaimed she belonged solely to me. And I walked up, and took her and (*agitated*) came between them. And that was wrong of me, and I don't know why I did it.

DR. A.: You feel very bad.

FLORA: Mmhmm, yes.

DR. A.: Think you committed a crime?

FLORA: Well, possibly. Then I got a bawling out from him.

DR. A.: You were claiming Mom for your very own mom.

FLORA: Yes.

DR. A.: And pushing him out.

FLORA: Yes.

DR. A.: Mm. You want to say something about that, Henry?

MR. C.: No, no. Uh, she had, she had the courage and decency to say exactly what I would have said. Well, this was an incident, it was an incident. And that's why I said that sometimes I think her words belie her actions. I think she knows at least the right things to say.

DR. A.: But what she felt was very hurt, very morose, angry. She felt like the tail end of the family that was forgotten. You two were spurting ahead, window shopping, enjoying each other.

MRS. C.: Well, it wasn't . . . At that moment, he wanted me to see a certain camera or something. And he said, "Leah, come over here and see

She reacts by reclaiming mother, but is made to feel criminal. The feelings of guilt induced in her are paralyzing. This is dramatically reflected in her stumbling repetitiveness.

Father's wrath is mollified by daughter's confession.

Therapist points out sharply how parents shut daughter out.

this." You know, you remember the leather goods or things like that?

MR. C.: Oh, oh, yes.

MRS. C.: I guess he didn't feel Flora would be interested particularly in that sort of thing, you know. Because if it's something that would interest Flora, then he'll, you know, point to it and say, "Well, you come over and look at this."

DR. A.: You mean he didn't forget Flora for the moment?

MRS. C.: No, I don't think so. And I just walked over. I didn't think about it. I just walked over casually to look at it. But Flora saw something in a different window that might interest us. But this goes on all the time, I mean, there's this pulling apart, you know.

DR. A.: (*To Flora, who had tried to interject something.*) You said Mother's wrong, Flora?

FLORA: I think she is wrong. Because even if, uh, even if, even if he had seen that, that camera or the luggage, leather goods, I don't think he would have signaled to me to come and look at them anyway.

MR. C. (*to Flora*): Would, would you have been interested in it? It was something that I felt had absolutely no interest for you.

FLORA: Maybe . . .

DR. A.: I wonder if that's the point. We need to understand why at the moment Flora felt forgotten, like she didn't exist.

MR. C.: In other words . . .

Father and daughter vie for mother who feels torn between them.

Again, therapist shows how parents rub daughter out.

DR. A.: You were walking ahead, you two were affectionately joined, good companions, you were sharing a certain interest in common.

FLORA: I didn't mean, I didn't mean to hurt you in any way. (*She reaches her hand out toward her father; he ignores it.*) But whenever we hurt those we love and can't get it out of our mind, you know, as the stanza goes, as the poem goes . . .

MR. C.: We hurt the things we love, eh? Is that what you're saying?

FLORA: No, no, another stanza, another . . .

DR. A.: Henry, she reached out her hand for your hand.

MR. C.: Well . . .

DR. A.: She didn't quite touch it.

MR. C.: She didn't quite make it, see. Well, I didn't want to make the mistake, I didn't want to make the heinous crime that Leah did of reaching out, so I just held my ground.

DR. A.: You, you felt her reach out toward your hand?

MR. C.: Mmhmm, but I didn't want to commit the same crime Leah did.

DR. A.: Mm.

MR. C.: So, uh, you know . . .

DR. A. (*to Flora*): You want to touch Pop's hand? It won't hurt.

FLORA: Well . . .

DR. A.: I think you do. You want him to understand . . . how badly that little action of yours made you feel.

FLORA: I didn't feel . . .

DR. A.: You really didn't want to bust up the marriage.

Daughter reaches out for father's forgiveness and is rebuffed.

Father makes an excuse for his rejection.

FLORA: No. Dr. A. . . .

DR. A.: You want him to forgive you.

FLORA: Yes, forgive . . . mitigate the circumstances for a while.

DR. A.: You want to take his hand?

FLORA: No, not particularly. I mean . . .

Daughter shows paralyzing fright and ambivalence.

MR. C.: I thought for a while there you wanted to reach out for my hand.

FLORA: Well, I, I, I don't know. Touching hands is personal, I mean, you know, I can't put my finger on it.

Note the phrase "put *my* finger on it."

MR. C.: She's using my theory.

Refers to prior session when Mr. C. had said he couldn't touch someone physically unless he had emotional contact with that person.

DR. A.: Put the finger on it, that's the point. (*Mrs. C. laughs.*)

Simultaneous with Mr. C.'s remark.

FLORA: I can't put my finger on it; that's the point.

MR. C.: She's using my theory. How horrible, how horrible. (*In jest.*)

DR. A.: Yes, that's right. That's your peculiarity.

MR. C.: Why didn't she . . . I may have one or two good characteristics. I may have, I'm not sure. I wish she'd sponge up one or two that I have, if I have them.

DR. A.: Well, Flora feels that you have more than one or two. She's admiring them.

MR. C.: If I do have any, I wish she'd sponge those up too.

DR. A.: I think she has sponged up the good qualities, too, not just the bad ones, not just that fear of yours about touching.

MR. C.: Well, I admit very freely, this . . .

DR. A.: Could we put it to a test and ask Flora if she wants to do it?

MR. C.: Well, let's put it to . . .

DR. A.: See if she can "put her finger on it."

FLORA: Hold, touch hands, hold hands?

MR. C. (*to Mrs. C.*): May I?

MRS. C.: (*Smilingly murmurs assent.*)

MR. C.: With your permission, Dr. A., may I help the situation, or do I have to be rigid?

Parents ritualize the joining of daughter and father.

DR. A.: You can meet her halfway. (*Father and Flora hold hands.*)

MR. C.: All right?

FLORA: All right. Well (*murmurs inarticulately*), all right, okay.

DR. A.: How did it feel?

FLORA: All right.

MR. C.: It's not killing anybody?

Father refers to fears of violence.

FLORA: No, no.

MR. C.: You don't feel like you're being killed?

FLORA: No.

MR. C.: Fine.

FLORA: No.

MR. C.: It also means that this incident is forgotten and forgiven?

FLORA: That it's forgotten and forgiven, all finished.

DR. A.: Did you feel the kind of warm, accepting, loving hand that you wanted to feel?

FLORA: Well, uh, I felt a hand that's as unsteady as mine, so to speak. But

I felt a hand that wants to, uh, understand.

DR. A.: Do you want to feel it again?

FLORA: Uh, yes.

Father and daughter hold
hands again, but both are
hesitant and uneasy.

MR. C.: All right?

FLORA: All right.

MR. C.: And it didn't, it's not killing
you?

FLORA: No, uh . . . uh, no.

MR. C.: We made progress. (*Pause.*)
Leah, you're not jealous? (*Laughs
nervously.*)

As if joking, father invites
mother to intrude.

MRS. C.: It's what I want more than
anything in the world. You know this
is the thing, if I could have things . . .
You know, there's something I
couldn't understand very much. Uh,
this was touching, uh . . . My mother
and father always fought very much.
Uh, this was touching, uh . . . If I
could have seen them touch each other
and be happy with each other, I
would have been, you know . . .

Mother tries to prove her
good intentions.

DR. A.: More trust and faith with
them.

MRS. C.: That's right, I would have
been much happier. If she could feel
that she's part of it and not an outsider. She would feel the same way.
She would be happy that we do touch
each other, providing she's in the picture also. And I understand that all
too well. That's why when he tells me
a story, or he tells me anything that
happens in the office, I want him to
include her in the thing. I always want
her to be in the picture. Now I don't
know. Maybe that's what's pushing

This is a good example of the
mother's vague denial of responsibility, covered over by
her preachy self-righteousness. Yet there is beneath
this, too, a true yearning for
something better.

him away, because I want it so badly,
I don't know. Don't I always say . . .

MR. C.: Leah, I told you many times,
when the mental barrier between us
breaks down, that will go a long way
toward solving the problem. And, and
you can see that she's . . . The barriers are slowly, slowly receding. You
can see that. She's improved. We all
agree to that. We are, we all feel that
way without any reservations, that she
is better.

Father does the same, imi-
tating mother.

After a year and a half of continued treatment, the patient lost
interest in her relations with Zena and Queendom. There was
progressively less mention of hallucinatory communications with
the planet's inhabitants. Finally, she ceased altogether to refer to
these experiences. Gradually, she seemed to resume her place in
the real life of her family on earth. It became clear that she was
progressively withdrawing her interest in her psychotic world and
investing more and more of her feeling in her struggle to find a
new place in her human family.

At the same time, she began again to attend school. Her ability
to concentrate on her studies was restored, and there were no
further failures in class. She worked better and, in fact, achieved
an average of 85 per cent. The change was striking and was remarked on with amazement by her teachers. She has since moved
on to college.

At another level, she improved her relations with her peers. She
now talks with the young people in her class and has developed a
friendship with a girl friend. She was able to attend a school dance
and to have contact with boys as well as with girls. In the over-all
picture, the patient showed marked improvement at home, in
school, and in the larger community.

10

A Closing Note

As a special method of intervention in human problems, family psychotherapy is in its infancy. Its ultimate capacities and limitations are not yet known, but gradually the practitioners of this type of treatment are defining its basic principles and learning how to apply them to various family types in different social conditions and at different stages of the family life cycle. As I have shown, family psychotherapy is applicable to a variety of types of psychiatric disorders and to the relations between husband and wife and between child and family. We are at a point now where each family group we see contributes to a new learning experience. At another level, therapists are learning to intertwine family therapy with other methods of treatment, reflecting the fundamental complementary relations and needs of family and individual. Finally, therapists are learning how to adapt the family method to their own therapeutic styles, to blend the science and art of this type of therapy.

Family psychotherapy reveals the promise of becoming a potent therapeutic instrument. It is not only unfolding as a method in its own right, but it may also serve to correct and improve some of the older therapeutic methods. Many psychoanalysts who have training in family therapy not only discover its values, but find that they become more effective individual therapists as a result of this training.

Family therapy leads to more realistic goals and procedures for many troubled people. It is a natural, not an artificial entry into problems of human distress. Its principles lead to more accurate location of the causes of individual difficulties within the network of family relationships and to earlier detection and prevention of mental disturbance. Treatment within the individual's natural family environment helps join the issues of social and mental health. It aids in linking the psychological disorders of the individual to the psychosocial disorders of the family and the community. Its potential for the study of problems in social psychopathology offers a powerful antidote to the forces of family decline resulting from rapid, disorganizing social change. Family process itself is seen as related to both social and mental health.

The basic approach has been strongly influenced by developments in social psychopathology, group dynamics, psychotherapy, and the related behavioral sciences. Causation of disorders of emotion and behavior has come to be seen as multiple and circular, direct and indirect, specific and nonspecific. The events in the present merge the multiple sources of causation. They embrace unconscious and conscious motivations and situational influences as well. The adaptation of the individual is evaluated within the context of his personal environment. In this setting the concept of homeodynamic balance assumes a position of focal importance.

The future of family psychotherapy is hinted at in the implications of the method which I have attempted to outline in this book. As we have seen, it leads to a new and different image of mental illness by focusing on the here and now, by joining past and future in the present. It encompasses the interdependent and interpenetrating relations of individual and group.

Family therapy has the quality of a touching experience, both for the family members and for the therapist. It counteracts the distorted use of verbal communication and reduces the defensive barricades among family members.

The importance of emotional contagion is highlighted, especially the contagion of anxiety in family interchange. The emotional events in the interview presented in Chapter 1 clearly exemplify this contagion—for example, in the therapist's opening response to the father's long sigh and in the therapist's reception of the outbursts of giggling from the mother and the daughter.

In family therapy, one can see clearly the transmission of pathogenic conflict and coping from person to person and from one generation to the next. The interplay of multiple disturbances among family members becomes clearly defined, as is vividly illustrated in the family interview in the chapter on schizophrenia. Here the identically patterned conflicts are passed down from the relationship of grandmother and mother to the relationship of mother and daughter.

Family therapy offers an effective means for the relief of guilt by penetrating the vicious circle of blame and accusation for things past and by producing an emotional matrix for enhancing mutual understanding, respect, and esteem. One part of the family is not healed at the expense of other parts. A good example is in the treatment interview of Henry's family, where we see a retransposition of the conflicts from the "bad seed," Henry, back to the original source, the parental relationship.

This same family is an excellent illustration of the manner in which the natural family setting used for therapy permits the continuous clash between dream and reality and opens an effective channel for the living out of pain and disillusionment deriving from this clash. It is possible to deal with the disparities of depth and surface and of inner and outer being; with the interplay of intrapersonal and interpersonal conflict; and with the relation, mutually supporting or oppositional, between family group defenses and individual defenses against anxiety. As dramatized in the treatment interview in the chapter on children's disorders, it is possible, within a single framework, to deal with elements of sameness and difference, or union and individuation among family members.

In family psychotherapy, the members are offered genuine satisfaction of valid emotional needs. The treatment supplies emotional elements which the family needs but lacks. At another level it becomes possible to counteract the splitting of the family into warring groups, the destructive effects of prejudicial scapegoating, and the exploitation of the secondary gains of illness. By enhancing complementarity, family relations can be realigned. The way can be opened for new kinds of feeling, action, and reaction. As can be seen, for example, in the treatment interview of husband and wife in Chapter 5, reality testing is maximized through modification of the images of self and others.

Injured individuals are not merely patched up, but an improved pattern of human relations evolves into a new way of life. Healthy rather than pathological healing of family disorders is fostered.

Family psychotherapy is joined with the prevention of illness and the maintenance of health. It is a true therapy of the emotions— emotions as they are felt and expressed toward those who are closest and most significant.

Finally, family psychotherapy, though currently still evolving in technique and theory, is full of challenge, full of surprise, and highly rewarding for the therapist as well as for the family. A science of family behavior, based on a system of family diagnosis and psychotherapy, holds the promise of an important addition to our armamentarium of mental health services. It may well become the very core of the newly emerging community psychiatry.

Bibliography

Ackerman, Nathan W. "Adolescent Problems: A Symptom of Family Disorder." *Family Process,* Vol. I (1962).

————. "Child and Family Psychiatry Today: A New Look at Some Old Problems." *Mental Hygiene,* Vol. XLVII (1963).

————. "The Emotional Impact of In-Laws and Relatives." In *Emotional Forces in the Family,* ed. S. Leibman. New York: J. B. Lippincott, 1959.

————. "The Family as a Unit in Mental Health." In *Proceedings of the Third World Congress of Psychiatry.* Toronto, 1963.

————. "The Family Group and Family Therapy." *International Journal of Sociometry,* Vol. I (1957).

————. "The Principles of Shared Responsibility for Child Rearing." *International Journal of Social Psychiatry,* Vol. II (1957).

————. *The Psychodynamics of Family Life.* New York: Basic Books, 1958.

————. "Symptom, Defense and Growth in Group Process." *Journal of the American Group Therapy Association,* Vol. XI (1961).

————. "Toward an Integrative Therapy of the Family." *American Journal of Psychiatry,* Vol. CXIV (1958).

————. "Transference and Counter-Transference." *Psychoanalysis and Psychoanalytic Review,* Vol. XLVI (1959).

———— and Marjorie L. Behrens. "A Study of Family Diagnosis." *American Journal of Orthopsychiatry,* Vol. XXVI (1956).

———— et al. (eds.). *Exploring the Base for Family Therapy.* New York: Family Service Association of America, 1961.

Alexander, I. E. "Family Therapy." *Marriage and Family Living,* Vol. XXV (1963).

Arlen, Monroe S. "Conjoint Therapy and the Corrective Emotional Experience." *Family Process,* Vol. V (1966).

Behrens, Marjorie L., and Nathan W. Ackerman. "The Home Visit as an Aid in Family Diagnosis and Therapy." *Social Casework,* Vol. XXXVII (1956).

Bell, John E. *Family Group Therapy.* Public Health Monograph No. 64, U. S. Department of Health, Education, and Welfare, 1961.

———. "Recent Advances in Family Group Therapy." *Journal of Child Psychology and Psychiatry,* Vol. III (1962).

Bell, N. W. "Extended Family Relations of Disturbed and Well Families." *Family Process,* Vol. I (1962).

———, and E. F. Vogel (eds.). *A Modern Introduction to the Family.* Glencoe, Ill.: Free Press, 1960.

Boszormenyi-Nagy, Ivan, and James L. Framo. *Intensive Family Therapy.* New York: Harper & Row, 1965.

Brody, Elaine H., and Geraldine M. Spark. "Institutionalization of the Aged: A Family Crisis." *Family Process,* Vol. V (1966).

Brown, B. S. "Home Visiting by Psychiatrists." *Archives of General Psychiatry,* Vol. VII (1964).

Burgess, E. W., and H. J. Locke. *The Family.* New York: American Book Company, 1950.

Caplan, Gerald (ed.). *Prevention of Mental Disorders in Childhood.* New York: Basic Books, 1961.

Caputo, D. V. "The Parents of the Schizophrenic." *Family Process,* Vol. II (1963).

Carroll, E. J. "Family Therapy: Some Observations and Comparisons." *Family Process,* Vol. III (1964).

——— et al. "Psychotherapy of Marital Couples." *Family Process,* Vol. II (1963).

Chance, Erika. *Families in Treatment.* New York: Basic Books, 1958.

Clower, C. G., and L. Brody. "Conjoint Family Therapy in Outpatient Practice." *American Journal of Psychotherapy,* Vol. XVIII (1964).

Coyle, G. L. "Concepts Relevant to Helping the Family as a Group." *Social Casework,* XLIII (1962).

Despert, Louise J. *Children of Divorce.* Garden City: Doubleday, 1937.

Ehrenwald, J. *Neurosis in the Family and Patterns of Psychosocial Defense.* New York: Harper & Row, 1963.

———. "Neurosis in the Family." *Archives of General Psychiatry,* Vol. III (1960).

Epstein, N. B., and W. A. Westly. "Parental Interaction as Related to the Emotional Health of Children," *Social Problems*, Vol. VIII (1960).

Ferreira, A. H. "Family Myth and Homeostasis." *Archives of General Psychiatry*, Vol. IX (1963).

———. "Interpersonal Perceptivity among Family Members." *American Journal of Orthopsychiatry*, Vol. XXXIV (1964).

——— et al. "Some Interactional Variables in Normal and Abnormal Families." *Family Process*, Vol. V (1966).

Fisch, R. "Home Visits in a Private Psychiatric Practice." *Family Process*, Vol. III (1964).

Fleck, S. "Family Dynamics and Origin of Schizophrenia." *Psychosomatic Medicine*, Vol. XXII (1960).

Friedman, A. S. "Family Therapy as Conducted in the Home." *Family Process*, Vol. I (1962).

———. "The 'Well' Sibling in the 'Sick' Family: A Contradiction." *International Journal of Social Psychiatry*, Special Ed., Vol. II (1964).

Galdston, Iago (ed.). *The Family in Contemporary Society.* New York: International Universities Press, 1958.

Gehrke, S., and J. Moxom. "Diagnostic Classifications and Treatment Techniques in Marriage Counseling." *Family Process*, Vol. I (1962).

Glasser, P. H. "Changes in Family Equilibrium during Psychotherapy." *Family Process*, Vol. II (1963).

Greene, Bernard L. *The Psychotherapies of Marital Disharmony.* Glencoe, Ill.: Free Press, 1965.

Grolnick, A. "Family Psychotherapy." *American Journal of Orthopsychiatry*, Vol. XXXII (1962).

Grotjahn, Martin. *Psychoanalysis and the Family Neurosis.* New York: W. W. Norton, 1960.

Hader, Marvin. "The Importance of Grandparents in Family Life." *Family Process*, Vol. IV (1965).

Haley, Jay. *Strategies of Psychotherapy.* New York: Grune and Stratton, 1963.

———. "Whither Family Therapy?" *Family Process*, Vol. I (1962).

Handel, G. "Psychological Study of Whole Families." *Psychological Bulletin*, Vol. LXIII (1965).

Henry, J. "Family Structure and the Transmission of Neurotic Behavior." *American Journal of Orthopsychiatry*, Vol. XXI (1951).

Howells, J. G. "The Nuclear Family as the Functional Unit in Psychiatry." *Journal of Mental Science*, Vol. CVIII (1962).

Jackson, D. D., and J. H. Weakland. "Conjoint Family Therapy: Some Considerations on Theory, Technique, and Results." *Psychiatry,* Vol. XXIV (1961).

Kempler, W. "Experiential Family Therapy." *International Journal of Group Psychotherapy,* Vol. XV (1965).

Kohl, R. N. "Pathologic Reactions of Marital Partners to Improvement of Patients." *American Journal of Psychiatry,* Vol. CXVIII (1962).

Laqueur, H. P., *et al.* "Multiple Family Therapy: Further Developments." *International Journal of Social Psychiatry,* Special Ed., Vol. II (1964).

Leighton, Alexander H., *et al. Explorations in Social Psychiatry.* New York: Basic Books, 1957.

Leik, R. E. "Instrumentality and Emotionality in Family Interaction." *Sociometry,* Vol. XXVI (1963).

Lidz, Theodore. *The Family and Human Adaptation.* New York: International Universities Press, 1961.

———— *et al.* "Schizophrenic Patients and Their Siblings." *Psychiatry,* Vol. XXVI (1963).

MacGregor, Robert. "Multiple Impact Psychotherapy with Families." *Family Process,* Vol. I (1962).

———— *et al. Multiple Impact Therapy with Families.* New York: McGraw-Hill, 1964.

Masserman, Jules (ed.). *Science and Psychoanalysis.* Vol. IV. New York: Grune and Stratton, 1960.

Midelfort, Christian F. *The Family in Psychotherapy.* New York: McGraw-Hill, 1957.

Mitchell, Celia. "The Use of Family Sessions in the Diagnosis and Treatment of Disturbances in Children." *Social Casework,* Vol. XLI (1960).

Morgan, Ralph W. "The Extended Home Visit in Psychiatric Research and Treatment." *Psychiatry,* Vol. XXVI (1963).

Parad, H. J., and G. Caplan. "A Framework for Studying Families in Crisis." *Social Work,* Vol. V (1960).

Parloff, Morris B. "The Family in Psychotherapy." *Archives of General Psychiatry,* Vol. IV (1961).

Perry, S. E. "Home Treatment and the Social System of Psychiatry." *Psychiatry,* Vol. XXVI (1963).

Rapoport, R. "The Family and Psychiatric Treatment." *Psychiatry,* Vol. XXIII (1960).

————. "Normal Crises, Family Structure and Mental Health." *Family Process,* Vol. II (1963).

Rosenbaum, C. P. "Patient-Family Similarities in Schizophrenia." *Archives of General Psychiatry,* Vol. V (1961).

Ryle, A., and M. Hamilton. "Neurosis in Fifty Married Couples." *Journal of Mental Science,* Vol. CVIII (1962).

Satir, Virginia. *Conjoint Family Therapy.* Palo Alto: Science and Behavior Books, 1964.

Shellow, R. S., *et al.* "Family Group Therapy in Retrospect: Four Years and Sixty Families." *Family Process,* Vol. II (1963).

Sherman, M. H., *et al.* "Non-Verbal Cues and Re-enactment of Conflict in Family Therapy." *Family Process,* Vol. IV (1965).

Spiegel, J. P. "The Resolution of Role Conflict within the Family." *Psychiatry,* Vol. XX (1957).

Stein, M. I. (ed.). *Contemporary Psychotherapies.* Glencoe, Ill.: Free Press, 1961.

Tharp, R. "Marriage Roles, Child Development and Family Treatment." *American Journal of Orthopsychiatry,* Vol. XXXV (1965).

Titchener, J. L., *et al.* "Family Transaction and Derivation of Individuality." *Family Process,* Vol. II (1963).

Watson, A. S. "The Conjoint Psychotherapy of Marriage Partners." *American Journal of Orthopsychiatry,* Vol. XXXIII (1963).

Wynne, L. C., *et al.* "Pseudo-Mutuality in the Family Relations of Schizophrenia." *Psychiatry,* Vol. XXII (1958).

Index

Italic figures refer to page numbers of the "Verbatim Records" of therapy sessions.